FAST TRACK TO A 5

Preparing for the AP*
Biology Examination

To Accompany

Biology: The Unity and Diversity of Life
12th and 13th Editions
by Cecie Starr, Ralph Taggart, Christine Evers, and Lisa Starr

Paula Petterson
Ridgeview Classical Schools, Fort Collins, Colorado

Katherine Silber
Highland Park High School, Highland Park, Illinois

BROOKS/COLE
CENGAGE Learning·

Australia · Brazil · Japan · Korea · Mexico · Singapore · Spain · United Kingdom · United States

*AP and Advanced Placement Program are registered trademarks of the College Entrance Examination Board, which was not involved in the production of, and does not endorse, this product.

ISBN-13: 978-1-111-58134-3
ISBN-10: 1-111-58134-7

Brooks/Cole
20 Davis Drive
Belmont, CA 94002-3098
USA

Cengage Learning is a leading provider of customized learning solutions with office locations around the globe, including Singapore, the United Kingdom, Australia, Mexico, Brazil, and Japan. Locate your local office at: **www.cengage.com/global**

Cengage Learning products are represented in Canada by Nelson Education, Ltd.

Cengage Learning products are represented in high schools by Holt McDougal, a division of Houghton Mifflin Harcourt.

To learn more about Brooks/Cole, visit **www.cengage.com/brookscole**

To find online supplements and other instructional support, please visit **www.cengagebrain.com**

Printed in the United States of America
1 2 3 4 5 6 7 16 15 14 13 12

CONTENTS

PREFACE

Although the original presentation of the material is important, we have found that the best learning is achieved through the process of review. Repetition of material enforces key concepts that are necessary for the AP test. We have worked hard to include everything that will be covered on the test, yet keep the book as abridged as possible. Due to recent extensive AP Biology curriculum changes, we have done our best to provide the most recent requirements and information.

We have the utmost gratitude for the knowledgeable teachers, Christine Woods and Mark Stephansky, who evaluated our work. Their attention to detail during their review was essential to the success of our endeavor. Most importantly, we must thank our students who motivate us every day to add to our tool box of teaching skills. You inspire us to continue to learn and grow as educators.

Paula Petterson
Katherine Silber

March 2012

ABOUT THE AUTHORS

PAULA C. H. PETTERSON is a member of the Ridgeview Classical Schools Science Department in Fort Collins, Colorado. She has been teaching for twenty-six years, has served as department chair, and comes to AP Biology with a Master's degree in Biology. She has been an AP exam reader since 2001. She has published two articles in *The Science Teacher* and most recently contributed a book review to *The American Biology Teacher* in 2011.

KATHERINE W. SILBER is a member of the Highland Park High School Science Department in Highland Park, Illinois. She has been teaching for nine years and comes to AP Biology with a Master's degree in Biology and Education. She was an AP exam reader in 2007 and will be again for 2012. Katherine has two research publications based on her thesis work, "Intra-specific host sharing in the manipulative parasite *Acanthocephalus dirus*: does conflict occur over host modification?" *Parasitology 2004 (129,* 1–6) and "Development-related effects of an acanthocephalan parasite on pairing success of its intermediate host" *Animal Behavior 2006 (71,* 439–448).

AP BIOLOGY EQUATIONS AND FORMULAS

Statistical Analysis and Probability

Standard Error

$$SE_{\bar{x}} = \frac{s}{\sqrt{n}}$$

Mean

$$\bar{x} = \frac{1}{n}\sum_{i=1}^{n} x_i$$

Standard Deviation

$$s = \sqrt{\frac{\sum (x_i - \bar{x})^2}{n-1}}$$

Chi-Square

$$\chi^2 = \sum \frac{(o-e)^2}{e}$$

Chi-Square Table

p	Degrees of Freedom							
	1	2	3	4	5	6	7	8
0.05	3.84	5.99	7.82	9.49	11.07	12.59	14.07	15.51
0.01	6.64	9.32	11.34	13.28	15.09	16.81	18.48	20.09

s = sample standard deviation (i.e., the sample based estimate of the standard deviation of the population)

$\bar{x}$ = mean

n = size of the sample

o = observed individuals with observed genotype

e = expected individuals with observed genotype

Degrees of freedom equals the number of distinct possible outcomes minus one.

Laws of Probability

If A and B are mutually exclusive, then P (A or B) = P(A) + P(B)

If A and B are independent, then P (A and B) = P(A) x P(B)

Hardy-Weinberg Equations

$$p^2 + 2pq + q^2 = 1$$

$$p + q = 1$$

p = frequency of the dominant allele in a population

q = frequency of the recessive allele in a population

Metric Prefixes

Factor	Prefix	Symbol
10^9	giga	G
10^6	mega	M
10^3	kilo	k
10^{-2}	centi	c
10^{-3}	milli	m
10^{-6}	micro	μ
10^{-9}	nano	n
10^{-12}	pico	p

Mode = value that occurs most frequently in a data set

Median = middle value that separates the greater and lesser halves of a data set

Mean = sum of all data points divided by number of data points

Range = value obtained by subtracting the smallest observation (sample minimum) from the greatest (sample maximum)

Rate and Growth

Rate

dY/dt

Population Growth

dN/dt=B-D

Exponential Growth

$$\frac{dN}{dt} = r_{max}N$$

Logistic Growth

$$\frac{dN}{dt} = r_{max}N\left(\frac{K-N}{K}\right)$$

dY= amount of change

t = time

B = birth rate

D = death rate

N = population size

K = carrying capacity

r_{max} = maximum per capita growth rate of population

Water Potential (Ψ)

$$\Psi = \Psi p + \Psi s$$

Ψp = pressure potential

Ψs = solute potential

The water potential will be equal to the solute potential of a solution in an open container, since the pressure potential of the solution in an open container is zero.

The Solute Potential of the Solution

$$\Psi_s = - iCRT$$

i = ionization constant (For sucrose this is 1.0 because sucrose does not ionize in water)

C= molar concentration

R= pressure constant (R = 0.0831 liter bars/mole K)

T = temperature in Kelvin (273 + °C)

(Continues)

AP BIOLOGY EQUATIONS AND FORMULAS (CONCLUDED)

Temperature Coefficient Q_{10}

$$Q_{10} = \left(\frac{k_2}{k_1}\right)^{\frac{10}{t_2 - t_1}}$$

Primary Productivity Calculation

mg O_2/L x 0.698 = mL O_2/L

mL O_2/L x 0.536 = mg carbon fixed/L

t_2 = higher temperature

t_1 = lower temperature

k_2 = metabolic rate at t_2

k_1 = metabolic rate at t_1

Q_{10} = the *factor* by which the reaction rate increases when the temperature is raised by ten degrees

---

Surface Area and Volume

Volume of Sphere
$V = 4/3\, \pi\, r^3$

Volume of a cube (or square column)
$V = l\, w\, h$

Volume of a column
$V = \pi\, r^2 h$

Surface area of a sphere
$A = 4\, \pi\, r^2$

Surface area of a cube
$A = 6\, a$

Surface area of a rectangular solid
$A = \Sigma$ (surface area of each side)

r = radius

l = length

h = height

w = width

A = surface area

V = volume

Σ = Sum of all

a = surface area of one side of the cube

Dilution - used to create a dilute solution from a concentrated stock solution
$C_i V_i = C_f V_f$

i=initial (starting)   C = concentration of solute
f=final (desired)   V = volume of solution

Gibbs Free Energy

$\Delta G = \Delta H - T\Delta S$

ΔG = change in Gibbs free energy

ΔS = change in entropy

ΔH = change in enthalpy

T = absolute temperature (in Kelvin)

$pH = -\log [H^+]$

Part I

Strategies for the AP Examination

PREPARING FOR THE AP*
BIOLOGY EXAMINATION

Advanced Placement can be exhilarating. Whether you are taking an AP course at your school or you are working on AP independently, the stage is set for a great intellectual experience. As the school year progresses you begin noticing the relationship of form to function. You will gain a better understanding of the molecular nature of life and how underlying themes, such as evolution, persist throughout all aspects of Biology.

But sometime after New Year's Day, when the examination begins to loom on a very real horizon, Advanced Placement can seem downright intimidating. In fact, even adults long out of high school refuse the opportunity to take the examination for fun. If you dread taking the test, you are in good company.

The best way to deal with an AP examination is to master it, not let it master you. If you can think of these examinations as a way to show off how your mind works, you have a leg up: attitude *does* help. If you are not one of those students, there is still a lot you can do to sideline your anxiety. This book is designed to put you on a fast track. Focused review and practice time will help you master the examination so that you can walk in with confidence and get a 5.

WHAT'S IN THIS BOOK

This book is keyed to *Biology: The Unity and Diversity of Life*, by Cecie Starr, Ralph Taggart, Christine Evers, and Lisa Starr; but because it follows the College Board Topic Outline, it is compatible with all textbooks. It is divided into four sections. Part I offers suggestions for getting yourself ready, from signing up to take the test and sharpening your pencils to organizing a free-response essay. At the end of Part I, you will find a Diagnostic Test. This test has all of the elements of the AP Biology Examination, including multiple-choice questions, grid-in questions, and free-response questions. The sixty-three multiple-choice questions each cover material outlined by the College Board's four Big Ideas. Page references at the end of each answer indicate where you will find the discussion on that particular point in the 12th and 13th editions of *Biology*. Scoring is explained, so you will have some idea of how well you can do.

Part II, made up of seven chapters—again, following the updated AP Biology curriculum which centers on the four Big Ideas—is especially valuable when preparing for the exam in the spring. These

---

*AP and Advanced Placement Program are registered trademarks of the College Entrance Examination Board, which was not involved in the production of, and does not endorse, this product.

chapters are not a substitute for your textbook and class discussion; they simply review the AP Biology course. At the end of each chapter you will find fifteen multiple-choice questions, one single-part free-response question, one multi-part free-response question, and one grid-in question based on the material in that chapter. You will find page references at the end of each answer directing you to the discussion on that particular point in *Biology*.

Part III provides information about the laboratory assignments that the College Board recommends. Completing these labs will reinforce many of the important concepts presented throughout the course. This section summarizes the labs and ties the concepts presented by the labs to appropriate sections in the 12th and 13th editions of *Biology*. You might not have done the same labs in your class as students in another class, but the lab skills learned will be the same. The AP test will include concepts learned in the laboratory experiences as well as data analysis and the scientific method.

Part IV has two complete AP Biology Examinations. At the end of each test, you will find the answers, explanations, and references to *Biology* for the sixty-three multiple-choice questions, six grid-in questions, and free-response questions (multi-part and single-part).

SETTING UP A REVIEW SCHEDULE

If you have been steadily doing your homework and keeping up with the coursework, you are in good shape. But even if you've done all that—or if it's too late to do all that—there are some more ways to get it all together.

To begin, read Part I of this book. You will be much more comfortable going into the test if you understand how the test questions are designed and how best to approach them. Then take the Diagnostic Test and see where you are right now.

Take out a calendar and set up a schedule for yourself. If you begin studying early, you can chip away at the review chapters in Part II. You'll be surprised and pleased by how much material you can cover with studying half an hour a day for a month or so before the test. Look carefully at the Diagnostic Test; if you missed a number of questions, allow more time for the chapters that cover that topic of the course. Spend a few minutes reviewing the labs in Part III. Make sure that you have a complete understanding of the concepts introduced in each laboratory. You should be able to design a controlled experiment to test a hypothesis and explain what the expected results should be. Once you understand the experiment thoroughly, be prepared to redesign it by altering a different variable. The Practice Tests in Part IV will give you more experience with different kinds of multiple-choice questions, grid-in questions, and the wide range of free-response questions.

If time is short, skip reading the review chapters. Spend about five minutes with each lab summarized in Part III and familiarize yourself with the general procedures and the major concepts presented. Look at the key concepts listed at the beginning of each chapter to be sure that you have a working knowledge of the vocabulary and general concepts that will be used in the examination, and work on the multiple-choice and free-response questions at the end of each review.

This will give you a good idea of your understanding of that particular topic. Then take the tests in Part IV.

If time is really short, go straight from Part I to Part IV. Taking practice tests over and over again is the fastest, most practical way to prepare.

BEFORE THE EXAMINATION

By February, long before the exam, you need to make sure that you are registered to take the test. Many schools take care of the paperwork and handle the fees for their AP students, but check with your teacher or the AP coordinator to make sure that you are on the list. This is especially important if you have a documented disability and need test accommodations.

The evening before the exam is not a great time for partying or cramming. If you like, look over class notes or drift through your textbook, concentrating on the broad outlines of the course rather than the small details. You might also want to skim through this book and read the AP Tips.

The evening before the exam *is* a great time to get your things together for the next day. Sharpen a fistful of No. 2 pencils with good erasers for the multiple-choice section; set out several black or dark blue ballpoint pens for the free-response questions; make sure that you have a simple four-function calculator that can perform a square root; turn off your watch alarm if it has one; get a piece of fruit or a power bar and a bottle of water for the break; make sure you have your Social Security number and whatever photo identification and admission ticket are required. Then relax and get a good night's sleep.

On the day of the examination it is wise not to skip breakfast; studies show that students who eat a hot breakfast before testing get higher grades. Be careful not to drink a lot of liquids, necessitating a trip to the bathroom during the test. Breakfast will give you the energy you need to power you through the test and more. You will spend some time waiting while everyone is seated in the right room for the right test. That's before the test has even begun. Be prepared for a long morning. You do not want to be distracted by a growling stomach or hunger pangs.

Be sure to wear comfortable clothes, taking along a sweater or jacket in case the heating or air-conditioning is erratic. Be sure to wear clothes you like—everyone performs better when they think they look better—and by all means wear your lucky socks.

You have been on the fast track. Now go get a 5!

TAKING THE AP BIOLOGY EXAMINATION

The AP Biology Examination consists of two sections: Section I has sixty-three multiple-choice questions and six mathematical grid-in questions; Section II is the free-response section. It has two multi-part free-response questions, one of which connects with a laboratory experience. It also contains six single-part questions. You will have 90 minutes for the multiple-choice portion. The questions are collected, and you will be given a short break. You then have a ten-minute reading period during which you will be able to read the free-response questions but not begin writing. You have 80 minutes to complete the free-response portion of the exam. Try to spend 20 minutes on each multi-part question and 7 minutes answering the single-part questions. You must respond to every free-response question. There is no choice in AP Biology.

STRATEGIES FOR THE MULTIPLE-CHOICE SECTION

Here are some rules of thumb to help you work your way through the multiple-choice questions:

- **There is no longer a guessing penalty.** There are four possible answers for each question. Each correct answer is awarded one point, and no points are deducted for incorrect answers. Test takers should therefore not leave an answer blank. The multiple-choice section is worth 50% of your score.
- **Read the question carefully.** Pressured for time, many students make the mistake of reading the questions too quickly or merely skimming them. By reading a question carefully, you might already have some idea about the correct answer. You can then look for it in the responses. Careful reading is especially important in EXCEPT questions.
- **Eliminate any answer you know is wrong.** You may write on the multiple-choice questions in the test book. As you read through the answer choices, draw a line through any answer you know is wrong.
- **Read all of the possible answers, then choose the best answer choice.** AP Examinations are written to test your precise knowledge of a subject. Sometimes there are a few probable answers, but one of them is more specific. For example: "Name an organelle that produces ATP in all eukaryotic cells." Two of the choices might be chloroplasts and mitochondria. Although chloroplasts produce ATP, they are only found in certain plant

and protist cells. Only mitochondria produce ATP and are found in all eukaryotic cells.

■ **Mark and skip tough questions.** If you are hung up on a question, mark it in the margin of the question book. You can come back to it later if you have time. Make sure you skip that question on your answer sheet too.

TYPES OF MULTIPLE-CHOICE QUESTIONS

There are various kinds of multiple-choice questions. Here are some suggestions for how to approach each kind:

CLASSIC BEST ANSWER QUESTIONS

The classic best answer is the most common type of multiple-choice question. It simply requires you to read the question and select the most correct answer. For example:

1. The noncoding portion of a mRNA transcript is a (an)
   (A) intron.
   (B) exon.
   (C) polysome.
   (D) codon.

ANSWER: **A.** Introns contain noncoding segments and are removed from the transcript before it leaves the nucleus.

EXCEPT QUESTIONS

In the EXCEPT question, all of the choices are correct but one. The best way to approach these questions is as true/false. Mark a T or F in the margin next to each possible choice. There should be only one false choice, and that is the one you should select. For example:

1. All of the following statements about ribosomes are true EXCEPT
   (A) They can be found attached to the endoplasmic reticulum.
   (B) They can be found floating free in the cytoplasm.
   (C) They are only found in eukaryotic cells.
   (D) They are composed of two subunits.

ANSWER: **C.** All of the choices are true except C. Ribosomes are found in BOTH eukaryotic and prokaryotic cells.

LIST AND GROUP QUESTIONS

In this type of question, there is a list of possible answers, and you must select the answer that contains the correct group of responses. These questions look hard, but you can simplify them by crossing out items from the list and then eliminating them in the choices below. For example:

1. Which of the following groups of organisms contain chloroplasts in some of their cells?

   I.   Photoautotrophic bacteria
   II. Protists
   III. Plants

   (A) I only
   (B) II only
   (C) III only
   (D) II and III

To approach the question, draw a line through item I. Although photoautotrophic bacteria are capable of photosynthesis, they do not contain chloroplasts. Then cross out any response that contains item I: choice (A). Continue to cross out items that are wrong and the responses that contain them. Now you have narrowed down the possible responses.

ANSWER: **D.** Both protists and plant cells contain chloroplasts.

CHART/GRAPH QUESTIONS

These questions require you to examine the data on a chart or graph. While these questions are not difficult, spending too much time interpreting a chart or graph can slow you down. To avoid this, first read the question and all of the choices so that you know what you are looking for. Before you look at the graph, you might be able to eliminate some obviously incorrect responses.

The following example refers to an experiment set up to determine the rate of photosynthesis on suspensions of chloroplasts exposed to different conditions. The suspensions were either not boiled and exposed to light, not boiled and kept in the dark, boiled and exposed to light, or had no chloroplast in them. As photosynthesis occurs, the reduced dye becomes transparent. A spectrophotometer measured transmittance over a fifteen-minute period.

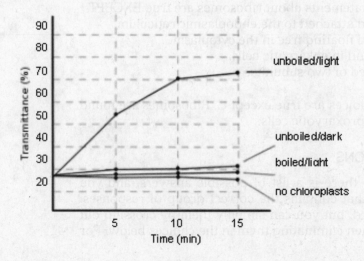

1. Which of the following conclusions is best supported by the data in the graph?
   - (A) Chloroplasts are not needed in photosynthesis.
   - (B) Photosynthesis occurs at a greater rate in unboiled chloroplasts exposed to light.
   - (C) The amount of carbon dioxide increases as photosynthesis occurs.
   - (D) The amount of oxygen used increases over time.

After interpreting the graph, eliminate choice (A) immediately—photosynthesis does not occur without chloroplasts and this condition had the lowest rate, not the highest. After reading the question and the responses, you could eliminate choices (C) and (D)—the graph displays the rate of photosynthesis only. Oxygen and carbon dioxide are not mentioned in the graph.

ANSWER: **B.** The only choice that showed an increase in transmittance, and thus photosynthesis, was unboiled chloroplasts exposed to light.

DIAGRAM QUESTIONS

These questions require you to interpret a simplified illustration. An underlying theme in biology is the relationship between form and function. Often you will need to have a complete understanding of the structure in the diagram. For example, the following question refers to the diagram of a neuron:

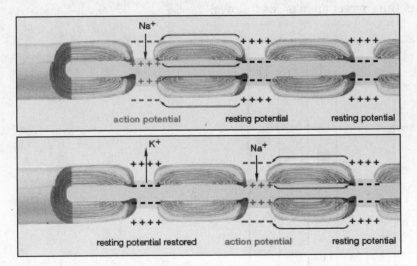

1. Which of the following explains the above diagram?
   - (A) Small gaps between the cells that make up the myelin sheath allow for ions to flow across the membrane
   - (B) Ions cannot flow through the myelin sheath, and therefore the action potential stops.
   - (C) Schwann cells only have a resting potential.
   - (D) Potassium ions rush into the cell and sodium ions out.

Answer: **A.** Sodium ions rush into the cell, and potassium ions rush out of the cell between the gaps that make up the myelin sheath. This allows the action potential to continue from node to node.

Grid-In Questions

These questions will require you to fill in the correct numerical answer. You may use a simple four-function calculator with a square root function on these questions. Use the Equations and Formulas guide as needed.

1. In *Drosophilia*, the allele for normal length wings is dominant over the allele for vestigial wings (vestigial wings are stubby little curls that cannot be used for flight). In a population of 1,000 individuals, 360 show the recessive phenotype. How many individuals would you expect to be homozygous dominant?

Answer:

$$p + q = 1$$
$$p^2 + pq = q^2 = 1$$
$$360/1000 = .36$$
$$q^2 = .36$$
$$q = .6$$
$$p = .4$$
$$p^2 = .16$$
$$.16 \times 1000 = 160$$

You would fill in 160 as the correct answer, as follows:

Free-Response Questions (single- and multi-part questions)

There are two multi-part free-response questions on the AP Biology Examination and six single-part free-response questions. At least one of the multi-part questions will be related to one of the lab experiences. Responses for free-response questions can be written in any order, but answers must appear in the writing section following each question. Questions are broken into parts (a) and (b). Be sure to label each part of your response.

These are not traditional English or History essay questions. They are typical science essay questions and require an analytical interpretation. You do not need to include an introduction, thesis, or conclusion, but do not restate the question and do not add fluff. You do not need to include an introduction, thesis, or conclusion. Although this sounds easier than writing a traditional essay, it is important that you know the material very well because these are targeted questions. Examination readers want specifics. They are looking for accurate information presented in clear, concise prose. You cannot mask vague information with elegant prose.

The free-response portion of the exam begins with a 10-minute reading period designed to allow you to read all questions before you answer any of them. During this time you will not be able to begin writing your final answers, but you will be able to record notes that will help you formulate your response. You will then have an 80-minute block of time for the entire free-response section, so watch your time. Allow about 20 minutes for each multi-part question and 7 minutes for each single-part question. Spend 5 minutes reading the question and any notes that you recorded during the reading period. Outline your response by jotting down a few words on each point you want to cover in your answer. Then spend about 15 minutes writing your response. Save the last few minutes to read over your response to make sure you have covered each point with enough detail. If 20 minutes have passed and you are not finished with a question, leave some space, and start a new question on the next page. You can come back later if you have time. Consider ranking them from easiest to most difficult and do the questions in that order—thus increasing confidence and reducing the chance of missing points because you run out of time.

Vocabulary

In answering the free-response questions, carefully read the question, and do exactly what it asks. It is important to note the word choices used in the questions:

■ **Define.** State the meaning of a word or phrase or to give a specific example. For instance, if a question asks you to define "anticodon," the response is "An anticodon is a sequence of three nucleotide bases in a tRNA molecule that are complementary to a codon on a mRNA molecule." Definitions are usually just one sentence.

- ▤ **Identify.** Select a factor, person, or idea and give it a name. For instance, if a question asks you to identify a major characteristic of mammals, one possible response is "Mammals are the only vertebrate whose females nourish young with milk produced by mammary glands."
- ▤ **Explain the data.** Give a cause or reason. Explanations usually include the word "because." For instance, if a question asks you to explain the difference between gross and net primary production, you could simply define each. You also might be asked to interpret the data presented in a graph or data table.

Scoring for Free-Response Questions

These questions are scored using a rubric that assigns points for each answer. For the multi-part questions, if a part requires you to identify and explain two factors, that part of the response will be worth 4 points (1 point for each identification and 1 point for each explanation). You can correctly satisfy the requirements of this part and earn all 4 points for part (a). If part (b) requires you to identify and describe two processes, that part of the response will also be worth 4 points (2 points for the identification and 2 points for the explanation). Again if you meet all of the requirements, you will earn the maximum of 4 possible points. If in part (c) you are asked to analyze and interpret data, it too could be worth 4 points (2 points for the analysis and 2 points for your interpretation). If you don't feel prepared for this part of the question, don't panic! If you can state a brief interpretation of the data, even without any analysis, you might pick up 1 point. This will give a total score of 9, which will not hurt your chance of earning a 5 on the exam. Remember, the question is only worth a total of 10 points, even though the sum of the three parts equals 12 points. This gives you the flexibility of earning the maximum points in your strong areas, while mitigating your weaknesses. You are not penalized for writing incorrect information, only given credit for correct information unless you contradict yourself.

For the single-part free-response questions, you will be answering the question in only 2-3 sentences. You will be asked a specific question and must answer what is being asked. These will also be graded using a rubric, and you will be given points for defining terms and explaining correctly.

Example of Single-Part Question

A spectrophotometer is an instrument used to determine the intensity of various wavelengths in a spectrum of light. Scientists put a sample into the spectrophotometer to determine the amount of light able to pass through the sample. The higher the rate of transmittance, the easier it is for light to travel through the substance. After running and walking up and down the stairs, students blew into a test tube with BTB indicator. They then put the samples in a spectrophotometer to determine the % transmittance. BTB indicates the acidity of a solution from dark to light where blue is a high pH, green a neutral pH, and yellow a low pH. Using the below information, explain what is occurring in this experiment in 2-3 sentences.

Number of Times Up and Down Stairs	Percent (%) Transmittance			
	Control	Walk	Jump	Run
0	31.9	31.8	32.0	30.8
2	32.1	33.3	50.0	45.4
4	32.2	38.9	56.4	55.4
6	32.5	40.5	60.7	58.7
8	32.1	46.7	65.4	62.1
10	32.2	45.9	69.8	65.7

ANSWER: As the amount of exercise increases, the % transmittance increases. This is because the amount of carbon dioxide (an acid) released from students during more intensive exercise increases, changing the BTB from dark to light. When the color change occurs, more light can travel through the sample giving a higher % transmittance.

EXAMPLE OF MULTI-PART QUESTION

For the following multi-part free-response question you will find three sample responses—one excellent, one mediocre, and one poor—and an explanation of how the responses were scored.

1. a. Describe the process within a mitochondrion and chloroplast that generates an imbalance of hydrogen ions across a membrane.
   b. Explain how this imbalance can contribute to the energy conversion within that organelle.
   c. Describe the type of organisms and tissues where you might find these two organelles and explain why they are found in these locations.

SAMPLE ESSAY ANSWER—EXCELLENT RESPONSE
Part (a): A mitochondrion has an inner membrane that divides this organelle into inner and outer compartments. Within the inner compartment the citric acid cycle (Krebs cycle) generates two coenzymes, NADH and FADH₂. Embedded in the inner membrane are a series of proteins that comprise the electron transport system (ETS). The imbalance begins as the coenzymes release H+ and pass electrons to the ETS. As the electrons move through the ETS, transport proteins move H+ across the membrane into the outer compartment. Oxygen is the final electron receptor and combines with two H+ from the inner compartment to form water. As this process ensues, a buildup of H+ in the outer compartment creates both an electrical and concentration gradient across the inner membrane. The imbalance is exacerbated by a depletion of H+ in the inner compartment as it combines with oxygen to form water.

A chloroplast is also compartmentalized. Within this organelle the inner membrane is folded into stacked disks called grana. The grana are surrounded by fluid in an outer compartment called the stroma. The membranes of the grana are called thylakoid membranes. Embedded within the thylakoid membranes are two photosystems, each followed by an ETS. The process begins as light energy and stimulates a chlorophyll molecule in the first photosystem to release electrons. These electrons move through the first ETS until they reach the second photosystem. The lost electrons are replaced as an enzyme catalyzes the photolysis of water. Water is split into oxygen, H+, and the electrons that replace the ones that are lost by the chlorophyll in the first photosystem. As electrons move through the ETS, transport proteins move H+ across the membrane into the thylakoid space. Meanwhile, the second photosystem releases electrons to its ETS as it too is stimulated by light energy. The electrons from the first ETS replace the ones released by the second photosystem. More H+ are pumped into the thylakoid space as the electrons move through the second ETS. At the end of the second ETS, a NADP+ picks up the electrons, and an H+ from outside the thylakoid space, to form NADPH. As this process continues, a buildup of H+ in the thylakoid space creates both an electrical and concentration gradient across the thylakoid membrane. This disparity is intensified by the depletion of H+ outside the thylakoid space as it combines with NADP+ to form NADPH.

Part (b): In both organelles, energy is converted to a more useful form as H+ finally seeks equilibrium. The H+ can only seek equilibrium by passing through a channel protein coupled with the enzyme ATP synthase. This enzyme transfers the energy from this flow of ions to inorganic phosphate and ADP forming ATP. In the chloroplast light energy is converted into the chemical energy of ATP and NADPH. In mitochondria chemical energy from organic molecules is converted to a more usable form in the energy carrier ATP.

Part (c): All tissues and cells of eukaryotic organisms contain mitochondria. The cells of animals, plants, fungi, and protists all require a constant supply of energy in the form of ATP. This energy must be generated locally and cannot be imported into a cell. Chloroplasts are absent in animals and fungi, but present in plants and many protists. Not all tissues in plants contain chloroplasts—generally, just the stems and leaves, the parts exposed to sunlight. Photosynthetic protists also contain chloroplasts. Unlike plants, which confine chloroplasts to certain tissues, protists tend to distribute them to nearly every cell.

Scoring 10/10. In Part (a), the response elaborates on the compartmental structure of both the mitochondrion and chloroplast. This understanding lays the foundation for the concept of ATP formation (1 point for each organelle). The causative factors in the creation of the H+ imbalance are explained (1/2 point each, max of 2 points). These include, in the mitochondria: 1) Coenzymes release electrons to the

ETS. As the electrons move through the ETS H+ are pumped into the outer compartment. 2) Oxygen combines with electrons from the ETS and two H+ from the inner compartment to form water. In the chloroplast: 1) Light stimulates electrons from chlorophyll to move through the ETS pulling in H+ into the inner compartment. 2) Photolysis splits water adding more H+ to the inner compartment. 3) NADP+ combines with H+ in the outer compartment.

In Part (b), the complete description of the movement of H+ through a channel protein coupled with the enzyme ATP synthase would yield 4 points.

The response in Part (c) completely describes the location of mitochondria to all eukaryotic cells. It also describes the reason for their ubiquitous presence. The explanation for the location of chloroplasts was also complete. The student listed only the groups of organisms that contain chloroplasts and the types of tissue where they might be found. This response would also yield 4 points for a total of 12. However, because the question is only worth 10 points, the student would only receive the maximum 10 points allowed.

SAMPLE ESSAY ANSWER—MEDIOCRE RESPONSE

Part (a): The membrane of a mitochondrion has a sequence of proteins called the Electron Transport System (ETS). As electrons pass through the ETS, hydrogen ions are transported to the outer compartment. The electrons pass through the ETS until they are captured by oxygen. Two hydrogen ions from the inner compartment and two electrons combine with oxygen to form water. This lowers the concentration of hydrogen ions in the inner compartment.

The chloroplast also has an ETS in its membrane. Electrons are passed to the ETS as light stimulates a chlorophyll molecule in a photosystem. As the electrons move through the ETS, hydrogen ions move across the membrane. This builds an imbalance of hydrogen across the membrane. Light splits water and releases electrons to replace the ones that the chlorophyll lost to the ETS. Oxygen gas is released and hydrogen ions are added to the compartment.

Part (b): ATP is produced as hydrogen seeks equilibrium. It moves from high to low concentrations as it passes through a protein equipped with an enzyme that makes ATP.

Part (c): Mitochondria are found in all eukaryotic cells. Chloroplasts are found in the stems and leaves of plants. They are also found in some protists.

Scoring 5/10. In part (a), although compartments are mentioned, their structure and importance are not described (0/2 points). Four factors that contribute to the imbalance were mentioned adequately enough (2/2 points).

In part (b), the explanation of energy conversion was incomplete. The mechanism of ATP formation and the resulting energy transfer were not described (1/4 points).

In Part (c), the student listed locations, but didn't explain why they would be found there (2/4 points).

Sample Essay Answer—Poor Response

Part (a): The mitochondrion uses proteins embedded within its membrane to move H+ from one part of the organelle to another. The energy that drives this process comes from organic molecules. This energy is carried by coenzymes that deliver electrons to proteins in the membrane. As electrons move through these proteins, H+ are pulled across the membrane and pass into its outer part. This process builds up an imbalance of H+.

In the chloroplast a similar process take place. It too has proteins in its membrane and uses them to move H+ from one side to the other. This process is also driven by the movement of electrons, but the source of electrons is chlorophyll. Light strikes the chlorophyll and stimulates it to release high-energy electrons to the membrane proteins.

Part (b): The hydrogen can only obtain equilibrium as it moves through a channel that has an enzyme that builds ATP.

Part (c): Mitochondria are found in animal cells, and chloroplasts are found in plants.

Scoring 3/10. In part (a), compartmentalization is referred to, but the structure of the organelles and how it was related to their function was not described (0/2) points). Only two factors that contribute to the imbalance were mentioned (half point each, 1/2 points).

In part (b), the explanation of energy conversion is incomplete. The mechanism of ATP formation and the resulting energy transfer were not described (1/4 points).

In part (c), the answer is incomplete. Mitochondria are not only found in animal cells, they are also found in the cells of all eukaryotic organisms, including plants. Protists were not mentioned as a type of organism containing chloroplasts. Although part of this response was vaguely correct, it didn't warrant any points.

A DIAGNOSTIC TEST

This diagnostic test will give you some indication of how you might score on the multiple-choice and grid-in portion as well as the free-response portion of the AP Biology exam. Of course, the exam changes every year, so it is never possible to predict a student's score with certainty. This test will also pinpoint strengths and weaknesses on the key content areas covered by the exam.

AP BIOLOGY EXAMINATION
SECTION I: Multiple-Choice and Grid-In Questions
Time—90 minutes
Number of Questions—63 MC and 6 GI

DIRECTIONS Each of the questions or incomplete statements of this portion of the exam is followed by four possible answers or suggestions. Choose the single response that best answers the question or completes the statement. There is no penalty for guessing. Simple four-function calculators may be used on this portion of the exam. Use the Equations and Formulas guide as needed for selecting the proper equation or formula to solve the Grid-In Questions.

MULTIPLE-CHOICE QUESTIONS

Questions 1-3 refer to the following diagram.

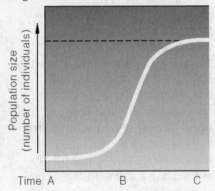

Change in growth pattern over time

1. The dotted line represents
   (A) the point at which emigration exceeds immigration.
   (B) the carrying capacity.
   (C) the maximum death rate.
   (D) the maximum growth rate.

2. At which point on the graph is the population growing at its biotic potential?
   (A) A
   (B) B
   (C) C
   (D) throughout the entire curve

3. At which point on the graph would limiting factors (food, shelter, predators) play a fundamental role in determining the population size?
   (A) A
   (B) B
   (C) C
   (D) at no point on the curve

Use the following terms to answer Questions 4-7. Match the terms with their functions. These terms may be used once, more than once, or not at all.
   (A) phospholipid
   (B) glucose
   (C) amino acid
   (D) guanine

4. This molecule is likely to form hydrogen bonds with a complementary molecule.

5. Peptide bonds could join this molecule to a similar one.

6. This molecule always has both hydrophobic and hydrophilic properties.

7. The light-independent (Calvin Cycle) reactions ultimately produce this molecule.

GO ON TO NEXT PAGE

17

8. Which of the following best describes the differences between positive and negative feedback?
    (A) Positive feedback amplifies a cellular response while negative feedback returns a cell to a target point.
    (B) Positive feedback returns a cell to a target point while negative feedback amplifies a cellular response.
    (C) Positive feedback only responds to internal stimuli while negative feedback responds to external stimuli.
    (D) Positive feedback only responds to external stimuli while negative feedback responds to internal stimuli.

9. All of the following statements about the cytoskeleton are true EXCEPT
    (A) Microtubules form scaffolding within a cell.
    (B) The cell wall is an external component.
    (C) Microfilaments form from actin subunits.
    (D) The inner surface of the nuclear envelope is supported by intermediate filaments.

10. In plants, the hormone ethylene is released from ripening fruit causing the production of specific enzymes which causes cells to have a cellular response to the hormonal signal. This is an example of
    (A) HOX genes.
    (B) mutation.
    (C) signal transmission.
    (D) phototropisms.

11. Which of the following does NOT cause genetic variation?
    (A) sexual reproduction
    (B) mutations
    (C) crossing over
    (D) mitosis

12. Which of the following is a correct statement?
    (A) Proteins are polymers in which the monomers are linked by peptide bonds.
    (B) Sugar monomers form large carbohydrates through the process called hydrolysis.
    (C) Lipids are polymers made of carbon, hydrogen, oxygen, and nitrogen atoms.
    (D) All nucleic acids exist as double strands.

13. An enzyme-mediated reaction
    (A) will usually speed up if a strong base is added.
    (B) is unaffected by salt.
    (C) will stop once all of the enzyme is used in the reaction.
    (D) has a faster rate of reaction at the beginning.

14. Which of the following statements accurately describes *Homo sapiens'* relationship with chimpanzees?
    (A) *Homo sapiens* are a direct descendant of chimpanzees.
    (B) *Homo sapiens* evolved before chimpanzees.
    (C) *Homo sapiens* evolved by allopatric speciation while chimpanzees evolved by peripatric speciation.
    (D) *Homo sapiens* evolved from a common ancestor with chimpanzees.

15. Scientific evidence shows that all life forms on Earth use the same genetic code to determine which amino acids match each mRNA codon. This is evidence of what idea?
    (A) All extant and extinct organisms shared a common ancestor at one time in Earth's history.
    (B) All extant and extinct organisms have the same genome.
    (C) All extinct organisms did not use the superior genetic code used by extant organisms today.
    (D) All extant organisms have the same genome.

16. Which of the following does not characterize most prokaryotic cells?
    (A) Golgi body
    (B) circular piece of DNA
    (C) ribosomes
    (D) cell wall

17. Which of the following is not a characteristic of animals?
    (A) multicellular
    (B) heterotrophic
    (C) capsule
    (D) no cell walls

18. All of the following are possible hypotheses on the formation of macromolecules EXCEPT
    (A) Formation of organic molecules was promoted at hydrothermal vents at the seafloor.
    (B) All macromolecules developed via spontaneous generation.
    (C) Positively charged amino acid molecules could stick to negatively charged clay particles in tidal flats and through radiation energy form protein molecules.
    (D) DNA self assembled and initiated directions for RNA and proteins.

19. Evidence for common ancestry among species includes
    (A) homologous structures.
    (B) analogous structures.
    (C) cladograms.
    (D) Hardy-Weinberg equilibrium.

20. A group of three codons contains how many nucleotides?
    (A) 3
    (B) 9
    (C) 27
    (D) 81

21. Viruses multiply by using which of the following?
    (A) mitotic cell cycle
    (B) binary fission
    (C) lytic cycle
    (D) reverse transcriptase

22. Which of the following is the correct pathway of the endomembrane system that would lead to an exported protein?
    (A) Golgi body → smooth ER → ribosome → plasma membrane
    (B) nucleus → lysosome → Golgi body → vesicle
    (C) rough ER → smooth ER → Golgi body → lysosome
    (D) nucleus → rough ER → Golgi body → plasma membrane

23. Who took and analyzed the first X-ray diffraction image of the DNA molecule?
    (A) Watson
    (B) Franklin
    (C) Jenner
    (D) Chargaff

24. A chromosome contains 30% guanine; how much adenine does it contain?
    (A) 20%
    (B) 30%
    (C) 40%
    (D) 60%

25. An individual with a genotype of AA BB Cc is able to produce how many different kinds of gametes?
    (A) 2
    (B) 3
    (C) 4
    (D) 7

26. If black hair (B) is dominant to blonde hair (b), then what fraction of the offspring produced by a cross of Bb × bb will be homozygous dominant?
    (A) 1/2
    (B) 1/4
    (C) 1/3
    (D) 0

27. Which pair of organisms could survive without other organisms?
    (A) fungi and secondary consumers
    (B) primary producers and decomposers
    (C) decomposers and primary consumers
    (D) deer and wolves

GO ON TO NEXT PAGE

28. Which of the following locations in cells does not have an electron transport chain that is used to set up an electrochemical gradient?
    (A) prokaryotic plasma membrane
    (B) inner mitochondrial membrane
    (C) thylakoid membrane
    (D) neuron cell membrane

29. A replicated chromosome has how many sister chromatids?
    (A) 0
    (B) 2
    (C) 4
    (D) 6

30. Which of the following is/are found in bacteria and plant cells, but not in animal cells?
    (A) cytoplasm
    (B) plasma membrane
    (C) cell wall
    (D) ribosomes

Questions 31–32 refer to the following diagram. The enzyme tyrosinase is involved in the production of the black pigment melanin. This colors the skin and hair of mammals while protecting them from excessive UV radiation.

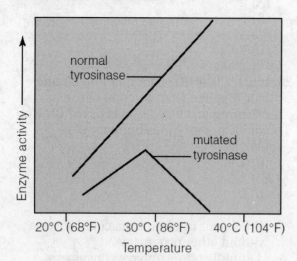

31. What happens to the enzyme produced by the mutated gene at about 28°C?
    (A) It denatures.
    (B) It produces more melanin.
    (C) It runs out of substrate.
    (D) The activation energy is finally reached.

32. What color would you expect the warmer parts of a mammal to be if it had the enzyme produced by a mutated gene?
    (A) It would be darker due to the ineffective enzyme.
    (B) It would be lighter due to the ineffective enzyme.
    (C) It would be darker due to better UV protection.
    (D) It would be lighter due to better UV protection.

33. Which would be the last species to appear on a newly formed island?
    (A) bacteria
    (B) insects
    (C) mammals
    (D) moss

34. RNAi is associated with
    (A) preventing digestion of mRNA by enzymes in the cytoplasm.
    (B) regulation of gene expression.
    (C) splicing of exons inside the nucleus.
    (D) the attachment of amino acids to tRNA molecules.

35. Why does the chromosomal abnormality Trisomy 21 occur?
    (A) an error in mitosis
    (B) an error in meiosis
    (C) an error in transcription
    (D) an error in replication

36. Which best describes a virus?
    (A) a cellular parasite
    (B) a non-cellular intracellular parasite
    (C) the common ancestor of protists
    (D) only has DNA

37. Rapid speciation in plants occurs through which of the following mechanisms?
    (A) natural selection
    (B) mass extinction
    (C) polyploidy
    (D) adaptive radiation

38. The flow of genetic information generally follows which path?
    (A) RNA → mRNA → trait → protein
    (B) DNA → mRNA → protein → trait
    (C) DNA → protein → mRNA → protein → trait
    (D) RNA → DNA → protein → trait

39. A chromosome undergoes replication twice. What percentage of the resulting chromosomes will contain some of the original DNA?
    (A) 0%
    (B) 25%
    (C) 50%
    (D) 75%

40. Which of the following is an adaptation that allows certain plants to survive in dry environmental conditions?
    (A) undergoing only the light-dependent reactions, not the Calvin cycle
    (B) undergoing only cellular respiration, not photosynthesis
    (C) doing gas exchange and binding carbon dioxide only at night
    (D) making NADH rather than NADPH

41. Which of the following is a true statement regarding mitosis and meiosis?
    (A) Mitosis is the process of making diploid daughter cells for growth and development while meiosis is the process of making haploid gametes for sexual reproduction.
    (B) Meiosis is the process of making diploid daughter cells for growth and development while mitosis is the process of making haploid gametes for sexual reproduction.
    (C) Mitosis is the process of making haploid daughter cells for growth and development while meiosis is the process of making diploid gametes for sexual reproduction.
    (D) Mitosis is the process of making diploid daughter cells for sexual reproduction while meiosis is the process of making haploid gametes for growth and development.

42. All of the following statements are true about transport proteins EXCEPT
    (A) They are peripheral proteins, located only on the cell's outer surface.
    (B) Channel proteins allow ions to move across the membrane with the concentration gradient.
    (C) The sodium-potassium pump uses ATP energy.
    (D) Facilitated diffusion requires a transport protein.

43. Primary productivity measures
    (A) the total amount of energy stored in all of the autotrophs in an ecosystem.
    (B) the total number of hours autotrophs run photosynthesis.
    (C) the total amount of energy required to maintain an ecosystem.
    (D) the total amount of energy stored in autotrophs less the amount of energy used by all organisms in the ecosystem.

44. Bacteria and fungi are essential to an ecosystem because
    (A) they cycle nutrients to the soil.
    (B) they form the base of food chains.
    (C) they release carbon dioxide into the atmosphere.
    (D) they store large amounts of carbon dioxide.

45. The monomers of nucleic acids are
    (A) fatty acids.
    (B) nucleotides.
    (C) 5 carbon sugars.
    (D) phosphate groups.

46. Carbon dioxide and oxygen rely on _____ to move them in and out of cells.
    (A) diffusion
    (B) active transport
    (C) exocytosis
    (D) passive diffusion

47. What is the major factor that limits cell size?
    (A) Large cells can't move efficiently.
    (B) The nucleus has trouble controlling a large cell.
    (C) A cell wall can't form around a cell if it's too large.
    (D) Large cells lack the surface area required to facilitate the movement of materials in and out of the cell.

GO ON TO NEXT PAGE

48. What is the product of photosynthesis?
    (A) glucose
    (B) carbon dioxide
    (C) ATP
    (D) NADPH⁺

The letters in the diagram below represent the answer options for Questions 49-52.

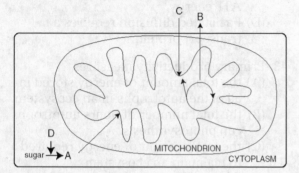

49. This molecule is carbon dioxide.

50. This molecule is renewed as letter A enters the mitochondria and also by lactic acid fermentation.

51. This is the final electron acceptor.

52. This molecule is a product of glycolysis.

53. From the relative positions of genes on the chromosome illustration below, we expect

(A) the lowest frequency of separating genes by crossing over is between genes C and D.
(B) genes C and D to be separated more often than genes D and B by crossing over.
(C) genes A and B to be separated more often than genes B and C by crossing over.
(D) the lowest frequency of separating genes from crossing over to occur between genes B and C.

54. The myelin sheath of a neuron acts as a
    (A) hormone.
    (B) ATP pump.
    (C) electrical insulator.
    (D) neurotransmitter.

55. Put the following major events in the history of life in the correct order from oldest to most recent.
    1. first eukaryotic cells
    2. universe forms
    3. first prokaryotic cells
    4. earth forms
    5. sun forms

    (A) 5, 4, 2, 3, 1
    (B) 2, 4, 5, 1, 3
    (C) 2, 5, 4, 3, 1
    (D) 1, 3, 4, 2, 5

Use the following answer options for Questions 56–58. Terms may be used once, more than once, or not at all.
(A) cytotoxic T-cell
(B) antigen
(C) antibody
(D) B-cell

56. This is the only type of cell that produces antibodies.

57. This recognizes and kills virus-infected cells.

58. This is recognized by certain white blood cells as nonself.

59. All of the following genotypes are possible F1 gametes for a dihybrid cross between Aa BB with Aa bb EXCEPT
    (A) Aa.
    (B) Ab.
    (C) AB.
    (D) aB.

60. Night length changes with the seasons (except at the equator), and organisms respond to this change in the length of night relative to the length of day. This phenomenon is termed
    (A) circadian rhythm.
    (B) photoperiodism.
    (C) phototropism.
    (D) germination.

61. During DNA replication
    (A) the leading and lagging strand diverge.
    (B) protein synthesis occurs.
    (C) the nucleotide sequence GGG starts the process.
    (D) mRNA is produced.

62. Nonspecific defenses include all of the following EXCEPT
    (A) fever.
    (B) inflammation.
    (C) mucus.
    (D) MHC markers.

63. How did Mendel ensure that his pea plants did not self-fertilize?
    (A) He removed the petals.
    (B) He kept them in cold storage.
    (C) He removed the pollen-producing anthers.
    (D) He removed them from the soil.

GRID-IN QUESTIONS

1. If 250 people out of a population of 1,000 are born with sickle-cell anemia, how many people in the population will be more resistant to malaria because they are heterozygous for the sickle-cell gene?

2. Cancerous cells from various patients were observed. One hundred cells from each sample were chosen at random and analyzed for the stage of the cell cycle in which the cell was. The table represents these data.

Cell Type	Inter-phase	Mitosis			
		Pro-phase	Meta-phase	Ana-phase	Telophase/Cytokinesis
Stomach cells	24	36	19	10	6
Pancreatic cells	26	35	10	9	10
Lung cells	21	42	15	8	7
Neurons	50	20	13	7	5
Liver cells	50	17	15	5	5

If cancer cells divide every hour when in mitosis, how many pancreatic cancer cells would be produced in 5 hours?

3. A spectrophotometer is an instrument used to determine the intensity of various wavelengths in a spectrum of light. Scientists put a sample into the spectrophotometer to determine the amount of light able to pass through the sample. The higher the rate of transmittance the easier it is for light to travel through the substance. After running and walking up and down the stairs, students blew into a test tube with BTB indicator. They then put the samples in a spectrophotometer to determine the % transmittance. BTB indicates the acidity of a solution from dark to light where blue is a high pH, green a neutral pH, and yellow a low pH.

Times up and down stairs	% Transmittance			
	Control	Walk	Jump	Run
0	31.9	31.8	32.0	30.8
2	32.1	33.3	50.0	45.4
4	32.2	38.9	56.4	55.4
6	32.5	40.5	60.7	58.7
8	32.1	46.7	65.4	62.1
10	32.2	45.9	69.8	65.7

What would be average % transmittance for walking up and down the stairs?

4. H_2O_2 is broken down to H_2O and O_2 by the enzyme catalase. The following data were taken over 5 minutes.

Time (min)	Amount of Oxygen Produced (mL)
1	2.3
2	3.6
3	4.2
4	5.5
5	5.9

What is the rate of enzymatic reaction in mL/min from 2 to 4 minutes?

5. In an 8-acre plot of forest there are 32 trees per acre. Each tree weighs 460 kg where 150 kg of each tree is water. Using the following formula, determine the biomass of all the trees in the forest.

Biomass = # of organisms × Weight of organisms (without water)

GO ON TO NEXT PAGE

6. In pea plants, smooth seeds are dominant to wrinkled, and purple flowers are dominant to white. In a dihybrid cross where a 9:3:3:1 ratio is expected, the following data were collected.

Smooth and Purple= 223
Smooth and White = 84
Wrinkled and Purple = 89
Wrinkled and White = 33

Determine the chi-square value.

STOP
END OF SECTION I

IF YOU FINISH BEFORE TIME IS CALLED, YOU MAY CHECK YOUR WORK ON THIS SECTION. DO NOT GO ON TO SECTION II UNTIL YOU ARE TOLD TO DO SO.

AP BIOLOGY EXAMINATION
SECTION II: Free-Response Essays
Suggested Writing Time—80 minutes
Number of Questions—2 MP and 6 SP

DIRECTIONS This section begins with a 10-minute reading period to allow you to read the questions. You may take notes, but you cannot begin your final response until this period is over. You will then have 80 minutes to answer the following questions. You can continue planning and organizing your response, but this time will come out of your 80 minutes. Answers must be in essay form. Outline form is unacceptable. Diagrams with labels may be used to supplement your answer. Diagrams alone, however, are inadequate. Unless the directions indicate otherwise, respond to all parts of each question. It is recommended that you take a few minutes to plan and outline each answer. Spend approximately 20–25 minutes per multi-part question and 3–10 minutes per single-part question. Support your essay with specific examples where appropriate. Be sure to number each of your answers. If a question has multiple parts, make sure the answer to each part is clearly labeled.

MULTI-PART QUESTIONS

1. Prokaryotes are Earth's most abundant organisms. There are many characteristics that make prokaryotes unique on Earth. Pick two of the following three comparisons and explain how they relate to prokaryotes:
   (a) bacteria vs. archaea
   (b) chemoautotrophs vs. chemoheterotrophs
   (c) transformation vs. transduction

2. Gregor Mendel's experiments with pea plants led him to describe laws or principles concerning the inheritance of traits. Yet, geneticists today realize that much inheritance does not follow these laws.
   (a) Explain Mendel's laws of segregation and independent assortment.
   (b) Describe how sex linked inheritance does not follow Mendel's conclusions.
   (c) Explain an example of nonnuclear inheritance.

SINGLE-PART QUESTIONS

1. Describe two ways in which human actions have had an effect on ecosystem diversity.

2. Describe the structure of DNA.

3. Explain the differences between chromatids, chromatin, chromosomes, and homologous chromosomes.

4. An aquatic plant in an aquarium with a light source has bubbles coming from it and surrounding the leaves. What are the bubbles and where are they coming from?

GO ON TO NEXT PAGE

5. Explain how this diagram shows the idea of a keystone predator.

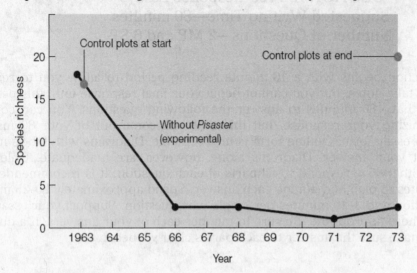

6. A group of biology students found a vial of flies in the back of a biology classroom and wanted to determine the genotype of the flies' ancestors. The data below show the number of red and white eye male and female flies. The students remember from past experiments that red eyes are dominant to white. Based on this information, what conclusion can be made about the genotypes of the parent generation?

Data of the F2 Generation		
Eye Color	Male	Female
Red eye	115	178
White eye	69	0

END OF EXAMINATION

ANSWERS FOR SECTION I

MULTIPLE-CHOICE ANSWER KEY

SCORING Using the table below, score the multiple-choice portion of the test. Correct answers earn points, while incorrect answers are not penalized. A greater number of correct answers would be associated with higher exam scores. You will find explanations of the answers below and on the following pages.

1. B	14. D	27. B	40. C	53. A
2. B	15. A	28. D	41. A	54. C
3. C	16. A	29. B	42. A	55. C
4. D	17. C	30. C	43. A	56. D
5. C	18. D	31. A	44. A	57. A
6. A	19. A	32. B	45. B	58. B
7. B	20. B	33. C	46. A	59. A
8. A	21. C	34. B	47. D	60. B
9. B	22. D	35. B	48. A	61. A
10. C	23. B	36. B	49. B	62. D
11. D	24. A	37. C	50. D	63. C
12. A	25. A	38. B	51. C	
13. D	26. D	39. C	52. A	

EXPLANATIONS FOR THE MULTIPLE-CHOICE ANSWERS

1. **B.** The carrying capacity is the maximum number of individuals the environment can sustain indefinitely (*Biology*, 12th ed., page 802/13th ed., page 796).

2. **B.** Biotic potential refers to the maximum rate of growth for a population (*Biology*, 12th ed., page 801/13th ed., page 795).

3. **C.** Limiting factors set a population's carrying capacity (*Biology*, 12th ed., page 802/13th ed., page 796).

4. **D.** In DNA, guanine forms three hydrogen bonds with its complementary nitrogen base, cytosine (*Biology*, 12th ed., page 207/13th ed., page 139).

5. **C.** Amino acids are held to each other by C-N (peptide) bonds in the formation of polypeptide chains (*Biology*, 12th ed., page 44/13th ed., page 46).

6. **A.** Phospholipids have hydrophobic fatty acid tails and a hydrophilic phosphate head (*Biology*, 12th ed., page 43/13th ed., page 44).

7. **B.** Glucose is a final product of photosynthesis. It is produced in the Calvin-Benson cycle during the light-independent reactions (*Biology*, 12th ed., page 115/13th ed., page 105).

8. **A.** Positive feedback amplifies a cellular response while negative feedback returns a cell to a target point. Both positive and negative feedback can respond to internal and external stimuli (*Biology*, 12th ed., pages 466–467/13th ed., pages 536 and 546).

9. **B.** The cell wall does offer external support, but it is not part of the cytoskeleton (*Biology*, 12th ed. page 72/13th ed., pages 68–69).

10. **C.** In signal transmission, an intercellular, intracellular, or extracellular signal causes a reaction by the cell such as transcription of a gene or regulation of gene expression (*Biology*, 12th ed., pages 526–527/13th ed., pages 506–507, 513).

11. **D.** Mitosis creates two identical diploid cells where no variation should be included unless mutations have occurred. Sexual reproduction and crossing over in meiosis both introduce unique variation (*Biology*, 12th ed., pages 144–145, 160–161/13th ed., pages 179, 194–195).

12. **A.** Amino acids are linked by peptide bonds in proteins. Polymers are formed through dehydration synthesis and are broken down by hydrolysis. Lipids do not contain nitrogen atoms. While DNA is double-stranded, RNA molecules, such as messenger RNA, are not (*Biology*, 12th ed. pages 40–48. 216–217/13th ed., pages 42–49, 150–152).

13. **D.** Due to a high concentration of substrate, therefore a greater probability of enzyme-substrate collisions, the rate of reaction will be the fastest at the beginning of the reaction (*Biology*, 12th ed., page 96/13th ed., pages 84–85).

14. **D.** Humans share an ancestor with chimpanzees. *Homo sapiens* did not directly evolve from chimps, and the mode of speciation is not clear from the fossil record (*Biology*, 12th ed., pages 454–456/13th ed., pages 444–447).

15. **A.** Genetic and molecular evidence shows that all extant and extinct organisms shared a common ancestor during the origin of life on Earth (*Biology*, 12th ed., page 308–309/13th ed., page 300–301).

16. **A.** Prokaryotic cells have no membrane-bound organelles (including no nucleus or Golgi body). They have a single chromosome, normally in a circle. They have ribosomes, which are the site of protein synthesis, and cells walls for protection (*Biology*, 12th ed., pages 340–342/13th ed., pages 58–59).

17. **C.** Animals are multicellular and heterotrophic. They are eukaryotic (have membrane-bound organelles) and do not have cell walls like plants, fungi, and bacteria. Bacteria have a capsule but not animal cells (*Biology*, 12th ed., pages 404–405/13th ed., page 394).

18. **D.** The only hypothesis that has not been proposed is that DNA came first, even though we know information flows from DNA to RNA to protein in prokaryotes and eukaryotes. However, viruses can use RNA first to make a copy of DNA; and RNA can act as enzymes that would catalyze protein synthesis (*Biology*, 12th ed., page 329/13th ed., page 311).

19. **A.** Homologous structures, along with similarities in development, a common genetic code, and other biochemical similarities point to common ancestry. Analogous structures have similar surface adaptations to the environment that are not accompanied by similarities in DNA or development. Cladograms are used to show common ancestry based on evidence such as homologous structures, but are not evi-

dence themselves. Hardy-Weinberg equilibrium is describing changes within a population, and is not used to compare species (*Biology*, 12th ed., pages 303–309/13th ed., pages 297–303).

20. **B.** Each codon consists of three nucleotides, so 3 codons would contain 9 nucleotides (*Biology*, 12th ed., page 221/13th ed., page 154).

21. **C.** Viruses are particles and are not made of cells. They multiply quickly using the lytic cycle, where they use their host cell's metabolism to quickly manufacture viral DNA and proteins and assemble them into new viruses that are released from the host cell. Reverse transcriptase is used by some viruses to produce DNA from its RNA; however, new viruses are not made immediately by the host cell (*Biology*, 12th ed. pages 336–337/13th ed., pages 326–327).

22. **D.** The process begins with transcription in the nucleus. The mRNA moves to a ribosome on the rough ER and a polypeptide forms. The polypeptides are packaged and sent to a Golgi body. After final modification, the proteins are again packaged into a vesicle that merges with the plasma membrane to expel its contents (*Biology*, 12th ed., page 66/13th ed., pages 64–65).

23. **B.** Rosalind Franklin's X-ray diffraction images assisted Watson and Crick in determining the structure of DNA (*Biology*, 12th ed., page 211/13th ed., page 143).

24. **A.** If 30% of the chromosome is guanine then 30% must be cytosine. This leaves 40% to be divided evenly between adenine and thymine (*Biology*, 12th ed., page 206/13th ed., page 138).

25. **A.** Genes are distributed into gametes independently of how other genes are distributed. In this example, an A is always passed on and so is a B. However, either a C or a c has a 50% chance of being passed on (*Biology*, 12th ed., page 174/13th ed., page 208).

26. **D.** A cross between a Bb and a bb will produce 50% Bb and 50% bb only (*Biology*, 12th ed., page 173/13th ed., page 209).

27. **B.** Primary producers are autotrophs and can provide their own energy source. Decomposers could recycle the nutrients in dead plants back to the soil for new plants to take up. All of the other combinations lack a means to either introduce energy into the system or recycle nutrients (*Biology*, 12th ed., page 840/13th ed., page 835).

28. **D.** Electron transport chains used in photosynthesis and cellular respiration are found embedded in the thylakoid membrane and inner mitochondrial membrane, respectively, in eukaryotes and in the plasma membrane of prokaryotic cells (*Biology*, 12th ed., pages 112–114, 130–131/13th ed., pages 106–108, 124–125).

29. **B.** A replicated chromosome is made up of two sister chromatids joined together by a centromere (*Biology*, 12th ed., pages 142–143/13th ed., page 179).

30. **C.** Animal cells lack a cell wall, but contain all of the other features typical of cells (*Biology*, 12th ed., page 56/13th ed., pages 58–61).

31. **A.** Enzymes only function correctly when they have the proper shape. The increased temperature disrupts the bonds holding the enzyme

together; it denatures, causing it to lose its effectiveness (*Biology*, 12th ed., page 99/13th ed., page 83).

32. **B.** The enzyme denatures at body temperature, and the pigment would not be produced on the core portion of the animal. However, the extremities—like the ears and nose—are likely to be cool enough to allow the enzyme to function (*Biology*, 12th ed., page 99/13th ed., page 83).

33. **C.** Mammals would appear last as they require lower trophic levels to provide them with feeding opportunities (*Biology*, 12th ed., page 828/13th ed., page 799).

34. **B.** RNAi, or RNA interference, is involved in the regulation of gene expression (*Biology*, 12th ed., page 231/13th ed., page 165).

35. **B.** Trisomy 21 is the result of a change in the chromosome number due to a nondisjunction event during meiosis (*Biology*, 12th ed., page 194/13th ed., page 228).

36. **B.** A virus is a non-cellular parasite that lives inside a cell. Viruses are not considered cells because they don't have plasma membranes. Viruses can have either DNA or RNA and are smaller than bacteria (*Biology*, 12th ed., page 334/13th ed., page 324).

37. **C.** Plants can be polyploid, meaning that they have more than two sets of chromosomes. When this occurs, it allows for rapid speciation due to the high amount of genetic variation (*Biology*, 12th ed., page 294/13th ed., page 288).

38. **B.** Gene expression begins with a sequence of DNA and converts into a structural or functional part of a cell or body (*Biology*, 12th ed., page 217/13th ed., page 150).

39. **C.** DNA replication is semi-conservative. After the first replication, both newly formed chromosomes will contain one original strand and one new strand of DNA. After the second replication, two of the four chromosomes will contain one original strand and one new strand, while the other two will consist of only new strands (*Biology*, 12th ed., page 208/13th ed., pages 140–141).

40. **C.** Certain plants, such as cacti, close their stomata during the day and fix carbon dioxide at night as an adaptation to dry conditions. This helps prevent water loss. The other options would not give plants an advantage in dry conditions (*Biology*, 12th ed., page 117/13th ed., page 111).

41. **A.** Mitosis makes 2 identical diploid somatic cells whereas meiosis makes 4 genetically different haploid gametes. (*Biology*, 12th ed., pages 164–165/13th ed., pages 198–199).

42. **A.** Transport proteins are transmembrane proteins which span the membrane. Peripheral proteins are on the inside of the membrane and are not used for transport. (*Biology*, 12th ed., page 83/13th ed., page 89).

43. **A.** Autotrophs or self feeders are photosynthetic and set the energy level in an ecosystem (*Biology*, 12th ed., page 844/13th ed., pages 834–835).

44. **A.** Fungi and many bacteria are decomposers and therefore break down material and cycle the nutrients back into the soil (*Biology*, 12th ed., page 840/13th ed., page 830).

45. **B.** Nucleotides consist of pentose sugars, phosphate groups, and nitrogenous bases. Nucleotides are linked together to form a DNA chain (*Biology*, 12th ed., page 206/13th ed., page 49).

46. **A.** The amount of surface area and the partial pressure gradients influence the rate of gas exchange across respiratory surfaces (*Biology*, 12th ed., page 682/13th ed., page 682).

47. **D.** As a cell enlarges, the surface area only increases by a square of its diameter while the volume increases by a cube of its diameter. Eventually there is not enough surface area to accommodate the required movement of material across the membrane (*Biology*, 12th ed., page 56/13th ed., page 55).

48. **A.** The process of photosynthesis takes light energy and converts it to sugar. ATP and NADPH$^+$ are used to make glucose, and water is also made (*Biology*, 12th ed., page 354/13th ed., page 105).

49. **B.** Two of the three carbons from each pyruvate are released in the Krebs cycle. The first carbon is released as acetyl-coA is formed in the mitochondrion before the Krebs cycle takes place (*Biology*, 12th ed., page 129/13th ed., page 122).

50. **D.** NAD$^+$ receives electrons and H$^+$ in glycolysis. It is renewed as a result of electron transport in aerobic respiration or when pyruvate is transformed during fermentation (*Biology*, 12th ed., page 48/13th ed., pages 126–127).

51. **C.** Oxygen is highly electronegative and therefore strongly attracted to electrons. It is poised at the end of the electron transport chain and is the final electron acceptor (*Biology*, 12th ed., page 131/13th ed., pages 124–125).

52. **A.** This molecule represents the pyruvate, the final product of glycolysis (*Biology*, 12th ed., page 126/13th ed., page 121).

53. **A.** The probability that a crossover event will separate two genes decreases as the distance between the two genes on the chromosome decreases (*Biology*, 12th ed., page 178/13th ed., page 194).

54. **C.** The myelin sheath surrounds Schwann cells and works to conduct the electrical impulse of an action potential down a neuron. This allows nerve impulses to travel quickly (*Biology*, 12th ed., page 564/13th ed., page 552).

55. **C.** The universe formed first, followed by the sun. It is hypothesized that Earth formed from rocks orbiting the sun, which indicates that the sun had to have formed first. Prokaryotes can live without oxygen, but eukaryotes cannot. Because early Earth had little free O$_2$, prokaryotes would have been able to survive, but eukaryotes would not (*Biology*, 12th ed., page 329/13th ed., pages 310–314).

56. **D.** During antibody-mediated immune responses, populations of B cells form and secrete antibodies that recognize and bind antigen (*Biology*, 12th ed., page 671/13th ed., page 662).

57. **A.** Cytotoxic T-cells recognize a cell that has been infected with a virus and is displaying viral proteins. It then releases factors that break apart the membrane of the cell and cause it to lyse (*Biology*, 12th ed., pages 672–673/13th ed., pages 664–665).

58. **B.** Antigens are the parts of pathogens that are recognized by lymphocytes in the specific immune response (*Biology*, 12th ed., page 660/13th ed., page 650).

59. **A.** The Law of Segregation states that pairs of homologous chromosomes separate during meiosis and end up in different gametes (*Biology*, 12th ed., page 173/13th ed., page 650).

60. **B.** Circadian rhythm is a 24-hour cycle of activity for an organism whereas gravitropism is a growth response to gravity. Photoperiodism is an organism's response to changes in the length of day (*Biology*, 12th ed. pages 532–533/13th ed., pages 514–515).

61. **A.** During DNA replication the two strands of DNA are separated and replicated. Both the leading and lagging strand are synthesized by DNA polymerase at the same time (*Biology*, 12th ed. page 208/13th ed. page 141).

62. **D.** Nonspecific defenses include barriers at body surfaces and internal reactions to tissue damage (*Biology*, 12th ed., page 660/13th ed., pages 656–657).

63. **C.** By removing the anthers, Mendel removed the source of pollen (*Biology*, 12th ed., page 170/13th ed., page 204).

GRID-IN ANSWERS

SCORING Answers and explanations for questions in this section are given below. When comparing your answer to the provided answer, pay close attention to the number of significant digits, and for answers with values between zero and one, to the inclusion of the place-holding zero before the decimal point. A correct answer in this section is weighted equally to a correct answer in the multiple choice section of the exam. There is no penalty for an incorrect answer.

1. 500

   $p + q = 1$

   $p^2 + 2pq + q^2 = 1$

   $q^2 = 250/1000 = .25$

   $q = .5$

   $p + q = 1$

   $p = .5$

   heterozygous is $2pq$

   $2(.5)(.5) = .5 \times 1000 = 500$

   (*Biology*, 12th ed., pages 280–281/13th ed., pages 274–275).

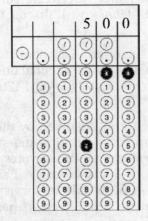

2. **1952**

   During interphase, cells are not actively dividing but rather preparing to divide or suspended. Therefore, the number of cells in mitosis are added together.

   35 + 10 + 9 + 10 = 64 cells

   1 hour: 64 × 2 = 122

   2 hours: 122 × 2 = 244

   3 hours: 244 × 2 = 488

   4 hours: 488 × 2 = 976

   5 hours: 976 × 2 = 1952

   (*Biology*, 12th ed. pages 144–145/13th ed., pages 178–179).

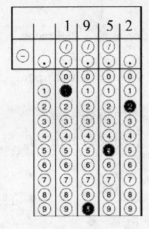

3. **39.52**

   Mean = Sum of all data points/ Number of data points

   31.8 + 33.3 + 38.9 + 40.5 + 46.7 + 45.9 = 237.1

   237.1 / 6 = 39.52

   (*Biology*, 12th ed., page 111/ 13th ed., pages 118–119).

4. **0.95**

   Rate = dY/dt

   Rate is the slope

   $m = (y_2 - y_1)/(x_2 - x_1)$

   $m = (5.5 - 3.6)/(4 - 2) = 0.95$

   (*Biology*, 12th ed., pages 98–99/13th ed., pages 82–83).

5. 79,360

8 acres × 32 trees per acre = 256 trees total

460 kg – 150 kg of water = 310 kg per tree

256 trees × 310 kg = 79,360 kg

(*Biology,* 12th ed., page 844/13th ed., page 834).

6. 3.84

Expected	Observed
241.3	223
80.43	84
80.43	89
26.81	33

$$X_2 = \frac{\Sigma (o - e)^2}{e}$$

$[(223 - 241.3)^2/241.3]$
$+ [(84 - 80.43)^2/80.43]$
$+ [(89 - 80.43)^2/80.43]$
$+ [(33 - 26.81)^2/26.81]$
$= 3.84$

(*Biology,* 12th ed., pages 188–189/13th ed., pages 206–208).

ANSWERS FOR SECTION II

SCORING It is difficult to come up with an exact score for this section of the test. Correct statements are awarded points. You are not penalized for incorrect statements unless you have contradicted one of your correct statements. Diagrams that are not explained by your statements and bullet points or lists are not awarded points. If you compare your answers to the answers provided below, you can get a general idea of the percentage of the questions for which you would get credit. More thorough answers will earn more points and are associated with higher exam scores of 4 or 5.

FREE-RESPONSE ANSWERS

MULTI-PART

1. (a) Bacteria can be both pathogenic and ecologically important. Many bacteria are helpful to ecosystems such as nitrogen-fixing bacteria, which take nitrogen from the atmosphere and turn it into ammonia, which is then used by plants. Some bacteria like cyanobacteria are photosynthetic and have provided oxygen to the atmosphere for billions of years. While some bacteria help specific ecosystems, others are extremely dangerous and cause deadly diseases—tuberculosis and tetanus, for example. Archaea are similar to bacteria in size and shape but differ in the environments they live in. Archaea are either methanogens (anaerobic and free oxygen kills), extreme thermophiles (live in extreme heat), or extreme halophiles (live in extreme salt).

   (b) Chemoautotrophs use carbon dioxide as a carbon source and get energy by removing electrons from inorganic molecules. Chemo-heterotrophs acquire carbon and energy by breaking down organic compounds. They can feed on both living and dead organisms.

   (c) Transformation and transduction both introduce genetic variation into bacteria cells which reproduce asexually (no genetic variation). Transformation is the random uptake of DNA from the environment. This DNA is then integrated into the bacteria cells' genome. In transduction, a bacteriophage (virus that infects bacteria cells) picks up DNA from a cell that it infects then transfers the DNA to the next host cell (*Biology*, 12th ed., Chapter 21/13th ed., Chapter 20).

2. (a) Mendel's law of segregation states that for a given inherited characteristic, an organism has two factors, now called genes, and the organism can only give one of its two factors to a given offspring. Thus, if the organism has the genotype Aa, it will give A or a to its offspring, not both. Mendel's law of independent assortment applies to the inheritance of two traits and states that the inheritance of one factor or gene does not affect the inheritance of the other factor. That is, if the organism has the genotype AaBb, it can pass on the combinations AB, Ab, aB, and ab with equal probability. Mendel's law of independent assortment is now known to not always apply because genes might be located close together on the same chromosome and therefore be inherited together.

   (b) Sex-linked traits fail to follow Mendel's conclusions that each trait is governed by the interaction of two alleles. Males have one X chromosome and one Y chromosome. Genes found on the X chromosome in a male will be expressed as the Y chromosome lacks those genes. For example, color-blindness is a gene that is carried on the X chromosome. Males who have a correctly functioning gene on the X chromosome will be able to differentiate between colors. However, males with a mutated form of this gene will express it, as the Y chromosome lacks this gene.

(c) Mitochondria and chloroplasts have nonnuclear DNA. Because these organelles may not be equally distributed during meiotic cytokinesis, their inheritance does not follow Mendel's laws. One example of this is that humans typically inherit their mitochondrial DNA maternally because the egg cell contains many mitochondria and the sperm does not contribute cytoplasm to the zygote (*Biology*, 12th ed., pages 172–174, 190–191, 291/13th ed., pages 206–209, 224–225, 285).

SINGLE-PART

1. One way in which humans have affected ecosystem diversity is by introducing a non-native species to an environment. For example, the introduction of kudzu to the southeastern United States allowed that species to become invasive. In the absence of naturally occurring predators or parasites, kudzu has spread and out-competed native plant species. A second way would be slash and burn agriculture in areas once occupied by tropical rain forests. When the already poor soil is further depleted of nutrients, desertification can result, with the area no longer able to support the variety of plants and animals native to that area (*Biology*, 12th ed., pages 830–831, 852–853, 855, 875, 892–903/13th ed., pages 822–823, 840–841, 843, 861, 877–891).
Note: You may choose other examples to answer this question.

2. DNA consists of two strands of nucleotides. Each nucleotide has a deoxyribose sugar and a phosphate group; linkages between these make up the "backbone" of the polymer. Also attached to each deoxyribose sugar molecule is a nitrogenous base. Four of these nitrogenous bases are found in DNA. Two have double ring structures and are called purines (adenine and guanine, abbreviated A and G); two have single ring structures and are called pyrimidines (thymine and cytosine, abbreviated T and C). The nitrogenous bases form pairs due to hydrogen bonds between them. Adenine pairs with thymine, and guanine pairs with cytosine. The attraction between these pairs holds the two strands together in the spiral structure called the double helix. The two strands are anti-parallel, with the phosphate group located at the ends referred to as 5', a name derived from the carbon atom in the deoxyribose to which it is attached. A segment of DNA is illustrated below and shows the anti-parallel nature of the molecule as well as the base pairing.

5' – A T C C G A T G G C C A – 3'

3' – T A G G C T A C C G G T – 5'

(*Biology*, 12th ed., pages 206–207/ 13th ed., pages 138–139).

3. Chromatin is uncondensed DNA. This is the normal state of DNA in a cell. During interphase of mitosis and meiosis the DNA condenses into chromosomes. There are two copies of each chromosome known as homologous chromosomes. Each of the duplicated chromosomes is made up of sister chromatids. Each chromatid contains the same genes

but might have different versions of the gene known as an allele (*Biology*, 12th ed., page 64/13th ed., pages 63 and 179).

4. The bubbles on the plant are oxygen. They are the result of the plant undergoing photosynthesis in the presence of light. In the process of photosynthesis a plant take light energy and transforms it into glucose. The first part of the process has two electrons being released from water and oxygen is the byproduct (*Biology*, 12th ed., pages 111–113/13th ed., pages 105–107).

5. The diagram shows how the removal of a keystone predator results in the decrease in biodiversity within a community. The control shows that when the keystone predator is not removed there is no significant decrease in the species diversity within the ecosystem (*Biology*, 12th ed., page 830/13th ed., page 822).

6. The parent generation would be $X^R X^R \times X^r Y$. If these two genotypes are crossed, all the female flies of the F_1 generation would be $X^R X^r$ and all the males would be $X^R Y$. When the F_1 generation is crossed, the F_2 generation would have all females with the phenotype of red eyes, half the males with the red eye phenotype, and half the males with the white eye phenotype, as the data show (*Biology*, 12th ed., page 175/13th ed., pages 207–209).

Part II
A Review of AP Biology

1

EVOLUTION

BIG IDEA 1

Physical, chemical, and biological processes are used to analyze the past, including the early Earth as well as life's origin. Geologic evidence helps to date and describe past events, while the fossil record can help to place species into the proper place in time. Both microevolution and macroevolution processes effect change in species and populations. Evidence from anatomical, fossil, and molecular comparisons allows patterns of development and relatedness to be established.

KEY TERMS

adaptive radiation

alleles

allele frequency

allopatric speciation

analogous structure

balanced polymorphism

biogeography

bottleneck effect

catastrophism

cladogram

coevolution

comparative morphology

directional selection

disruptive selection

endosymbiosis

evolution

extant

extinction

fitness

fossils

founder effect

gene flow

gene pool

genetic drift

Hardy-Weinberg
 equilibrium

half life

homologous structures

Hox genes

hydrothermal vents

lethal mutation

macroevolution

mass extinctions

microevolution

morphological
 convergence

morphological
 divergence

natural selection

neutral mutation

plate tectonics

phylogeny

41

population	ribozymes	stabilizing selection
protocells	RNA world hypothesis	sympatric speciation
radiometric dating	sexual selection	uniformity
reproductive isolation	speciation	

KEY CONCEPTS

▪ There are different theories about how approximately 3.8 million years ago life might have begun on Earth, from the origin of organic compounds to evolution and diversification of prokaryotic and eukaryotic species.

▪ Organisms continually evolve over time depending on environmental conditions.

▪ The evidence of evolution supports Darwin's theory of natural selection, including descent with modification.

▪ Darwin's theory of natural selection explains how species evolve.

▪ All organisms on Earth are decedents of a common ancestor.

▪ Phylogenetic trees are used to show evolutionary relationships between species.

For a full discussion of evolution, see *Biology* 12th ed., Chapters 17, 18, 19, and 20/13th ed., Chapters 16, 17, 18, and 19.

CHANGE IN GENETIC MAKEUP
Enduring Understanding 1.A

Pre-Darwinian thought on the history of Earth and living organisms was supported by the idea of a creator and fixity of species. This started to change in the mid-nineteenth century, when the work of scientists such as Linnaeus (Scala nuturae and classification of permanent species), Lyell and Hutton (geology's theory of uniformity), Lamarck (inheritance of acquired characteristics), Malthus (economic analogy of supply and demand), and Cuvier (catastrophism and extinction) caused an attempt to reconcile the traditional beliefs with the new physical evidence. Building on Malthus's idea, Wallace and Darwin demonstrated that a population will grow until the demand is greater than the supply of resources. At that point, the individuals must compete for food, shelter, mates, water, etc. Those that had the characteristics to survive and had reproductive success could pass on adaptive traits to the next generation, imparting greater fitness to certain populations. The idea of differential reproductive success and survival are the basis of Darwin's theory of natural selection.

Scientists employ a variety of studies to support the theory of evolution. These include biogeography of extant (living) species, comparative morphology, fossils, and molecular comparisons. Biogeographers study the geographic distribution of species. For example, the South American rhea, the Australian emu, and the African ostrich all have similarities but are indigenous to different continents. The study of biogeography establishes relatedness among species that would otherwise be geographically isolated. Comparative morphology is the study of body plans and structures, looking to compare outward appearances with underlying structures. For example, the wings of a bat, an insect, and a bird have similarities in surface structure and function but do not have a common ancestor. This is an example of morphological convergence in which similar body parts evolve from different lineages. Alternatively, the forearms of a penguin, a human, and an elephant have similarities in structure because of a common ancestor. This is known as morphological divergence and referred to as homologous structures.

Structures that are similar as a result of morphological convergences are called analogous structures. For example, bird, bat, and insect wings all perform the same function but evolved independently, not from a common ancestor. Most fossil evidence is found in sedimentary rock and is from the hard body parts of once-living organisms. Though there are fossils for over 250,000 species, many potential fossil finds are destroyed from decay and decomposition due to the oxidizing atmosphere along with natural disasters and human destruction. In addition, many marine invertebrates, such as jellyfish, do not have any hard parts that would become fossilized. Radiometric dating is a method used to determine the age of a fossil by measuring the content of radioisotopes. Scientists can determine the relative age based on the half life of each type of radioisotope. Finally, comparing DNA and proteins shows the evolutionary relationship among species due to the biochemical similarities. Two species with many identical proteins are likely to be close relatives, while two species with very few similar proteins have most likely not shared an ancestor for a long time.

One way that scientists can determine what drives evolution is by using the Hardy-Weinberg formula. The Hardy-Weinberg equation states that $p^2 + 2pq + q = 1$ and $p + q = 1$ where p^2 represents the homozygous dominant individuals, $2pq$ represents the heterozygous individuals, and q^2 represents the homozygous recessive individuals. Only if all five conditions of Hardy-Weinberg equilibrium are met can a population be considered to be stable. The five criteria for the Hardy-Weinberg equation are:

1. Population size must be large.
2. There can be no gene flow.
3. There can be no mutations.

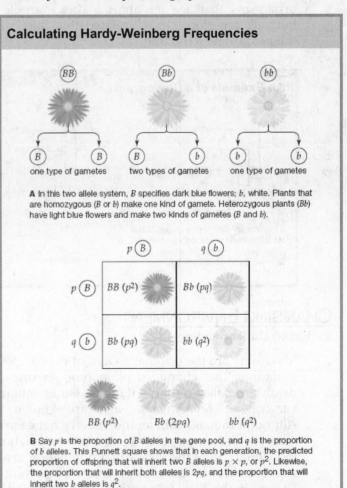

Calculating Hardy-Weinberg Frequencies

A In this two allele system, B specifies dark blue flowers; b, white. Plants that are homozygous (B or b) make one kind of gamete. Heterozygous plants (Bb) have light blue flowers and make two kinds of gametes (B and b).

B Say p is the proportion of B alleles in the gene pool, and q is the proportion of b alleles. This Punnett square shows that in each generation, the predicted proportion of offspring that will inherit two B alleles is $p \times p$, or p^2. Likewise, the proportion that will inherit both alleles is $2pq$, and the proportion that will inherit two b alleles is q^2.

4. Mating must be random.
5. There can be no natural selection.

COMMON ANCESTRY

Enduring Understanding 1.B

Similarities between organisms are often the result of shared common ancestry. Body parts that are a result of a common ancestor are termed homologous structures. One example of a homologous structure is the bone pattern in the limb of a mammal. Whales, humans, bats, and other mammals have the same bone pattern in the limbs even though they are used for different purposes. One group of genes, called Hox genes, controls body form and is present in most phyla of animals. These genes are highly conserved and function in most animals, showing that all animals evolved from a common ancestor.

Phylogenetic trees or cladograms are pictorial representations of evolutionary relationships. Scientists look at specific shared and derived characteristics in order to organize species. A clade is a group of organisms that shares one or more defining, derived traits. Scientists can also use molecular comparisons to determine how closely related two species are. Organisms that are closer on a phylogenetic tree share a more recent common ancestor than organisms that are far apart. This example shows that mice and humans are more closely related than humans and tuna because of their location on the tree.

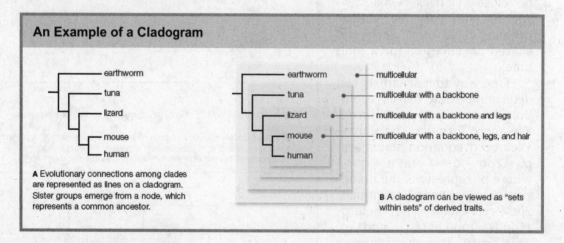

An Example of a Cladogram

A Evolutionary connections among clades are represented as lines on a cladogram. Sister groups emerge from a node, which represents a common ancestor.

B A cladogram can be viewed as "sets within sets" of derived traits.

CHANGING ENVIRONMENT

Enduring Understanding 1.C

Mutations are the original source of new alleles in a population. Some mutations that change a phenotype so drastically that it results in death are called lethal mutations. Other mutations have no effect on survival or reproduction and are known as neutral mutations. Although mutations in an individual's genes are the original source of new alleles in a population, it is the population that evolves, not the individual. All of the alleles in a population are called a gene pool and are influenced by both micro- and macroevolution. Microevolution is a change in the allele frequency within a population. Under the umbrella of natural selection, microevolution includes directional, stabilizing and disruptive selection, sexual selection, genetic drift, gene flow, bottleneck effect, and founder effect:

- Directional Selection—allele frequencies shift in a consistent direction.
- Stabilizing Selection—intermediate form of a trait is favored.
- Disruptive Selection—traits on both ends of a range of variation are favored.
- Sexual Selection—some version of a trait gives an individual an advantage in securing a mate.
- Balanced Polymorphism—multiple alleles are maintained in a population at relatively high freqencies.
- Genetic Drift—random change in allele frequencies.
- Gene Flow—physical movement of alleles in and out of a population via immigration and emigration.
- Bottleneck Effect—drastic reduction in a population due to severe pressures.
- Founder Effect—small group of individuals leave a population to start a new population.

Sometimes genetic changes that lead to the evolution of a new species occur, and this is called speciation. When a physical barrier is present to prevent gene flow, forming a new population, it is called allopatric speciation. If no physical barrier is present and a new species forms within the home range it is called sympatric speciation. The final type of speciation occurs when a population maintains contact along a common border and evolves into distinct species. This is termed parapatric speciation. Each of these speciation events occurs due to reproductive isolation (prezygotic or postzygotic) events, and all lead to new species as seen in the following table.

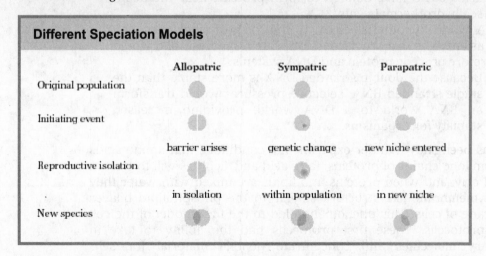

Different Speciation Models

	Allopatric	Sympatric	Parapatric
Original population			
Initiating event	barrier arises	genetic change	new niche entered
Reproductive isolation	in isolation	within population	in new niche
New species			

Macroevolution is based on changes in large scale patterns of evolution including stasis, exaptation, adaptive radiation, coevolution, and extinction.

- Stasis—there is very little change over time.
- Exaptation—occurs when the same structure starts being used for a new purpose.
- Adaptive radiation—occurs when species occupy different habitats and changes emerge based on new niches.
- Coevolution—when two species closely interact with each other due to the interdependence among the different species.
- Extinction—the loss of species, of which there have been up to 20 mass extinctions, including five catastrophic extinctions in which the majority of species on Earth disappeared.

ORIGIN OF LIVING SYSTEMS
Enduring Understanding 1.D

The big bang theory states that the universe formed 13 to 15 billion years ago and that Earth formed over 4 billion years ago from rocky debris that orbited the sun. It is assumed that the early atmosphere of Earth contained water vapor, methane, and ammonia, but very little free oxygen. Along with the first atmosphere, the origin of the Earth's crust and the first seas brought about a molecular evolution that led to living organisms, starting from the first protocells to anaerobic prokaryotic cells to eukaryotic cells.

Lab simulations, like those of Stanley Miller, support the idea that organic compounds such as amino acids and nucleotides could self-assemble under the presumed conditions of primitive Earth. There are multiple different hypotheses regarding the origin of proteins and metabolism.

- Protein first hypothesis—protein enzymes needed to be in place before any other chemical reactions leading to self-replication or metabolism could occur. This is supported by the Clay hypothesis.
  - The Clay hypothesis suggests that amino acids stuck to clay, forming proteins when energized by the sun. Amino acids could have bonded to form proteins near the deep-sea hydrothermal vents.
- RNA world hypothesis—RNA, in the form of ribozymes, can act as enzymes that are needed for protein synthesis and would therefore precede protein and DNA systems.
  - Because the double stranded DNA is more stable than the single stranded RNA, selective pressures would transform an RNA world to a DNA world, providing increased stability for organisms.

It has been shown under experimental conditions that amino acids will form long chains of proteins, fatty acid and alcohols will form sacs around clay, and when proteins and lipids are mixed with water they form a membrane-like structure similar to the phospholipid bilayer membrane of cells. This phenomenon led to the first model of the cell called protocells. These first protocells had the ability to take in necessary molecules and concentrate genetic material for self-replication, leading to evolution of the first prokaryotes.

Evidence from fossils and genes suggests that the first prokaryotes evolved 3.2 to 4.3 billion years ago. The two modern domains of prokaryotes, the archaeans and bacteria, branched from a common ancestor about 3.5 million years ago. The archaeans probably used light energy from hydrothermal vents to support their anaerobic metabolism, which is a cyclic process that does not produce oxygen. Once they colonized sunlit, surface waters, the noncyclic pathway of photosynthesis, which produces oxygen and ATP, evolved. Due to the new oxygen-rich atmosphere, self-assembly of organic molecules stopped, aerobic respiration evolved, and an ozone layer formed. With the onset of aerobic respiration came the rise of organelles and eukaryotes. About 2.1 billion years ago, red algae arose as some of the first eukaryotes. Organelles, such as the nucleus, endoplasmic reticulum, and Golgi body, arose from infolding of the plasma membrane as seen in the figure below. They remain part of the endomembrane system in which all maintain the bilayer structure of the plasma membrane and are connected structurally via cellular processes.

Diagram of Endosybiotic Theory

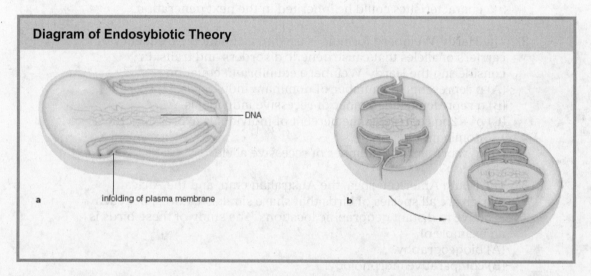

Mitochondria and chloroplasts are most likely descendants of bacteria. They are thought to have been engulfed by cells through a process known as endosymbiosis. Dr. Lynn Margulis brought the endosymbiosis hypothesis to the forefront of the study of the evolution of the cell. The hypothesis states that structures once free living became engulfed in the cell, but rather than being destroyed, they survived using the nutrients and ATP inside the cell to replicate. Eventually they became permanent organelles necessary for the cell's survival and evolved so that neither could live independently.

AP Tip

Remember when answering questions related to evolution, the smallest unit that can evolve is a population. Individuals do not evolve.

Multiple-Choice Questions

1. Before and during Darwin's time, many theories of evolution had been proposed. With which of the following theories would Darwin most agree?
    (A) Malthus suggested that species and populations were limited by the available resources and lack of resources created competition. That competition drove evolution.
    (B) Cuvier's theory of catastrophism supported the theory that there were abrupt changes and that the survivors of the catastrophes were not new species at all.
    (C) Lyell's theory of uniformity stated that there was a steady, gradual, and lengthy molding of Earth and its species.
    (D) Lamarck suggested that single simple forms could become more complex in an individual and that change in characteristics could be inherited in the next generation.

2. The Hardy-Weinberg formula is used to estimate the frequency of carriers of alleles that cause genetic disorders and traits. In considering the Hardy-Weinberg equilibrium equation
    (A) p represents the number of dominant individuals.
    (B) q represents the number of recessive individuals.
    (C) $p^2 + 2pq$ represents the percent of individuals expressing the dominant phenotype.
    (D) q^2 represents the number of recessive allele.

3. The South American rhea, the Australian emu, and the African ostrich are all species of birds that share similar features, but each is native to distant geographic locations. The study of these birds is an example of
    (A) biogeography.
    (B) comparative morphology.
    (C) natural evolution.
    (D) geologic dispersion.

4. Differential reproductive success is a main idea of
    (A) acquired characteristics.
    (B) natural selection.
    (C) uniformity.
    (D) catastrophism.

5. Which of the following is true regarding the fossil record?
    (A) The youngest fossils are found in the deepest layer of sedimentary rock.
    (B) The fossil record is complete.
    (C) Different geologic events have altered the fossil record.
    (D) The fossil record is not substantial enough to really piece together history.

6. Unlike a lethal mutation, a neutral mutation
   (A) does not change the sequence of bases in DNA.
   (B) is affected by natural selection.
   (C) will occasionally be favored by a change in the environment.
   (D) has been altering the phenotypes for billions of years.

7. All of the following mechanisms drive evolution EXCEPT
   (A) changes in allelic frequencies.
   (B) differential reproductive success.
   (C) genetic drift.
   (D) populations in genetic equilibrium.

8. Changes in allelic frequencies that lead to a shift in phenotypes to
   one extreme, as in the pepper moth population, are an example of
   (A) directional selection.
   (B) stabilizing selection.
   (C) disruptive selection.
   (D) sexual selection.

9. Balanced polymorphism, as in the case of malaria and sickle-cell
   anemia, is a state in which natural selection maintains
   (A) the homozygous recessive condition.
   (B) the homozygous dominant condition.
   (C) the heterozygous condition.
   (D) sexual dimorphism.

10. All of the following are prezygotic isolating mechanisms EXCEPT
    (A) temporal isolation.
    (B) hybrid sterility.
    (C) gamete incompatibility.
    (D) behavioral isolation.

11. The most common mode of speciation is
    (A) allopatric.
    (B) sympatric.
    (C) parapatric.
    (D) semipatric.

12. Morphological divergence is to _____ as morphological
    convergence is to _____.
    (A) disruptive selection; directional selection
    (B) homologous structures; analogous structures
    (C) allopatric speciation; sympatric speciation
    (D) dimorphism; polymorphism

13. All of the following statements regarding molecular comparisons
    are true EXCEPT
    (A) Biochemical similarities can show evolutionary relationships.
    (B) DNA and amino acid sequences are greatest among lineages
        that diverged long ago.
    (C) There are some essential genes that have evolved very little.
    (D) Recent lineages have the greatest differences in their DNA.

14. Early Earth was considered to have a reducing atmosphere rather than the oxidizing atmosphere of today. If this is true, which of the elements would be present in the least amount in early Earth's atmosphere?
    (A) oxygen
    (B) hydrogen
    (C) nitrogen
    (D) carbon monoxide

15. Stanley Miller's apparatus and experiment supported
    (A) the big bang theory.
    (B) that organic molecules could have formed spontaneously on Earth.
    (C) amino acids came from interstellar clouds.
    (D) spontaneous generation.

Grid-In Question

1. The allele for the ability to roll one's tongue is dominant over the allele for the lack of this ability. In a population of 1000 individuals, 25 percent show the recessive phenotype. How many individuals would you expect to be homozygous dominant for this trait?

Free-Response Questions

MULTI-PART QUESTION

1. There are a number of reasons and ways that populations evolve. Describe the mechanisms of micro- and macro-evolution by:
   (a) comparing the level of occurrence for each
   (b) explaining at least three different mechanisms for each
   (c) giving a specific example for each mechanism

SINGLE-PART QUESTION

2. Fossils and molecular comparisons among modern organisms inform us about the early history of life including links from prokaryotes to eukaryotes. Describe the evolution of eukaryotic cells.

Answers

MULTIPLE-CHOICE QUESTIONS

1. **A.** Darwin's theory of natural selection and survival of the fittest would be most in line with Malthus's economic perspective of supply and demand. If there is more demand for a resource than is available, species have to compete for that resource in order to survive. The species with the traits needed to obtain the resource would be the species that survived to reproduce, passing those traits on to the next generation (*Biology*, 12th, ed. page 265/13th ed., pages 256–259).

2. **C.** p and q represent the frequencies of the dominant and recessive alleles, not the number of individuals. q^2 represents the frequency of the homozygous recessive individuals whereas p^2 represents the frequency of homozygous dominant individuals. The dominant trait will be expressed in both the homozygous dominant individuals (p^2) and the heterozygous individuals ($2pq$) (*Biology*, 12th ed., pages 280–281/13th ed., pages 274–275).

3. **A.** Because the study of these birds is focused on the fact that they have similarities while being indigenous to different continents, biogeography, the study of geographic distribution of species, would be the correct answer. Comparative morphology is the study of body forms and function within a group of organisms and focuses more on homologous structures like the arm of the whale, bat, and human. There has yet to be a term coined for natural evolution; geologic dispersion is when species leave their home area and reestablish themselves elsewhere, and is more closely connected to ecology (*Biology*, 12th ed., page 260/13th ed., pages 298–299).

4. **B.** Natural selection is based on differential reproductive success and survival. Acquired characteristics and catastrophism are ideas that are not readily accepted as accurate today. Uniformity supports that Earth formed due to gradual and repetitive changes (*Biology*, 12th ed., page 286/13th ed., pages 256–259).

5. **C.** Due to geologic events that have altered the fossil record, the fossil record is not complete. Due to stratification of sedimentary rock, the oldest fossils are actually in the deepest layer. There is still enough fossil record, however, to establish patterns in evolutionary history. There have been many similar fossils that have been found in different geographic locations (*Biology*, 12th ed., pages 266–267/13th ed., page 255).

6. **C.** The base sequence changes in both a lethal and neutral mutation. Because neutral mutations do not affect reproduction or survival, they are not subject to pressures of natural selection. Mutations in general have been changing the course of history

for billions of years. On occasion, however, changes in the environment will benefit a previous neutral mutation (*Biology*, 12th ed., page 279/13th ed., pages 272–273).

7. **D.** Differential reproductive success and genetic drift contribute to changes in allelic frequencies, leading to different phenotypes that are subject to pressures from their environment. Genetic equilibrium is referring to a population that is not evolving and therefore not driving evolution (*Biology*, 12th ed., pages 288–298/13th ed., pages 282–283).

8. **A.** In directional selection, one extreme form becomes more common over time whereas in disruptive selection, both extremes are favored. In stabilizing selection, the average form becomes more common. Sexual selection has to do with mating behaviors that lead to the most adaptive forms being chosen (*Biology*, 12th ed., page 282/13th ed., pages 276–277).

9. **C.** Balanced polymorphism keeps two or more alleles at relatively high frequencies because there is a benefit due to environmental pressures, as in the case of malaria and sickle-cell anemia. Heterozygotes are more likely to survive malaria and make enough normal hemoglobin to survive, giving them the heterozygote advantage (*Biology*, 12th ed., page 287/13th ed., page 281).

10. **B.** Temporal and behavior isolation keep the species from inter-breeding. In gamete incompatibility, they breed but fertilization cannot occur; therefore, it is still considered prezygotic. In hybrid sterility, a zygote does form, but the individual or its offspring does not produce functioning gametes (*Biology* 12th ed., pages 290–291/13th ed., page 284).

11. **A.** In allopatric speciation, a geographic barrier ends potential gene flow, resulting in a new species. Although, in sympatric and parapatric speciation, new species can arise while they are within the same population or along the same border, it is not as common as when there is a physical divide (*Biology* 12th ed., pages 292–293/13th ed., pages 286–289).

12. **B.** Homologous structures are shared body parts that reflect a common ancestor and morphological divergence is a change in the body part from a common ancestor. Analogous structures are structures that look alike but do not have a common ancestor. Morphological convergence is the evolution of these similar body forms (*Biology* 12th ed., pages 304–305/13th ed., pages 298–299)

13. **D.** DNA and amino acid sequences are most similar among those species that have diverged most recently and greatest among those that diverged further back in the species ancestors. Both A and C are also accurate because scientists use biochemical similarities to establish relationships, and there are some genes, like the one that encodes for cytochrome C, that are conserved in many species (*Biology* 12th ed., pages 308–309/13th ed., pages 300–301).

14. **A.** There was little free oxygen in the Earth's first atmosphere. Evidence from ancient iron-containing rocks indicates that the iron did not combine with oxygen to form rust until much later (*Biology*, 12th ed., page 318/13th ed., page 310).

15. **B.** Stanley Miller circulated water vapor, hydrogen gas, methane, and ammonia in a glass chamber and exposed it to an electrode to simulate lightning. This experiment simulated conditions on early Earth and tested the hypothesis that organic molecules could have formed spontaneously given the right conditions (*Biology*, 12th ed., page 319/13th ed., page 311).

GRID-IN QUESTION

1. 250

   calculated as follows:

   $p^2 + 2pq + q^2 = 1$

   $q^2 = .25$

   $q = .5$

   $p + q = 1$

   $p = .5$

   $p^2 = .25$

   $.25 \times 1000 = 250$

(*Biology*, 12th ed., pages 274–275/13th ed., pages 274–275).

FREE-RESPONSE QUESTIONS

MULTI-PART

1. *Microevolution* is small scale changes in allele frequencies occurring within a single species or population. Genetic mutations, gene flow, and genetic drift are all causes of microevolution. In most organisms, the condition of polymorphism exists—meaning that due to a genetic mutation, there is more than one phenotype for a trait. A neutral mutation, like having attached versus detached ear lobes, may not have an impact on a population. A lethal mutation or a beneficial mutation, however, can cause a change in the gene pool due to loss of lethal genes or gain of beneficial genes. Gene flow is the movement of alleles between populations, causing the gene pools to become more similar to each other. When blue jays carry acorns from one oak tree population to the next, gene flow is seen between two otherwise separate populations. Genetic drift occurs when the allele frequencies change in a population due to chance. Two examples

of genetic drift are the bottleneck effect and the founder effect. The bottleneck effect is when a drastic reduction in a population is brought about by a severe pressure. The northern elephant seals experienced the bottleneck effect when there were only 20 known survivors in the world in the 1890s. The traits of the 20 that survived were the only traits that could then be passed on to future generations. The founder effect is when a small group of individuals starts a new population. Through mild inbreeding, the founder effect has occurred in the Old Order Amish populations in Lancaster County, Pennsylvania. Forms of nonrandom mating such as assortive mating and sexual selection could also be included with the discussion of microevolution.

Macroevolution occurs on a larger scale and has occurred over millions of years. Coevolution, stasis, exaptation, adaptive radiation, and extinction are all causes of macroevolution. Coevolution is when two organisms evolve side by side. In fact they can become dependent on each other, like pollinators and flowers. Stasis occurs when a species lineage stays the same for millions of years, like the coelacanth, an ancient lobe-finned fish. Exaptation is the adaptation of a particular feature for a completely different purpose. For example, feathers on dinosaurs were used for insulation, not flight, but evolved for use in flight in modern birds. Adaptive radiation is when a single lineage leads to many new species, as in the Hawaiian honeycreepers when they adapted to new niches they encountered in the Hawaiian Archipelago. Maintaining some characteristics of the original population, a distinct form of honeycreepers is now found on each island. Extinction is when species are irrevocably lost. There have been more than 20 mass extinctions and 5 catastrophic extinctions which caused the majority of species on Earth to disappear (*Biology*, 12th ed., pages 288–297/13th ed., pages 272–273 and 282–290).

SINGLE-PART

2. Mitochondria and chloroplasts, which are genetically similar to different types of free-living prokaryotes, are thought to have initially been engulfed by cells through a process known as endosymbiosis. Structures that were once free living became engulfed in the cell, but rather than being destroyed, they survived using the nutrients and ATP inside the cell to replicate. Eventually they became permanent organelles necessary for the cell's survival and evolved so that neither could live independently (*Biology*, 12th ed., pages 320–325/13th ed., pages 316–317).

2

BIOCHEMISTRY AND ENERGY/ENZYMES

BIG IDEAS 2, 4

The most important molecule to life is water. Life evolved in water and all of the chemical reactions of life take place in water. Carbohydrates, lipids, proteins, and nucleic acids are the four main groups of organic molecules that build and sustain life. All living things require a constant supply of energy and raw materials from the environment. Most chemical reactions within organisms cannot happen without the presence of enzymes. These organic catalysts position reactants such that products are more likely to form at the organism's body temperature.

KEY TERMS

activation energy	denature	hydrogen bond
active site	disaccharides	hydrophilic
allosteric enzymes	endergonic	hydrophobic
amino acids	entropy	ionic bonds
ATP	enzymes	lipids
carbohydrates	exergonic	monosaccharides
chitin	feedback inhibition	nucleotides
cofactors	free energy	oligosaccharides
cohesion	first law of thermodynamics	oxidation/reduction reaction
condensation reactions		
covalent bonds	functional group	pH

polar	R-group	steroids
polymers	saturated fats	surface tension
polypeptide	second law of	triglycerides
polysaccharides	thermodynamics	unsaturated fats
proteins	solvent	waxes

KEY CONCEPTS

- The unique properties of water make it essential to life.
- All molecules of life are built of carbon atoms.
- Life is built mostly of organic molecules that are categorized as carbohydrates, lipids, proteins, or nucleic acids.
- Living things transform energy from one form to another, but they must conform to the physical laws of the universe.
- Enzymes enable chemical reactions to take place at temperatures that cells can tolerate.
- Enzyme function can be measured, and it is affected by environmental conditions such as temperature and pH, as well as by the presence of regulatory molecules.

For a full discussion of biochemistry and energy/enzymes, see *Biology* 12th ed., Chapters 2, 3, and 6/13th ed., Chapters 2, 3, and 5.

WATER
Enduring Understanding 4.A

Water is a major component of all life forms. Most biologists think that the evolution of life took place in water and this process was greatly influenced by many of water's unique properties. Living things are composed mostly of water, and the chemical reactions needed for life must take place in an aqueous environment. Water molecules are held together by polar covalent bonds. Its polarity, along with its widespread occurrence in its liquid state, has given water the properties that have made life on Earth possible.

Water is an excellent solvent. Its ability to dissolve polar substances makes it an ideal medium for the chemistry of life. Ionic substances, such as NaCl, easily dissolve in water. The poles of water intervene between the Na+ and Cl-, separating them into ions. Non-ionic solids, such as sugar molecules, dissolve easily in water because their molecules can form hydrogen bonds with water molecules. Hydrogen bonding dissolves a solid substance by pulling its molecules away from one another and keeping them apart. Substances that dissolve easily in water are hydrophilic. Nonpolar substances, such as oil, are said to be hydrophobic (water-fearing) and are insoluble in water.

Another important property of water is its ability to stabilize temperature. All matter has kinetic energy. The total amount of this kinetic energy is heat. Temperature is a measurement of this molecular motion. This movement is restricted in liquid water due to the extensive hydrogen bonding between molecules. The hydrogen bonding keeps water molecules from moving as much as they would otherwise; therefore, it takes more heat to raise the temperature of water compared to other liquids. When water freezes, the hydrogen bonds form a rigid lattice, causing ice to be less dense than liquid water, forcing it to float. This property allows ice to insulate a body of water, keeping it from freezing solid, and allowing aquatic life to persist over the winter.

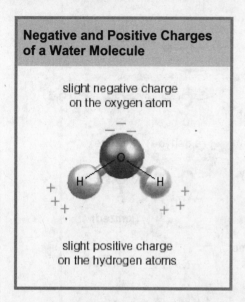

Negative and Positive Charges of a Water Molecule

slight negative charge on the oxygen atom

slight positive charge on the hydrogen atoms

The ability of water to form hydrogen bonds with itself gives it strong cohesion and creates high surface tension. In the process of transpiration, the cohesion of water allows it to move up hundreds of feet in tall trees, hydrating even the top-most leaves. As one molecule of water evaporates, the molecules below are pulled up to replace it. Water tension is created on the surface of a pond allowing small insects, like the water strider, to glide around without sinking.

ORGANIC MOLECULES
Enduring Understanding 4.A

Organic molecules contain carbon and build all living things. Carbon's ability to combine with four different atoms allows it to be the backbone of very large molecules. These large molecules are often referred to as macromolecules or polymers. Four major classes of biochemical molecules exist in living things. Carbohydrates, lipids, proteins, and nucleic acids are the major components of all living things. They are usually composed of repeating subunits called monomers. The different classes of macromolecules often have similar properties due to common functional groups. A functional group is a cluster of atoms covalently bound to a carbon in a macromolecule. The functional groups in the following table impart chemical characteristics to organic molecules and contribute their function in biological molecules.

Functional Groups

Group	Character	Location	Structure
hydroxyl	polar	amino acids, sugars, and other alcohols	—OH
methyl	nonpolar	fatty acids, some amino acids	H—C—H (with H above and H below)
carbonyl	polar, reactive	sugars, amino acids, nucleotides	(aldehyde) (ketone)
carboxyl	acidio	amino acids, fatty acids, carbohydrates	C—OH C—O⁻ (ionized)
amine	basic	amino acids, some nucleotide bases	—N—H —NH⁺ (ionized)
phosphate	high energy, polar	nucleotides (e.g., ATP), DNA and RNA, many proteins, phospholipids	—O—P—O⁻ ℗ ion
sulfhydryl	forms disulfide bridges	cysteine (an amino acid)	—SH —S—S— (disulfide bridge)

Polymers are often built by condensation reactions. Enzymes remove an OH– from one monomer and an H+ from another, forming water. A covalent bond forms between the molecules as the polymer grows. Conversely, macromolecules are broken down in a reverse reaction called hydrolysis. Here an enzyme adds an OH– and H+ from water as it severs the bond between molecules, releasing the monomers.

Polymers Built by Condensation Reactions

glucose + fructose ⟶ sucrose + water

CARBOHYDRATES

Carbohydrates are macromolecules that are composed of carbon, hydrogen, and oxygen in a 1:2:1 ratio. They are built from monomers of simple sugars like glucose. The three main types of carbohydrates found in nature are monosaccharides, oligosaccharides, and poly-saccharides. Most monosaccharides have a backbone of five or six carbon atoms. Common examples include deoxyribose and glucose.

Examples of Monosaccharides

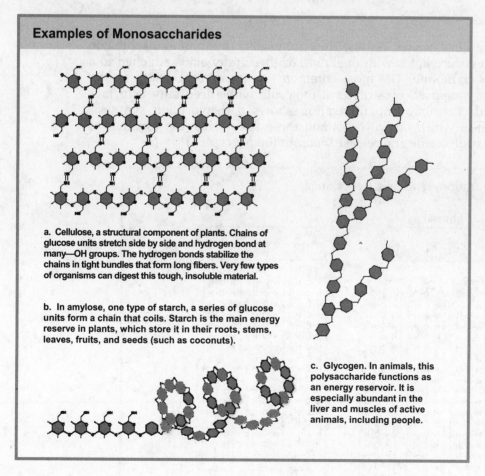

a. Cellulose, a structural component of plants. Chains of glucose units stretch side by side and hydrogen bond at many—OH groups. The hydrogen bonds stabilize the chains in tight bundles that form long fibers. Very few types of organisms can digest this tough, insoluble material.

b. In amylose, one type of starch, a series of glucose units form a chain that coils. Starch is the main energy reserve in plants, which store it in their roots, stems, leaves, fruits, and seeds (such as coconuts).

c. Glycogen. In animals, this polysaccharide functions as an energy reservoir. It is especially abundant in the liver and muscles of active animals, including people.

Disaccharides are composed of just two monosaccharides. Sucrose, common table sugar, and lactose, the sugar in milk, are two familiar examples. Oligosaccharides are short polysaccharide chains composed of three to six monosaccharides. Oligosaccharides can be attached to lipids or proteins embedded in the cell membrane. The largest carbohydrates are the polysaccharides. They are composed of hundreds of monosaccharides linked together and are usually used as a source of quick energy. Starch is built when glucose molecules join to form a long and sometimes spiral molecule. Starch is the main chemical storage molecule of glucose in plants. Glycogen is also an energy storage molecule, but found in animals and fungi. Animals store glycogen in their muscles and liver to give us a quick burst of energy whenever we need it. This carbohydrate is composed of branched chains of glucose monomers. Cellulose is a structural component of plants. In this polymer, the glucose molecules are arranged side by side in sheets. Hydrogen bonds between adjacent glucose molecules make it tough, insoluble, and difficult for most organisms to digest. The cell walls of plants are composed of this tough carbohydrate. Chitin is a structural polysaccharide found in the exoskeletons of arthropods. It is composed of a modified monosaccharide containing nitrogen.

LIPIDS

Lipids are fats, waxes, or oils. They are usually greasy and insoluble in water. Fats are lipids with one, two, or three fatty acids attached to a glycerol backbone. The most common fats in animals, triglycerides, are fats composed of a glycerol molecule with three fatty acid tails attached. The following illustration shows a dehydration synthesis reaction in which one glycerol and three fatty acids join together to make a triglyceride and release water in the process.

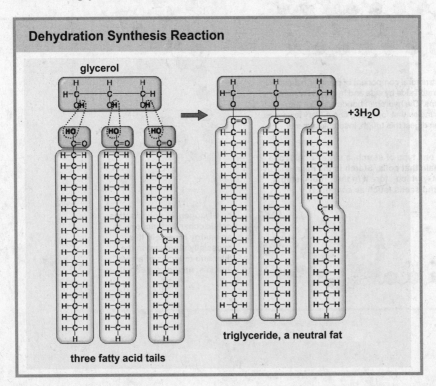

Dehydration Synthesis Reaction

glycerol

+3H₂O

triglyceride, a neutral fat

three fatty acid tails

If the fatty acid tails all contain carbons that are joined together with single bonds only, they contain the maximum number of hydrogen atoms, and are considered saturated. Unsaturated fats result when at least one double bond exists between carbon atoms. Saturated fats form straight chains that pack close together and usually form solids at room temperature. The double bonds of unsaturated fats cause the carbon chains to kink, allowing only the loose packing that result in liquids at room temperature. Like triglycerides, phospholipids have a glycerol framework, but only two fatty acid tails. In the place of the third fatty acid is a hydrophilic phosphate head. The membranes of all cells are composed of phospholipids bilayers. The phosphate heads of this molecule dissolve easily in the cell's aquatic environment, while the hydrophobic tails are repelled, and seek each other, forming a sandwiched layer on the inside.

Phospholipid

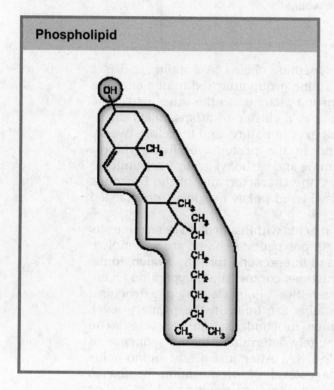

Steroids are lipids with a backbone of four carbon rings. The attached functional groups give them different properties. The most common steroid in animal tissue is cholesterol. It is the foundation of many other steroids such as estrogen, testosterone, and vitamin D.

Waxes are complex mixtures of lipids, with long fatty acid tails bound to carbon rings or long-chain alcohols. They help provide a water repellent covering to plants and animals.

PROTEINS

Of all of the organic molecules associated with life, proteins are the most diverse in form and in function. Amino acids are the monomers that build proteins. Amino acids have an amine group at one end and a carboxyl group at the other. Amino acids also have an R-group, which is made up of one or more atoms. The figure below is an example of one amino acid valine with the R-group shaded dark gray. The illustration on the left is the general structure, and the diagram on the right is a specific amino acid where the R-group (variable region) changes.

Amino Acid

amine group   carboxyl group

valine

They are linked into long polypeptide chains. An amino acid is a small organic molecule with an amine group attached to one end of a central carbon and a carboxyl group attached to the other end. Also extended from the central carbon is a cluster of atoms called an R-group. Twenty different R-groups exist in nature, and therefore twenty different amino acids are found in the proteins of living things. Although the properties of the amine and carboxyl groups are uniform among the different amino acids, the characteristics of the R-groups are unique. Amino acids are considered polar, nonpolar, or charged based on the R-group.

The sequence of specific amino acids within a protein determines its shape, and thus its properties. As polypeptide chains are assembled, the atoms of the R-groups begin to interact and form hydrogen, ionic, and covalent bonds. These interactions contort the polypeptide chain, helping to define its characteristics. Four levels of structural organization are present as proteins are built. In the primary level, amino acids are joined together in condensation reactions. The sequence of amino acids is ultimately determined by the sequence of nitrogen bases in an organism's DNA. After just a few amino acids have been joined, the secondary level of organization begins to emerge. The amino acids interact, causing the growing chain to coil or form a sheet-like structure. Hydrogen bonds form between the backbones of adjacent amino acids to stabilize the arrangement. In a protein's tertiary structure, significant folds and twists fashion the chain into a distinct three-dimensional molecule. As the shape develops, functional domains such as barrels or pockets stabilize the polypeptide. In the quaternary structure two or more polypeptide chains join together to form a protein.

The unique shape of a protein is usually only stable within a narrow range of conditions. Slight changes in temperature, pH, or salinity could influence the forces that are maintaining the protein's shape, and cause it to distort. Hydrogen bonds are especially susceptible and are often severed when a protein's environment changes. Without the bonds holding it together, the protein will unfold, losing its properties. This change is referred to as denaturation.

AP Tip

Know the four levels of protein structures:

- **Primary Structure**—A unique sequence of amino acids is joined together by carbon-nitrogen (peptide) bonds.

- **Secondary Structure**—Hydrogen bonds begin to form between adjacent amino acids. This often results in coiled or pleated sheet structure.

- **Tertiary Structure**—The chain is folded or twisted into stable arrangements called domains. These are held together by hydrogen, ionic, or covalent bonds.

- **Quaternary Structure**—Two or more polypeptide chains are held together to form a single protein.

NUCLEIC ACIDS

Nucleotides are the monomers that build nucleic acids such as DNA and RNA. They are composed of a five-carbon sugar, bound to a nitrogen-containing base, and one or more phosphate groups. Nucleotides are named based on the nitrogen base that they contain. The nucleotide ATP (adenosine triphosphate) is the major energy-carrying molecule used by cells.

DNA Nitrogenous Bases

The nucleotides that build the nucleic acids DNA and RNA share three common nitrogen bases. Adenine, guanine, and cytosine are found in both nucleic acids, while thymine is only found in DNA and uracil is unique to RNA. These nucleic acids also differ in the sugar that they contain. Deoxyribose is present in DNA and ribose is the sugar that helps build RNA. Structural differences are also apparent in these macromolecules. DNA consists of two strands of nucleotides forming a double helix, or twisted ladder shape, while RNA is composed of a single strand. The strands of DNA are held together by hydrogen bonds, joining adjacent nitrogen bases. Hereditary information is encoded in the sequence of nitrogen bases contained within the DNA molecule. This provides a template to assemble amino acids into the specific sequence that will form a protein with specific characteristics. RNA assists in the formation of proteins.

ENERGY TRANSFORMATIONS
Enduring Understanding 2.A

Energy is the ability to do work. Energy cannot be created or destroyed (first law of thermodynamics) but can only be converted from one form to another. For example, plants take solar energy and turn it into chemical energy but do not create new energy. Energy tends to spread out spontaneously. The tendency for entropy (measure of disorder) to increase in the universe is the second law of thermodynamics.

Chemical reactions allow cells to store and retrieve energy as they make and break chemical bonds. In a reaction, the starting molecules are the reactants and the ending molecules are the products. The amount of energy that a molecule has available to do work is its free energy. The amount of free energy in a molecule varies and is a result of entropy and the bond energy holding the molecule together.

In a chemical reaction, the amount of free energy of the reactants and products usually differs. If the products require more energy than the reactants have to offer, additional energy will need to be added. This type of reaction is said to be endergonic, which means "energy in." One source of energy that could drive this type of reaction could be heat from the environment. The area surrounding the reaction would cool down as heat is absorbed. When the reactants have greater free energy than the products, an exergonic reaction would result. The burning of paper would be considered an exergonic reaction. The excess free energy from the paper would be converted to heat and light as it burned.

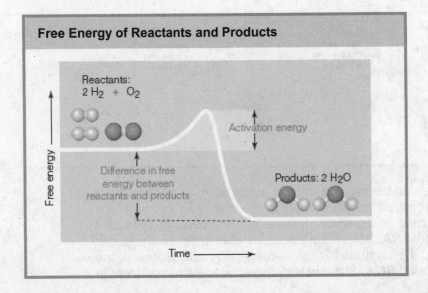

Free Energy of Reactants and Products

Reactants: $2 H_2 + O_2$

Activation energy

Free energy

Difference in free energy between reactants and products

Products: $2 H_2O$

Time

Both endergonic and exergonic reactions require an energy input in order to begin. Activation energy is the minimum amount of energy required to initiate a chemical reaction. For example, you use a match to start a fire. The match provides the needed activation energy. This would be an exergonic reaction, and the excess heat released would provide the activation energy to keep the fire burning.

Various chemical reactions are continually taking place in all cells. Many of these are endergonic and require a source of energy. Endergonic reactions are frequently coupled with exergonic reactions in cells. Without the constant supply of energy from these exergonic reactions, the important endergonic reactions cannot occur and cells will die.

The energy carrier, ATP (adenosine triphosphate), typically supplies energy for endergonic reactions in cells. ATP is a nucleotide with three phosphates attached. The bonds holding the phosphates can be easily broken to release their energy in an exergonic reaction. This released energy can be easily transferred. When an endergonic reaction needs energy, an ATP can transfer its third phosphate group in a process called phosphorylation. Cells require a constant supply of ATP, so it is continually renewed in the ATP/ADP cycle. The energy from organic molecules is used to recombine the third phosphate to an ADP molecule.

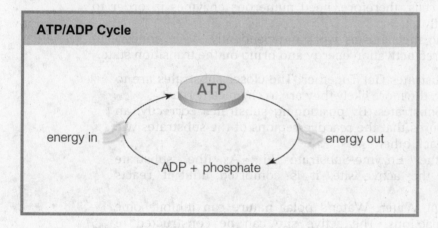

ATP/ADP Cycle

ATP

energy in

energy out

ADP + phosphate

ENZYMES

Chemical reactions require activation energy in order to begin. This energy is usually in the form of heat. Unfortunately, the temperature required to initiate most reactions would damage a cell. Catalysts are a group of molecules that lower activation energy. Their presence allows reactions to proceed at a much faster rate than they would on their own, and at temperatures that cells can tolerate.

Biological catalysts are typically proteins called enzymes, although some are composed of RNA, referred to as ribozymes. Enzymes' polypeptide chains are folded into a specific three-dimensional shape. The shape of a certain area, the active site, is crucial to how a specific enzyme functions. The active site is the region of the enzyme where reactants are altered. The reactants in enzyme-catalyzed reactions are

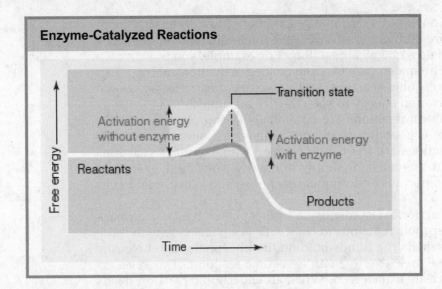

Enzyme-Catalyzed Reactions

usually referred to as substrates. When substrates are in the active site, they can be pushed close together, their charges can be altered, or some other change can occur. This alteration brings on the transition state and the product is formed. The active site is so specific that only a certain substrate will fit into it tightly enough to be catalyzed. Our cells, therefore, need numerous enzymes in order to function correctly.

The following mechanisms work independently, or in concert, to lower the required activation energy and bring on the transition state:

- Helping Substrates Get Together: The closer substrates are to one another, the more likely they are to chemically react.
- Orienting Substrates: By positioning substrates correctly, an enzyme ensures that the reactive regions of the substrates will encounter each other.
- Inducing the Enzyme-Substrate Fit: As the substrate encounters the active site, it is contorted until it reacts chemically.
- Shutting Out Water: Water's polar nature can inhibit some chemical reactions. The active site can be constructed of nonpolar amino acids creating a microenvironment that will allow hydrophobic molecules to get close enough to react chemically.
- Alter pH: Enzymes can create a suitable microenvironment by altering the pH with appropriate amino acid R groups.
- Form Temporary Double Bonds: Enzymes can participate in reactions by forming some covalent bonds with the substrate or a cofactor.

Enzymes are not altered when they catalyze a reaction and can be used over and over. Nevertheless, their ability to function can be impaired by different environmental conditions, such as temperature, pH, and salinity. Heat speeds up molecular motion and therefore increases reaction rates. Excessive increases in temperature, however, could cause the enzyme to denature. If the shape of its active site changes as a result, it is likely to lose its effectiveness as an enzyme. Similarly, changes in pH or salinity can cause denaturation. Therefore, enzymes have an optimum condition and any variance decreases its effectiveness.

AP Tip

Remember that enzymes are proteins and therefore are made of amino acids. They are specific to a substrate, and only a few amino acids in the active site will interact with the substrate and allow for extreme specificity.

Enzymes often need assistance. Cofactors are atoms or molecules that are associated with enzymes and are essential to their ability to function properly. Only when a cofactor binds to a certain enzyme does that enzyme's active site become an effective shape for its function. Some cofactors are metal ions while others are organic molecules referred to as coenzymes. Many vitamins are coenzymes or their precursors. Some coenzymes are tightly bound to an enzyme while others move freely through the cytoplasm.

A series of enzyme-mediated reactions is a metabolic pathway. Biosynthetic or anabolic pathways build large molecules from smaller ones. Degradative or catabolic pathways break molecules apart. Metabolic pathways can be linear, branched, or cyclic and can construct many intermediate molecules before the final products are formed. Enzymatic reactions typically run from reactants to products, but they also can flow in reverse, depending on the concentrations of products and reactants.

Allosteric Activator/Inhibitor

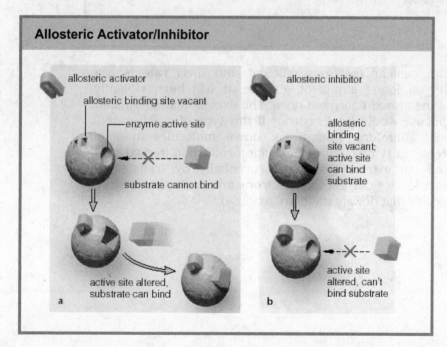

Cells tend to conserve energy and resources, only carrying out reactions that are needed at any given moment. Feedback mechanisms are used to control the rate of enzyme formation or can activate or inhibit the enzymes that are already present. In addition to an active site, allosteric enzymes have a second location, called the allosteric site, which is used by a regulatory substance. The allosteric substance alters the shape of the enzyme's active site when it attaches. This change in shape will activate or inhibit the enzyme. In feedback inhibition, an end product of a series of enzymatic reactions inhibits the first enzyme in the series either by binding to it allosterically or by binding to the active site itself, competitively blocking the substrate from binding there. This ensures that the reaction stops or slows down when adequate amounts of the product are present.

Redox

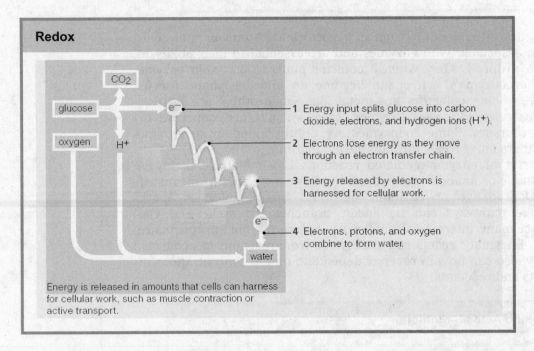

1 Energy input splits glucose into carbon dioxide, electrons, and hydrogen ions (H^+).

2 Electrons lose energy as they move through an electron transfer chain.

3 Energy released by electrons is harnessed for cellular work.

4 Electrons, protons, and oxygen combine to form water.

Energy is released in amounts that cells can harness for cellular work, such as muscle contraction or active transport.

Not only are cellular reactions efficient, but their rate is also controlled. If you ignite a pile of glucose, it will burn violently, releasing all of the stored energy at once. The excess heat and instant depletion of glucose would be disastrous if this type of reaction took place in a cell. Therefore, cells break down molecules in small manageable steps. Enzyme-mediated oxidation-reduction (redox) reactions allow cells to extract the energy gradually by transferring electrons. The molecules that receive electrons are said to be reduced, while the molecules that donate them are oxidized.

Multiple-Choice Questions

1. A reaction in which the products have more free energy than the reactants had is
   (A) a reaction that doesn't require activation energy.
   (B) an endergonic reaction.
   (C) an exergonic reaction.
   (D) contrary to the first law of thermodynamics.

2. A specific reactant that is altered by an enzyme is called a(n)
   (A) active site.
   (B) product.
   (C) substrate.
   (D) coenzyme.

3. The crevice of an enzyme where substrates bind is the
   (A) transition state.
   (B) cofactor.
   (C) coenzyme.
   (D) active site.

4. All of the following are true about water EXCEPT
   (A) Water is composed of two hydrogen atoms held to an oxygen atom by covalent bonds.
   (B) Water has temperature stabilizing effects.
   (C) Water is polar, due to the strong electronegative hydrogen atoms that it contains.
   (D) Water is a good solvent.

5. All of the following statements are true about allosteric enzymes EXCEPT
   (A) They have a second bonding site in addition to the active site.
   (B) They can be altered by an activator.
   (C) They can be altered by an inhibitor.
   (D) They raise the activation energy required to initiate a chemical reaction.

Questions 6–10 refer to the diagram below.

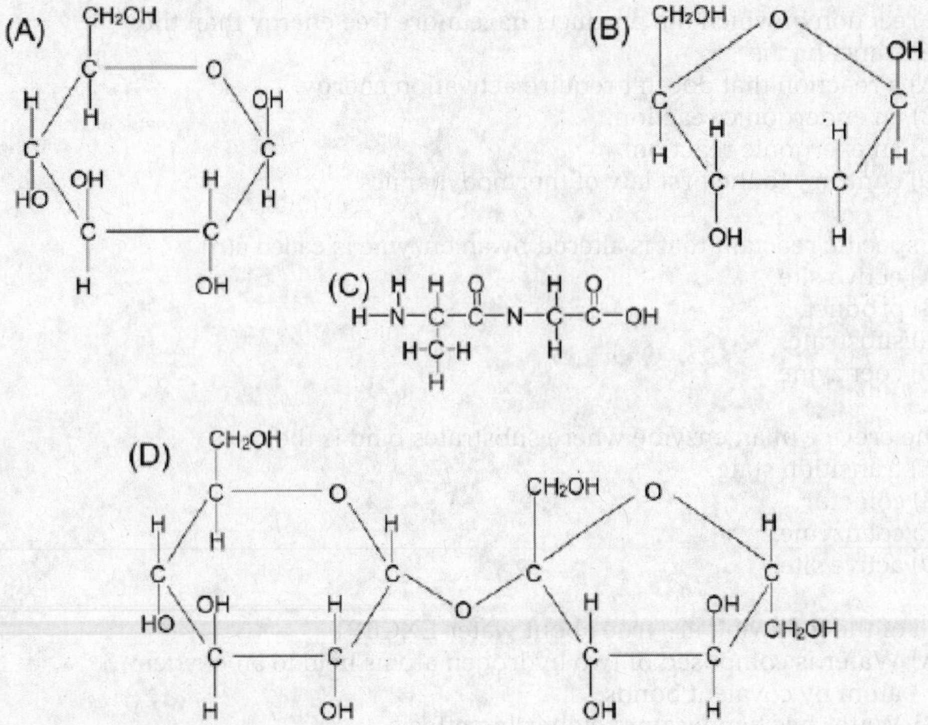

6. This molecule is a disaccharide.

7. This molecule is part of a nucleotide.

8. This molecule could be part of a polypeptide chain.

9. This molecule is the monomer that builds polysaccharides.

10. This molecule represents the primary level of organization of a protein.

11. All of the following represent organic molecules important to living things EXCEPT
    (A) water.
    (B) carbohydrates.
    (C) lipids.
    (D) proteins.

12. Which of the following represents a polysaccharide that is used to store energy within muscles?
    (A) glycogen
    (B) starch
    (C) ATP
    (D) glucose

13. The two strands of a DNA molecule are held together by
    (A) ionic bonds.
    (B) covalent bonds.
    (C) disulfide bridges.
    (D) hydrogen bonds.

14. A triglyceride is a lipid composed of
    (A) one glycerol molecule and three cholesterol molecules.
    (B) three glycerol molecules and one cholesterol molecule.
    (C) three fatty acid molecules and one cholesterol molecule.
    (D) three fatty acid molecules and one glycerol molecule.

15. Saturated fats have
    (A) all carbon atoms with the maximum number of hydrogen
        atoms attached to them.
    (B) all single carbon-carbon bonds and normally form liquids at
        room temperature.
    (C) some double carbon-carbon bonds and normally form liquids
        at room temperature.
    (D) some double carbon-carbon bonds and normally form solids at
        room temperature.

Grid-In Question

1. If 200 glucose molecules were put together to form starch, how
   many water molecules would come out of the reaction?

Free-Response Questions

MULTI-PART QUESTION

1. Discuss the following:
   (a) The levels of organization of a protein.
   (b) What could cause a protein's function to become ineffective?
   (c) How does DNA determine a protein's structure?

SINGLE-PART QUESTION

2. Enzymes are vital to the metabolism of all cells. Describe how their
   form is related to their function and what conditions could alter
   their form, rendering them useless.

Answers

Multiple-Choice Questions

1. **B.** Endergonic reactions result in products that have more free energy that the reactant had (*Biology*, 12th, ed. page 96/13th ed., page 81).

2. **C.** Reactants catalyzed by enzymes are referred to as substrates (*Biology*, 12th ed., page 98/13th ed., pages 82–83).

3. **D.** The properties of the amino acids that line the active site influence the bonding of the substrate (*Biology*, 12th ed., pages 98–99/13th ed., pages 82–84).

4. **C.** All of the properties of water are true except the last choice. The strong electronegative atom in water is oxygen, not hydrogen (*Biology*, 12th ed. page 28/13th ed., pages 30–31).

5. **D.** Like all enzymes, allosteric enzymes lower, NOT raise, the activation energy required to start a chemical reaction (*Biology*, 12th ed., pages 266–267/13th ed., page 255).

6. **D.** Disaccharides are composed of just two monosaccharides. This molecule represents sucrose composed of two monosaccharides (*Biology*, 12th ed., page 40/13th ed., pages 42–43).

7. **B.** Nucleotides are composed of a phosphate, 5-carbon sugar, and a nitrogen base. This molecule represents the sugar deoxyribose, a component of DNA nucleotides (*Biology*, 12th ed., page 48/13th ed., page 49).

8. **C.** Polypeptides are chains of amino acids. The N-C-C sequence is the backbone of any amino acid (*Biology*, 12th ed., page 44/13th ed., pages 46–47).

9. **A.** This molecule represents the simple sugar glucose. It is combined in different patterns to create the various polysaccharides (*Biology*, 12th ed., page 40/13th ed., page 42).

10. **C.** The sequence of amino acids is known as a protein's primary structure. This molecule is two amino acids joined together (*Biology* 12th ed., page 44/13th ed., pages 46–47).

11. **A.** Although water is very important to life, it lacks carbon and therefore is not considered to be an organic molecule (*Biology* 12th ed., page 36/13th ed., page 38).

12. **A.** All of the choices are associated with energy, but only glycogen is both a polysaccharide and found in muscles (*Biology* 12th ed., pages 304–305/13th ed., pages 298–299)

13. **D.** The cell must routinely extract the information coded in DNA. For this reason, the relatively weak hydrogen bonds are ideal (*Biology*, 12th ed., page 47/13th ed., page 49).

14. **D.** Triglyceride molecules are lipids composed of a glycerol backbone with three fatty acid tails (*Biology*, 12th ed., page 40/13th ed., page 44).

15. **A.** Saturated fats have all single carbon-carbon bonds freeing up bonding sites so that each carbon can have the maximum number of hydrogen atoms attached (*Biology*, 12th ed., page 40/13th ed., page 44).

GRID-IN QUESTION

1. 199

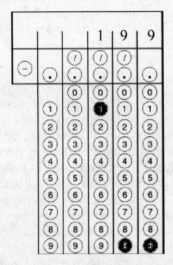

(*Biology*, 12th ed., page 39/13th ed., page 40).

FREE-RESPONSE QUESTIONS

MULTI-PART

1. (a) Four distinct levels of structural organization are apparent in the formation of proteins. Amino acids are joined together in condensation reactions forming a polypeptide chain in primary level of organization. As the polypeptide grows, the second level of a protein's organization begins to emerge. Adjacent amino acids begin to interact, forming hydrogen bonds that cause the chain to adopt a coiled alpha helix or sheet-like arrangement called a beta pleated sheet. In the third level of organization, enough interactions occur to fold the peptide into discrete three-dimensional regions called domains. Two or more polypeptide chains join together in the quaternary structure, the final level of organization in protein formation. The completed protein has a specific shape that gives it unique properties..

   (b) The shape of a protein determines its function. The structure of a protein is largely due to hydrogen bonds that hold it together. These bonds are numerous, but individually weak. They are easily influenced by several environmental conditions. Changes in temperature, pH, and salinity can alter the bonding within a protein and have adverse affects on its shape. If only slight modifications occur, a protein can regain its original shape. However, if drastic changes occur, the deformation is permanent, and the protein will no longer function normally, rendering it ineffective. At this point, the protein is said to be denatured.

(c) Proteins are composed of specific sequences of amino acids. The shape, and therefore the function, of a protein are due to this arrangement. The DNA of an organism contains the "recipe" for its proteins. The sequence of nitrogen bases in a DNA molecule determines the sequence of amino acids in a protein. Even a single nitrogen base alteration in DNA can have an adverse affect on the function of a protein. The genetic disorder sickle-cell anemia is caused by a single nitrogen base change in DNA. This change in DNA is translated into a malformed polypeptide in a hemoglobin molecule (*Biology*, 12th ed., pages 44–49/13th ed., pages 46–48).

SINGLE-PART

2. Most enzymes are proteins composed of multiple polypeptide chains. Like all proteins they have a distinct three-dimensional shape that is based on the sequence of amino acids in the polypeptide chains that build them. Enzymes have at least one area where their shape is crucial to their ability to function properly. This area is usually a crevice within the enzyme and is called the active site. This is where the reactant(s), called the substrate(s) is (are) altered. The amino acids in this area have the properties that allow the enzyme to lower the activation energy needed to initiate the reaction. The shape of an enzyme, like other proteins, is easily influenced by environmental conditions. The shape of an enzyme is in part due to the hydrogen bonds that form between adjacent amino acids. Several factors such as temperature, pH, and salinity will break or cause changes in the bonds that are maintaining the enzyme's shape. The hydrogen bonds responsible for maintaining an enzyme's shape are easily influenced by these changes. Enzymes are so specific that even a slight change in the active site will render them ineffective (*Biology*, 12th ed., pages 98–100/13th ed., pages 82–83).

3

ENERGY FOR CELLS

BIG IDEAS 2, 4

Living things require a continuous supply of energy. Different types of energy surround us, but most of it is not in a form that cells can utilize. Autotrophs convert energy from light, or some inorganic molecules, into the chemical bonds that hold complex organic molecules together. When heterotrophs consume other organisms, they acquire chemical energy stored in these organic molecules. Without the constant supply of energy from the sun, most ecosystems would perish.

The energy that cells need for single activities, such as the synthesis of a macromolecule, cell movement, and active transport, is less than that stored within complex molecules such as glucose. Cells break down glucose and other organic molecules in a series of reactions that transfer smaller amounts of energy, more suitable for cell activities, to other molecules such as ATP.

KEY TERMS

aerobic respiration

anaerobic fermentation

carbon fixation

chemiosmosis

chloroplast

electron transport chain

facultative anaerobes

Krebs cycle

light-dependent reactions

light-independent reactions

obligate anaerobes

phosphorylation

photolysis

photons

photosystems

pigment

products

reactants

reaction center

rubisco

stroma

substrate-level phosphorylation

substrate

thylakoid membrane

wavelength

KEY CONCEPTS

- In photosynthesis and aerobic respiration alike, energy is used to establish a proton electrochemical gradient across a membrane. When the protons diffuse back through ATP synthase, energy is transferred to form ATP.

- Chloroplasts are the organelles of photosynthesis in plants and other photosynthetic eukaryotes. Pigments found there can absorb light energy of different wavelengths.

- The reactions of photosynthesis form two series: the light-dependent reactions occur in the thylakoid membrane, and the light-independent reactions take place in the surrounding stroma.

- The light-dependent reactions convert light energy into the energy of chemical bonds of ATP and NADPH. These molecules transfer energy to the light-independent reactions.

- As water molecules donate electrons to the light-dependent reactions, oxygen gas is produced as a byproduct. When $NADP^+$ finally accepts the electrons, NADPH is formed.

- The light-independent reactions synthesize organic molecules. In the first step of these reactions, carbon fixation, carbon dioxide is used.

- Glycolysis occurs in the cytoplasm of cells and begins the breakdown of carbohydrates. This anaerobic process can be followed by fermentation or aerobic respiration.

- Fermentation lets cells continue glycolysis to make a small amount of ATP in the absence of oxygen because it frees up the necessary NAD^+.

- The mitochondrion is the organelle of aerobic respiration in eukaryotes, where the Krebs cycle and electron transport occur.

- The products of glycolysis and other organic molecules are broken down in the Krebs cycle, forming carbon dioxide. Most of their energy is transferred to coenzymes.

- Oxygen gas is not directly used in the Krebs cycle, but the NAD^+ and FAD necessary for the Krebs cycle are only available when oxygen is present.

- Coenzymes NADH and $FADH_2$ carry electrons to the electron transport chain of the mitochondrial cristae. The transfer of these electrons leads to the greatest formation of ATP in aerobic respiration.

- The final electron acceptor of the aerobic respiration electron transport chain is oxygen gas. The oxygen gas reacts to form water.

For a full discussion of cell energy, see *Biology* 12th ed., Chapters 6, 7 and 8/13th edition, Chapters 5, 6, and 7.

PROTON GRADIENTS AND ATP PRODUCTION
Enduring Understanding 2.A

The major energy processes in cells, photosynthesis and aerobic respiration, both involve the production of ATP by means of an electrochemical gradient. The specifics of their gradient formation and the fate of their ATP differ, but this type of ATP production is key to understanding both processes.

The reactions occurring in the thylakoid membrane of the chloroplast and in the cristae of the mitochondrion not only move electrons, but also change the concentration of protons (H^+) on the two sides of the membrane. The protons (H^+) can only attain equilibrium by passing through the enzyme ATP synthase. When these protons diffuse through the membrane protein ATP synthase, energy is transferred, enabling the attachment of a third phosphate group to a molecule of ADP, forming ATP. The coupling of the electron transport system to production of ATP by the movement of protons (H^+) is sometimes referred to as chemiosmosis.

While in both photosynthesis and aerobic respiration an electrochemical gradient is established, the details of how it is set up differs for the two processes. In both, protons (H^+) are pumped from one side of the membrane to the other and the energy for this is provided by the movement of electrons in the electron transport chain of the membrane. Protons (H^+) also accumulate or are removed due to chemical reactions at the inner or outer surface of the membrane. One notable difference is that the excess protons (H^+) accumulate in the compartment surrounded by the thylakoid membrane of chloroplasts, but in the compartment outside the cristae of mitochondria.

Prokaryotic cells also use proton gradients to form ATP, even though they do not have chloroplasts or mitochondria. Instead, they use their cell membrane to establish the electrochemical gradient.

AP Tip

The concept of chemiosmosis is critical for making comparisons between photosynthesis and cellular respiration as well as for simply understanding energy transfer in both processes. It occurs across the thylakoid membrane of chloroplasts and across the inner mitochondrial membrane (cristae). It can also occur across either the plasma membrane or inner membranes of prokaryotic cells. As electrons move between molecules of the electron transport chain located in the membrane, protons are concentrated on one side of the membrane. When the protons diffuse back through ATP synthase, energy is transferred to ATP.

PHOTOSYNTHESIS: CAPTURING ENERGY FROM THE SUN
Enduring Understanding 2.A

Visible light represents only a small segment of the electromagnetic radiation that is emitted by the sun. This energy travels in waves and the distance between successive crests is its wavelength. A wavelength of visible light is very short and is measured in nanometers (nm). Longer wavelengths of light, such as red, are bent more when they pass through a prism. This action separates light into the colors of the rainbow. The colors with the shortest wavelengths are the most energetic. Wavelengths of radiation longer than red include infrared (IR), and those shorter than violet include ultraviolet (UV). Photosynthesis occurs specifically within the light spectrum between IR and UV and is powered by wavelengths between 380 and 750 nm.

Wavelengths						
shortest wavelengths (highest energy)			range of most radiation reaching Earth's surface	range of heat escaping from Earth's surface		longest wavelengths (lowest energy)
			visible light			
gamma rays	x-rays	ultraviolet radiation	near-infrared radiation	infrared radiation	micro-waves	radio waves

The wavelengths of light reflected from an object are responsible for the colors that we perceive. An apple appears red because it reflects red light and absorbs other color wavelengths. Plants use pigments to color their fruits and other parts like flowers. A pigment is an organic molecule that selectively absorbs certain wavelengths of light while reflecting others. The most common photosynthetic pigment is chlorophyll a. This pigment is very abundant in plants and reflects green light, giving them their characteristic color.

In addition to chlorophyll a, photosynthetic organisms typically use a variety of other pigments. These auxiliary pigments capture much of the energy that chlorophyll a does not. Collectively, nearly all wavelengths of visible light are absorbed. Compared to chlorophyll a, these secondary pigments are found in very low quantities and usually do not contribute to the color of a plant's leaves. In autumn, many plants stop producing their pigments. Chlorophyll tends to break down first, revealing the other pigments.

As pigments absorb light, they capture energy packets called photons. When photons are absorbed, some of the pigment's electrons are boosted to a higher energy level. This excitement only lasts for an instant, and the electrons quickly return to their original position. As they drop back they emit energy, which is harvested by certain pigments and used to drive photosynthesis.

PHOTOSYNTHESIS: AN OVERVIEW
Enduring Understanding 2.A, 4.A

In eukaryotic cells of plants and algae, the chloroplast is the organelle of photosynthesis. It is surrounded by two outer membranes and filled with a semifluid mixture called the stroma. Suspended within the stroma is a highly folded membrane system that forms disk-like structures called thylakoids. The thylakoid membranes form a continuous network of channels and disks. Organized stacks of these thylakoid disks are called grana. The thylakoid membranes have multiple clusters of light-capturing pigments, especially chlorophyll. The pigments and other molecules are organized into clusters called photosystems. Two kinds of photosystems, type I and type II, are found embedded in thylakoid membranes. These are the components of the chloroplast that capture the light energy and begin its conversion into chemical energy.

The process of photosynthesis can be summarized by a simple equation that itemizes the reactants and products:

$$6H_2O + 6CO_2 \xrightarrow[\text{enzymes}]{\text{light energy}} 6O_2 + C_6H_{12}O_6$$

water   carbon   oxygen   glucose
       dioxide

The equation shows the reactants water and carbon dioxide, which are low in free energy, as well as the product glucose, which is high in free energy. It also shows the byproduct oxygen and that light and enzymes are also required. Photosynthesis is much more complex than this equation portrays. It is actually a series of multiple reactions that occur in two main stages.

Stages of Photosynthesis

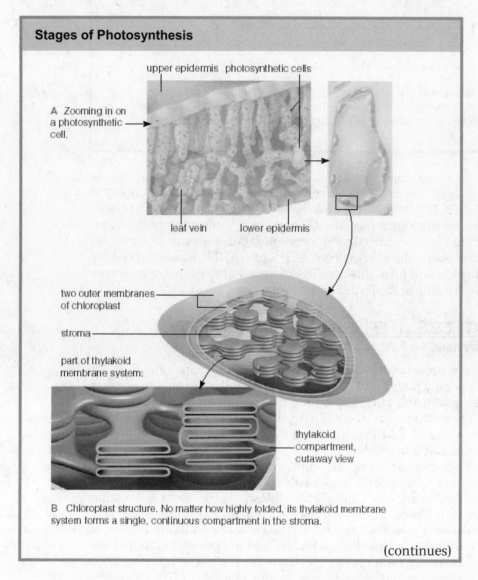

upper epidermis   photosynthetic cells

A Zooming in on a photosynthetic cell.

leaf vein   lower epidermis

two outer membranes of chloroplast

stroma

part of thylakoid membrane system:

thylakoid compartment, cutaway view

B Chloroplast structure. No matter how highly folded, its thylakoid membrane system forms a single, continuous compartment in the stroma.

(continues)

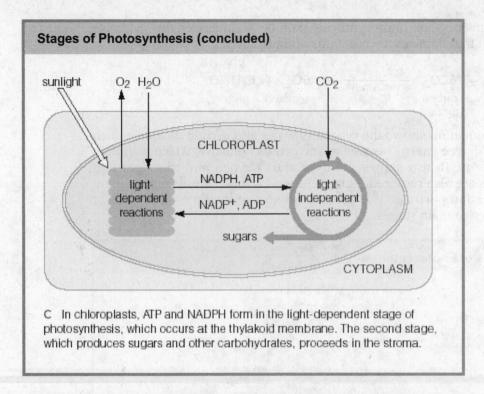

Stages of Photosynthesis (concluded)

C   In chloroplasts, ATP and NADPH form in the light-dependent stage of photosynthesis, which occurs at the thylakoid membrane. The second stage, which produces sugars and other carbohydrates, proceeds in the stroma.

The first stage consists of the light-dependent reactions. This is where the light energy is captured and transferred to the chemical bonds of ATP. In addition, the coenzyme NADPH is formed and water is split, releasing oxygen gas. The second stage, consisting of the light-independent reactions, occurs concurrently, but does not directly use light. In this stage, the energy from ATP and NADPH is used to reduce carbon dioxide and form glucose. The diagram above illustrates where these stages occur in the larger context of a plant's leaf.

PHOTOSYNTHESIS: THE LIGHT-DEPENDENT REACTIONS
Enduring Understanding 2.A

All cells are able to transform chemical energy from one form to another, but only plants and other photoautotrophs are able to convert light energy into the chemical bonds of organic compounds. In this first set of reactions, the solar energy is transferred to the chemical energy of ATP and NADPH. During this process water is split and O_2 gas is released as a byproduct.

The energy conversion of the light-dependent reactions takes place in the clusters of pigments and proteins that are embedded in the thylakoid membranes of each chloroplast. These light-harvesting complexes are called photosystems. Within each photosystem is a complex called a reaction center. This complex contains a pair of special chlorophyll a molecules which, when properly stimulated, are capable of releasing high-energy electrons. Two types of photosystems exist and are arranged in sequence in the membrane. The two are optimized to absorb energy of slightly different wavelengths. The first to be discovered is called photosystem I, while the other is photosystem II.

The Light-Dependent Reactions of Photosynthesis

A Light energy drives electrons out of photosystem II.

B. Photosystem II pulls replacement electrons from water molecules, which dissociate into oxygen and hydrogen ions (photolysis). The oxygen leaves the cell as O_2.

C Electrons from photosystem II enter an electron transfer chain.

D Energy lost by the electrons as they move through the chain causes H^+ to be pumped from the stroma into the thylakoid compartment. An H^+ gradient forms across the membrane.

E Light energy drives electrons out of photosystem I, which accepts replacement electrons from electron transfer chains.

F Electrons from photosystem I move through a second electron transfer chain, then combine with $NADP^+$ and H^+. NADPH forms.

G Hydrogen ions in the thylakoid compartment are propelled through the interior of the ATP synthases by their gradient across the thylakoid membrane.

H H^+ flow causes the ATP synthases to attach phosphate to ADP, so ATP forms in the stroma.

Normally these two photosystems work in concert, producing a linear flow of electrons in what is called the noncyclic pathway. The process begins when photosystem II's chlorophyll a molecules are energized by light and a pair of high-energy electrons are transferred to an adjacent molecule in the thylakoid membrane. As these electrons depart, water is split by a membrane protein which acts as an enzyme; this process is called photolysis. A pair of electrons from the water molecule replaces those removed from the chlorophyll. The hydrogen nuclei (H^+) accumulate in the fluid surrounded by the thylakoid membrane. The oxygen from pairs of split water molecules forms oxygen (O_2), which diffuses out of the chloroplast and, ultimately, into the organism's surroundings. The high-energy electrons are transferred along the electron transport chain of photosystem II, and lose energy as protons (H^+) are pumped from the stroma, across the membrane and into the thylakoid space.

Photosystem I is also stimulated by the appropriate wavelength of light to release a second pair of high-energy electrons. The pair lost from photosystem II immediately replaces these escaping electrons. The excited electrons are passed to another electron transport chain. At the end of this chain $NADP^+$ receives the two electrons and bonds to one proton (H^+) from the stroma to form NADPH. The $NADP^+$ is referred to as the final electron acceptor.

ATP is made as a result of chemiosmosis. This is made possible due to the difference in concentrations of protons (H^+) on the two sides of the thylakoid membrane. Three factors contribute to this gradient:

1. H^+ accumulates in the thylakoid-bound fluid when water breaks apart in photolysis.

2. As electrons move from the reaction center of photosystem II to that of photosystem I, along the electron transport chain, H^+ is pumped from the stroma into the thylakoid-bound fluid.

3. The formation of NADPH from $NADP^+$ removes H^+ from the stroma.

The energy captured during the noncyclic pathway of the light-dependent reactions is transferred to ATP and NADPH with O_2 released as a byproduct. This energy is transferred to carbohydrates in the light-independent reactions.

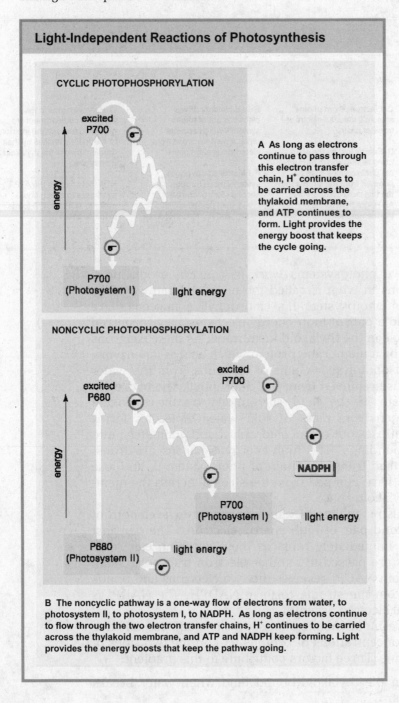

Light-Independent Reactions of Photosynthesis

CYCLIC PHOTOPHOSPHORYLATION

A As long as electrons continue to pass through this electron transfer chain, H^+ continues to be carried across the thylakoid membrane, and ATP continues to form. Light provides the energy boost that keeps the cycle going.

NONCYCLIC PHOTOPHOSPHORYLATION

B The noncyclic pathway is a one-way flow of electrons from water, to photosystem II, to photosystem I, to NADPH. As long as electrons continue to flow through the two electron transfer chains, H^+ continues to be carried across the thylakoid membrane, and ATP and NADPH keep forming. Light provides the energy boosts that keep the pathway going.

The noncyclic pathway will only continue if $NADP^+$ is available as an electron receptor. More ATP than NADPH is used in the light-independent reactions. This causes NADPH to accumulate and therefore stops the renewal of $NADP^+$ needed by the light-independent reactions. The noncyclic reactions will then pause until more $NADP^+$ becomes available. At this point the chloroplast will slip into the cyclic pathway of ATP production.

The cyclic pathway only involves photosystem I and doesn't produce any NADPH. Photolysis does not occur either, so water is not split and no O_2 is released as a byproduct. The only product is ATP. This pathway begins as two high-energy electrons are released by the chlorophylls in the reaction center of photosystem I. The electrons move through the electron transport chain, pumping protons (H^+) into the thylakoid-bound fluid. They then cycle back to the chlorophylls in the reaction center. The buildup of protons (H^+) drives the formation of ATP, just as it does in the noncyclic pathway. When there is enough ATP produced to resume the light-independent reactions, $NADP^+$ will be renewed, and the chloroplast will revert back to the noncyclic pathway.

PHOTOSYNTHESIS: THE LIGHT-INDEPENDENT REACTIONS
Enduring Understanding 2.A

In the light-independent reactions the Calvin-Benson cycle converts the energy stored in ATP and NADPH into the energy of glucose. The carbon atoms used to built these organic molecules are captured from carbon dioxide in a process called carbon fixation. The Calvin-Benson cycle begins as the enzyme rubisco attaches six CO_2 molecules to six five-carbon RuBP molecules. This forms six unstable six-carbon intermediates that quickly split into twelve three-carbon PGA molecules. Each of these receives a phosphate from ATP and hydrogen from NADPH. Two of the resulting three carbon PGAL molecules are used to form one glucose molecule. ATP is used to reorganize the other ten PGAL molecules back into the six RuBP molecules to which CO_2 was bound at the beginning of the cycle. (Note: the names rubisco, RuBP, PGA, and PGAL are details not required for AP Biology.).

The light-independent reactions build glucose from the carbons and oxygen contained in CO_2 and the hydrogen carried by the NADPH. Most of the energy in glucose is derived from the ATP produced in the light-dependent reactions. Once formed, the glucose is usually converted to sucrose for transport or to starch for storage. It can also be used as a building block for other organic molecules.

Cross-Section of Chloroplast with the Light-Independent Reactions Cycling in Stroma

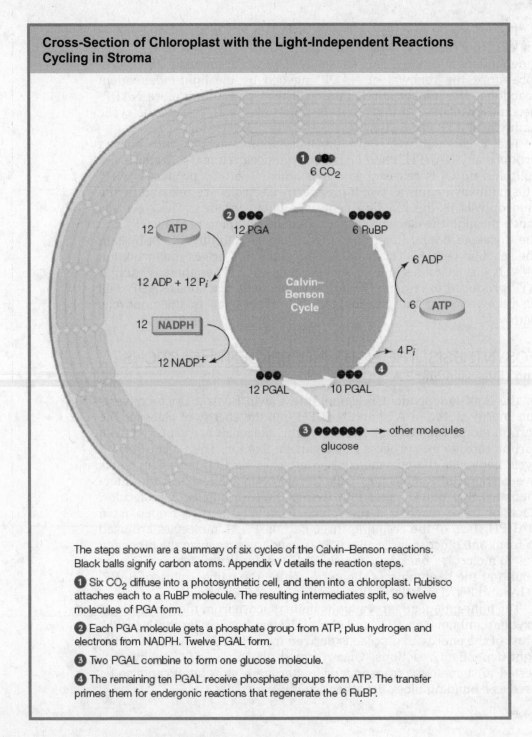

The steps shown are a summary of six cycles of the Calvin–Benson reactions. Black balls signify carbon atoms. Appendix V details the reaction steps.

❶ Six CO_2 diffuse into a photosynthetic cell, and then into a chloroplast. Rubisco attaches each to a RuBP molecule. The resulting intermediates split, so twelve molecules of PGA form.

❷ Each PGA molecule gets a phosphate group from ATP, plus hydrogen and electrons from NADPH. Twelve PGAL form.

❸ Two PGAL combine to form one glucose molecule.

❹ The remaining ten PGAL receive phosphate groups from ATP. The transfer primes them for endergonic reactions that regenerate the 6 RuBP.

GLYCOLYSIS: STARTING TO ACCESS THE ENERGY OF ORGANIC MOLECULES

Enduring Understanding 2.A

The metabolism of most organisms is powered by the chemical energy stored in carbohydrates. Aerobic respiration and anaerobic fermentation are the two main pathways of energy extraction. In eukaryotes, aerobic respiration occurs in the mitochondria, requires oxygen, and extracts a great deal of energy from food. Fermentation only extracts a small portion of the energy in food, but can occur without the presence of oxygen. Eukaryotic cells rely almost exclusively on the aerobic respiration pathway. Certain tissues, however, such as our skeletal muscles, or cells, such as yeast, will switch to the anaerobic pathway when oxygen is in short supply.

The first stage of either pathway is glycolysis. In glycolysis, one molecule of glucose is broken down into two pyruvate molecules. This breakdown occurs in the cytoplasm and yields four ATP. Two ATP, however, are required to initiate this process, so there is a net gain of just two ATP. The ATP result from the direct transfer of phosphates from a substrate to ADP in a process called substrate-level phosphorylation. Also, during the reaction electrons and hydrogen ions originating from glucose are transferred to two NAD^+ to produce two NADH molecules.

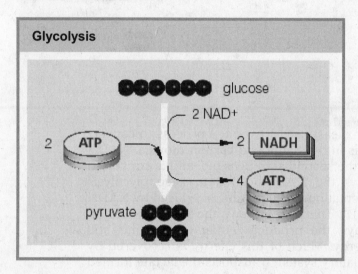

Glycolysis

FERMENTATION: ANAEROBIC RESPIRATION
Enduring Understanding 2.A

Fermentation is the breakdown of carbohydrates without the use of oxygen. Many groups of prokaryotes are obligate anaerobes, meaning not only do they not use oxygen, but also exposure to oxygen will kill them. Depending on oxygen availability, some single-celled fungi like yeast are facultative anaerobes, able to switch between aerobic respiration and fermentation. Animal muscle cells usually produce ATP using aerobic means. When the oxygen in the muscles has been depleted, however, the cells in these tissues will produce ATP through fermentation. Regardless of which organism is undergoing fermentation, the process always begins with glycolysis and takes place within the cytoplasm.

The actual fermentation pathway doesn't directly produce any ATP. All of it is made in glycolysis. The fermentation pathway replenishes the NAD^+ required by glycolysis. Without it, glycolysis could not form any ATP. By renewing the NAD^+, glycolysis can continue producing ATP, as long as glucose is available. Two fermentation pathways are well understood.

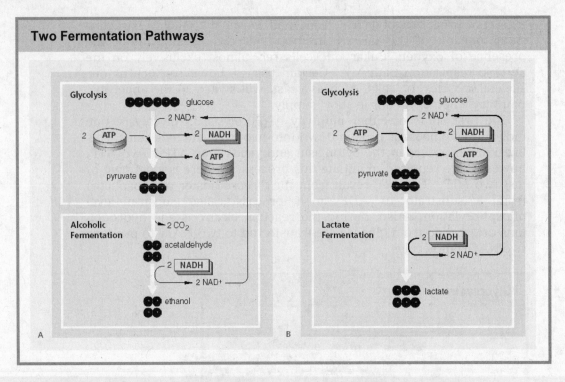

Two Fermentation Pathways

In alcoholic fermentation, yeast uses a two-step process to convert the pyruvate from glycolysis into ethanol and carbon dioxide. NADH donates electrons to make the second step possible, and is converted to NAD^+. This step renews the NAD^+ needed to keep glycolysis functioning. In lactate fermentation, the pyruvate is reduced by NADH to produce lactate and NAD^+. This, too, renews the NAD^+ needed in glycolysis. In both pathways, the products, ethanol or lactate, still contain a great deal of energy. Much of this energy is recovered by muscle cells when the circulatory system transports the lactate formed in muscles to the liver, where it is converted back to glucose.

AEROBIC RESPIRATION: THE KREBS CYCLE
Enduring Understanding 2.A, 4.A

If oxygen is present, cells can perform aerobic respiration after glycolysis. The next stage involves the mitochondria and includes two sets of reactions. The pyruvate formed in glycolysis is broken down first, in acetyl-CoA formation. This reaction occurs as the pyruvate enters the inner compartment of the mitochondrion. As each three-carbon pyruvate arrives, an enzyme splits it, forming a two-carbon molecule and releasing a CO_2 molecule. The two-carbon molecule joins with a coenzyme to make the intermediate molecule acetyl-CoA. As this molecule is formed, electrons and H^+ are released, and they combine with NAD^+ to make NADH. Although no oxygen gas is used in this step, adequate NAD^+ is necessary in the mitochondrion, and that only happens if oxygen gas is present.

The second reaction of this stage begins as the acetyl-CoA enters the Krebs cycle and undergoes a series of enzyme-mediated reactions. First, the acetyl-CoA combines with a four-carbon molecule, making a six-carbon molecule. Next, one and then a second CO_2 are removed. Each time this occurs, one NAD^+ combines with electrons and a

Mitochondrion

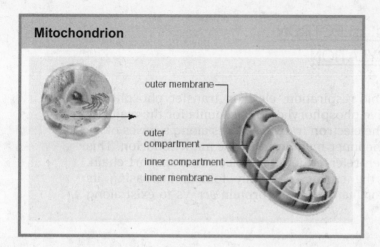

outer membrane

outer compartment

inner compartment

inner membrane

proton (H^+) to form the coenzyme NADH. Then, through substrate-level phosphorylation, an ATP forms from an ADP and a phosphate ion, and more electrons are passed to form another NADH and one molecule of another coenzyme, $FADH_2$. The original four-carbon molecule is formed and the cycle begins again. As with the previous step, no oxygen gas is used in the Krebs cycle, but the necessary NAD^+ and FAD are only available when oxygen gas is present.

Acetyle-CoA Formation

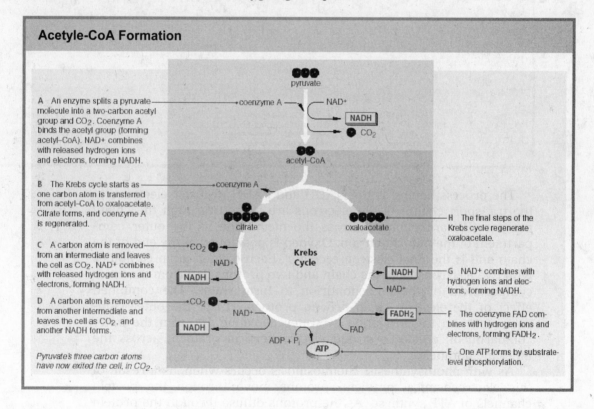

A   An enzyme splits a pyruvate molecule into a two-carbon acetyl group and CO_2. Coenzyme A binds the acetyl group (forming acetyl–CoA). NAD+ combines with released hydrogen ions and electrons, forming NADH.

B   The Krebs cycle starts as one carbon atom is transferred from acetyl–CoA to oxaloacetate. Citrate forms, and coenzyme A is regenerated.

C   A carbon atom is removed from an intermediate and leaves the cell as CO_2. NAD+ combines with released hydrogen ions and electrons, forming NADH.

D   A carbon atom is removed from another intermediate and leaves the cell as CO_2, and another NADH forms.

Pyruvate's three carbon atoms have now exited the cell, in CO_2.

H   The final steps of the Krebs cycle regenerate oxaloacetate.

G   NAD+ combines with hydrogen ions and electrons, forming NADH.

F   The coenzyme FAD combines with hydrogen ions and electrons, forming $FADH_2$.

E   One ATP forms by substrate-level phosphorylation.

pyruvate
coenzyme A
NAD^+
NADH
CO_2
acetyl-CoA
coenzyme A
citrate
oxaloacetate
Krebs Cycle
NAD^+
NADH
NADH
NAD^+
CO_2
CO_2
NADH
NAD^+
FADH2
NAD^+
FAD
ADP + P_i
ATP

AEROBIC RESPIRATION: ELECTRON TRANSFER PHOSPHORYLATION

Enduring Understanding 2.A, 4.A

The final stage of aerobic respiration, electron transfer phosphorylation (also called oxidative phosphorylation), accounts for the majority of ATP that is formed. The electron transfer occurs along a series of enzymes embedded in the inner membrane of the mitochondrion. This series of enzymes is often referred to as the electron transport chain. The inner membrane, the cristae, is highly folded, increasing its surface area, allowing for many of these protein arrays to exist along its length.

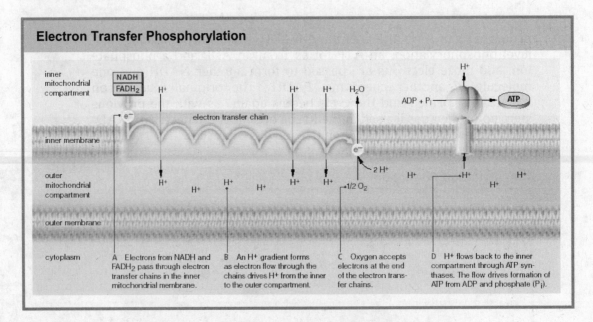

Electron Transfer Phosphorylation

A Electrons from NADH and FADH₂ pass through electron transfer chains in the inner mitochondrial membrane.

B An H⁺ gradient forms as electron flow through the chains drives H⁺ from the inner to the outer compartment.

C Oxygen accepts electrons at the end of the electron transfer chains.

D H⁺ flows back to the inner compartment through ATP synthases. The flow drives formation of ATP from ADP and phosphate (Pᵢ).

The process begins as the NADH and FADH₂ transfer electrons to the transport chain. As the electrons are passed through the chain, protons (H⁺) are pumped across the membrane to the outer compartment of the mitochondrion. Oxygen is positioned at the end of the chain and is the final electron receptor. Each oxygen atom combines with two electrons from the chain and two protons (H⁺) from the inner compartment of the mitochondrion to form water. The combined effect of the electron chain driving protons (H⁺) to the outer compartment, and the formation of water depleting H⁺ from the inner compartment, creates a strong electrochemical gradient across the inner membrane.

As with photosynthesis, chemiosmosis occurs when, as a result of this electrochemical gradient, protons move through the protein channels of ATP synthase. As the protons diffuse through the protein channels, free energy is transferred and ATP is formed from ADP and phosphate ions. This electron transfer phosphorylation accounts for most of the ATP formed in aerobic respiration. This allows the cell to gain many times more ATP than it would from fermentation.

Multiple-Choice Questions

1. Glycolysis occurs
   (A) only in eukaryotic cells.
   (B) in the mitochondria.
   (C) in the cytoplasm.
   (D) only in aerobic respiration.

2. A product of glycolysis is
   (A) NAD^+.
   (B) NADPH.
   (C) $FADH_2$.
   (D) pyruvate.

3. The Krebs cycle takes place in
   (A) the cytoplasm.
   (B) the inner mitochondrial compartment.
   (C) the inner mitochondrial membrane.
   (D) only prokaryotic cells.

4. Most of the ATP produced in aerobic respiration occurs in
   (A) glycolysis.
   (B) the Krebs cycle.
   (C) substrate level phosphorylation.
   (D) electron transfer phosphorylation.

5. The final electron acceptor at the end of the mitochondrial electron transport chain is
   (A) oxygen.
   (B) water.
   (C) NAD^+.
   (D) NADH.

6. All of the following are true of BOTH alcoholic and lactate fermentation EXCEPT
   (A) They start with pyruvate.
   (B) They recycle NAD^+ so glycolysis can continue.
   (C) They produce one CO_2 molecule for each pyruvate molecule used.
   (D) They occur in the cytoplasm.

7. During aerobic respiration, oxygen (O_2) is used
   (A) to make carbon dioxide.
   (B) as a source of electrons for chemiosmosis.
   (C) in the cytoplasm.
   (D) to accept electrons and make water.

8. The color of a green leaf is due to
   (A) abundant pigment molecules that absorb green light.
   (B) abundant pigment molecules that reflect green light.
   (C) chlorophyll's location in the outer membrane of the chloroplast.
   (D) the absence of any pigments other than chlorophyll.

9. All of the following are true of the light-dependent reactions of photosynthesis EXCEPT
   (A) NADPH is produced.
   (B) Water is a source of electrons.
   (C) ATP is produced.
   (D) Glucose is produced.

Questions 10–12 refer to the diagram of a photosynthetic cell below.

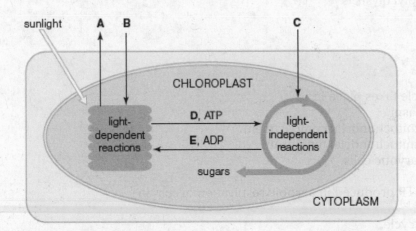

10. This compound is the source of the oxygen that is released during photosynthesis.
    (A) substance "A"
    (B) substance "B"
    (C) substance "C"
    (D) substance "E"

11. This substance is the source of the carbon that is fixed during photosynthesis.
    (A) substance "B"
    (B) substance "C"
    (C) substance "D"
    (D) substance "E"

12. This substance accepts the electrons at the end of the light-dependent reactions.
    (A) substance "A"
    (B) substance "B"
    (C) substance "D"
    (D) substance "E"

13. Which of the following is NOT associated with electron transfer phosphorylation?
    (A) membrane proteins
    (B) proton gradient
    (C) ATP synthase
    (D) carbon dioxide

14. The light-independent reactions of photosynthesis occur in the
    (A) stroma.
    (B) plasma membrane.
    (C) thylakoid membrane-bound.
    (D) cytoplasm.

15. Which of the following statements is FALSE?
    (A) Light energizes electrons that move during the light-dependent reactions of photosynthesis.
    (B) NADPH is found only in cells of photoautotrophs, and NADH is found only in cells of heterotrophs.
    (C) ATP synthase is found in the inner membrane of both chloroplasts and mitochondria.
    (D) The Krebs cycle is part of aerobic respiration; the Calvin-Benson cycle is part of photosynthesis.

Grid-In Question

1. Ten young bean plants were placed in a closed, transparent container, and the amount of carbon dioxide was measured over the course of a lab period. The plants were found to have used 0.036 moles of carbon dioxide gas. How many moles of glucose would the plants have been able to produce during this time?

Free-Response Questions

MULTI-PART QUESTION

1. Aerobic respiration and anaerobic fermentation can be used by cells to produce ATP.
   (a) Describe how these two pathways are different.
   (b) Describe the major advantages of each.
   (c) Distinguish between the two types of fermentation.

SINGLE-PART QUESTION

2. A student investigating photosynthesis measures the pH of the stroma and the inner thylakoid compartments of spinach leaf cells. Her results are shown in the following table.

Source of Fluid	pH
Stroma	8.2
Inner compartment of thylakoid	5.6

Explain these results, using your understanding of photosynthesis.

Answers

MULTIPLE-CHOICE QUESTIONS

1. **C.** Glycolysis occurs in the cytoplasm of eukaryotic and prokaryotic cells. It precedes both aerobic respiration and fermentation (*Biology*, 12th ed., page 126/13th ed., page 120).

2. **D.** In glycolysis, each glucose molecule is broken down into two pyruvate molecules (*Biology*, 2th ed., page 126/13th ed., page 120).

3. **B.** In eukaryotic cells, the Krebs cycle takes place in the inner compartment of mitochondria. The produced NADH and FADH2 are used to drive the electron transport chain (*Biology*, 12th ed., page 128/13th ed., pages 122–123).

4. **D.** For one glucose molecule, electron transfer phosphorylation yields 32 ATP while glycolysis and the Krebs cycle only yield two ATP each (*Biology*, 12th ed., page 130/13th ed., page 125).

5. **A.** Oxygen has a very high electronegativity and captures the electrons when they are at the end of the chain. It then combines with two H^+ to form water (*Biology*, 12th ed., page 130/13th ed., pages 124–125).

6. **C.** Only alcoholic fermentation releases CO2 (*Biology*, 12th ed., page 132/13th ed., pages 126–127).

7. **D.** Even though the Krebs cycle, where CO_2 is made, is part of aerobic respiration, oxygen does not play a role until it accepts electrons and combines with H^+ at the end of the mitochondrial electron transport chain (*Biology*, 12th ed., page 130/13th ed., pages 124–125).

8. **B.** Abundant chlorophyll molecules in the thylakoid membranes of plant chloroplasts reflect green light (*Biology*, 12th ed., pages 108–111/13th ed., pages 102–103).

9. **D.** Glucose is a product of photosynthesis, but it is produced during the light-independent reactions, not the light-dependent reactions (*Biology*, 12th ed., page 111/13th ed., page 105).

10. **B.** Substance B in the diagram represents water which is the only reactant that enters the light-dependent reactions. It is broken down releasing O_2 during photolysis (*Biology* 12th ed., page 111/13th ed., page 105).

11. **B.** Substance C in the diagram represents CO_2 and it is the source of carbon that is fixed during photosynthesis (*Biology* 12th ed., page 111/13th ed., page 105).

12. **D.** Substance E in the diagram represents $NADP^+$. $NADP^+$ joins with electrons and a proton (H^+) to form NADPH at the end of the electron transport chain of the thylakoid membrane. During the light-independent reactions, NADPH donates electrons, forming $NADP^+$ which cycles back to pick up more electrons from the light-dependent reactions (*Biology* 12th ed., page 115/13th ed., page 109).

13. **D.** Carbon dioxide is associated with the Krebs cycle. Electron transfer phosphorylation occurs in the cristae of the mitochondrion and involves protons moving through ATP synthase. In prokaryotes, the proton gradient is set up across the plasma membrane. During photosynthesis, a proton gradient across the thylakoid membrane generates ATP during the light-dependent reactions; carbon dioxide is fixed during the light-independent reactions (*Biology*, 12th ed., pages 112–113, 130/13th ed., pages 106–107, 124–125).

14. **A.** The light-independent reactions take place in the stroma (*Biology*, 12th ed., page 115/13th ed., page 109).

15. **B.** Aerobic respiration occurs in plants as well as in heterotrophic eukaryotes (*Biology*, 12th ed., page 124/13th ed., page 118).

GRID-IN QUESTION

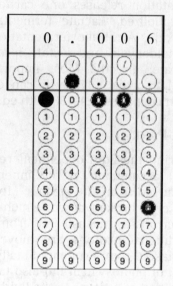

1. **0.006**

According to the balanced chemical equation for aerobic respiration, 6 moles (or molecules) of carbon dioxide are required for 1 mole (or molecule) of glucose; this occurs during the Calvin-Benson cycle.

Thus, 0.036 moles CO_2 × (1 mole glucose/6 moles CO_2) = 0.006 moles glucose.

(*Biology*, 12th ed., page 115/13th ed., page 109).

FREE-RESPONSE QUESTIONS

MULTI-PART

1. (a) Both types of processes are preceded by glycolysis. Fermentation takes place in the cytoplasm and doesn't use oxygen. Neither alcoholic nor lactate fermentation produce any ATP directly. These pathways simply regenerate the NAD^+ needed by glycolysis. But by renewing the NAD^+, they are indirectly responsible for the two ATP produced in glycolysis. The byproducts, ethanol or lactate, still contain a great deal of chemical energy. On the other hand,

aerobic respiration usually occurs in the mitochondria and always requires oxygen. It too renews the NAD⁺ needed by glycolysis. It, however, extracts most of the energy stored in glucose. Most of that energy is from the last stage, electron transfer phosphorylation. The byproducts, carbon dioxide and water, contain very little energy. Aerobic respiration is therefore much more efficient and is able to extract most of the energy from each glucose molecule.

(b) Although fermentation accounts for very little ATP, it does have a couple of advantages. First and foremost, it doesn't require oxygen. This feature allows some organisms to inhabit environments that lack oxygen. It also allows some aerobic organisms or tissues to obtain ATP when oxygen is not available. For example, yeast and skeletal muscle cells can obtain at least some ATP when their oxygen supply has been depleted. Fermentation is also a relatively simple process. It does not require an organelle and can generate a small amount of ATP very quickly. The major advantage of aerobic respiration is its ability to produce large amounts of ATP. This feature is essential to all eukaryotic cells because of their high-energy requirements. A second advantage is its efficiency. It extracts nearly all of the available energy stored in food.

(c) Alcoholic and lactate fermentation have several similarities, but they also differ in a few ways. The byproduct of alcoholic fermentation is a two-carbon ethanol, whereas lactate fermentation produces a three-carbon lactate as a byproduct. Alcoholic fermentation releases one carbon dioxide per pyruvate molecule metabolized. Lactate fermentation doesn't release any carbon dioxide. Alcoholic fermentation also produces an intermediate, acetaldehyde, and lactate fermentation produces its byproduct, lactate, directly. Most importantly, both processes regenerate NAD⁺ so that glycolysis can continue to produce ATP (*Biology*, 12th ed. pages 124–133/13th ed., pages 118–127).

SINGLE-PART

2. During the light-dependent reactions of photosynthesis, protons (H⁺) accumulate in the inner thylakoid compartment and are removed from the stroma. In the inner thylakoid compartment, water is broken down, which adds protons to that solution. As electrons are transferred from photosystem II to photosystem I, additional protons are moved from the stroma to the inner thylakoid compartment. Finally, as NADP⁺ accepts electrons at the end of photosystem I, it also takes a proton from the stroma. The addition of protons to the fluid of the inner thylakoid compartment lowers its pH, while the removal of protons from the stroma raises its pH. It is this difference in proton concentration on the two sides of the membrane that powers the production of ATP as the excess protons diffuse back into the stroma (*Biology*, 12th ed. pages 30, 112–114/13th ed., pages 106–108).

4

CELLS

Big Ideas 2, 3, 4

The most fundamental building block of life is the cell. Cells are the smallest living structures capable of carrying out all life activities. All of the chemical reactions that sustain life occur within cells. From simple prokaryotes, such as bacteria, to complex eukaryotes, such as humans, all living things are composed of cells. The cell is the basic unit of structure and function in multicellular organisms. In addition to obtaining usable energy from the environment via processes such as photosynthesis and cellular respiration, cells have important roles in homeostasis, heredity, and coordination within multicellular organisms.

Since the invention of the microscope over 400 years ago, our understanding of cells, as well as how they function, has steadily improved. The observations of multiple scientists have led to four generalizations that today constitute the cell theory:

1. All living things are composed of one or more cells.
2. The cell is the basic unit of structure and function for all organisms. The cell is the smallest unit to carry out all life functions.
3. Cells come from pre-existing cells.
4. Cells contain hereditary material and pass it on to their offspring.

Cells differ greatly in form and in function, but they share three common features. All cells are enveloped by a plasma membrane, include a DNA containing region, and have a semi-fluid interior called cytoplasm, in which are located protein assembly units called ribosomes. Furthermore, cells can be categorized as either prokaryotic or eukaryotic. The major difference between these two cell types is that prokaryotic cells lack a nucleus and other specialized, membrane-bound compartments, while eukaryotic cells have these structures.

95

KEY TERMS

active transport	endocytosis	nucleus
adhering junctions	endoplasmic reticulum (ER)	organelles
allele		osmosis
asexual reproduction	extracellular matrix (ECM)	passive transport
cancer	facilitated diffusion	phagocytosis
cell plate	flagella	pili
cell wall	gametes	plasma membrane
central vacuole	Golgi body	plasmid
centromere	haploid (1n)	plasmodesmata
chloroplasts	histones	prokaryotic
chromatin	homologous chromosomes	receptor proteins
chromoplasts		recognition proteins
chromosomes	hypertonic	ribosomes
cilia	hypotonic	sexual reproduction
concentration gradient	interphase	sister chromatids
crossing over	isotonic	somatic cells
cytokinesis	lysosomes	sperm
cytoplasm	meiosis	tight junctions
cytoskeleton	mitochondria	transport proteins
diffusion	mitosis	turgor pressure
diploid (2n)	nuclear envelope	vesicles
DNA replication	nucleoid	
egg	nucleolus	

KEY CONCEPTS

▦ Cells function by maintaining internal environments different from their external environments.

▦ The structure and function of a cell is derived from its components.

▦ In multicellular organisms, differences in gene expression result in cell specialization.

▦ The cell cycle involves passing hereditary information to another generation by asexual or sexual reproduction.

▦ Cells communicate with other cells.

For a full discussion of cells, see *Biology* 12th edition, Chapters 4, 5, 9, 10, 15, 21, 22, 33, and 35/13th edition, Chapters 4, 11, 12, 20, 21, 32, and 34.

THE BOUNDARY OF THE CELL
Enduring Understanding 2.B

The plasma membrane separates the contents of cells from their external environment. This membrane is composed mostly of a phospholipid bilayer, steroids, and proteins. A phospholipid has a hydrophilic phosphate-containing head and two hydrophobic fatty acid tails. The bilayer forms as the fatty acid tails are repelled by water and attract each other. Meanwhile, the phosphate heads dissolve easily in the aquatic environment found both inside and outside of the cell. This results in a stable barrier that confines the contents of the cell. Embedded proteins regulate the movement of many substances across the membrane, giving it a selective permeability property.

A Phospholipid

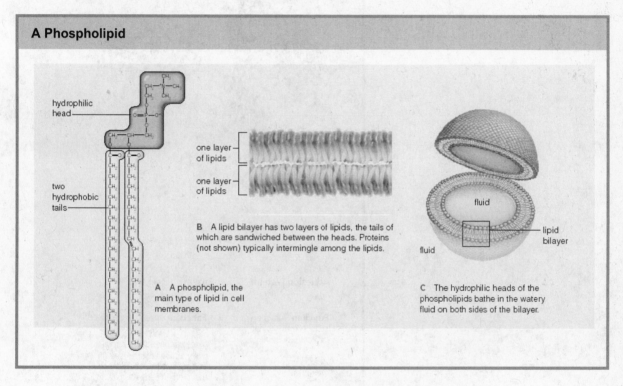

hydrophilic head

two hydrophobic tails

one layer of lipids

one layer of lipids

B A lipid bilayer has two layers of lipids, the tails of which are sandwiched between the heads. Proteins (not shown) typically intermingle among the lipids.

A A phospholipid, the main type of lipid in cell membranes.

fluid

fluid

lipid bilayer

C The hydrophilic heads of the phospholipids bathe in the watery fluid on both sides of the bilayer.

The fluid mosaic model is often used to describe the organization of the cell membrane. Although the phospholipids are compelled to form a bilayer, they freely move sideways and wiggle throughout the membrane. This gives the cell membrane a liquid behavior. Unsaturated fatty acid tails increase the fluidity of the membrane. This results from the kinks caused by double bonds in the fatty acid. The kinks prevent phospholipids from packing close together, increasing the membrane's fluidity. Its mosaic appearance is due to proteins, steroids, and other molecules dispersed within the bilayer. Cholesterol is the most common steroid in animal cell membranes. Its hydrophobic ring structure blends with the fatty acid portion of the bilayer, while the attached hydroxyl group dissolves in the aquatic environment on the outside. Phospholipid movement is restricted by cholesterol, thus limiting the fluidity of the membrane.

Oxygen, carbon dioxide, and other small non-polar molecules can easily pass across the membrane. The lipid bilayer, however, is a formidable barrier to large molecules, ions, and polar substances. Some of the proteins embedded in the membrane serve as conduits for the movement of materials to which the lipid bilayer is impermeable, such as ions and large hydrophilic molecules. Water moves both through the lipid bilayer and through proteins called aquaporins. The transport proteins tend to be specific to certain substances; therefore a variety of transport proteins are needed. Some of these proteins are gated and will only let materials through

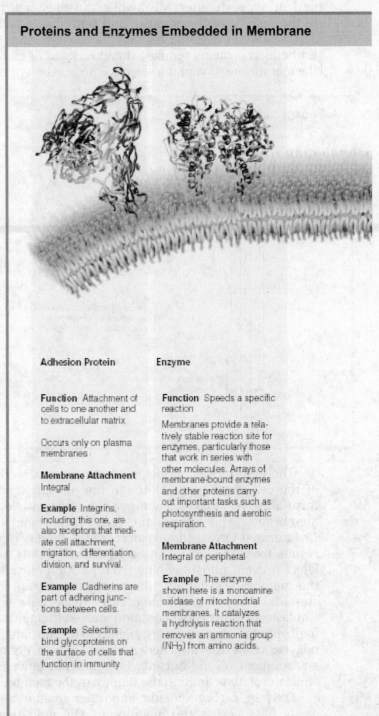

Proteins and Enzymes Embedded in Membrane

Adhesion Protein

Function Attachment of cells to one another and to extracellular matrix

Occurs only on plasma membranes

Membrane Attachment Integral

Example Integrins, including this one, are also receptors that mediate cell attachment, migration, differentiation, division, and survival.

Example Cadherins are part of adhering junctions between cells.

Example Selectins bind glycoproteins on the surface of cells that function in immunity

Enzyme

Function Speeds a specific reaction

Membranes provide a relatively stable reaction site for enzymes, particularly those that work in series with other molecules. Arrays of membrane-bound enzymes and other proteins carry out important tasks such as photosynthesis and aerobic respiration.

Membrane Attachment Integral or peripheral

Example The enzyme shown here is a monoamine oxidase of mitochondrial membranes. It catalyzes a hydrolysis reaction that removes an ammonia group (NH_3) from amino acids.

part of the time. Others can act like pumps, moving substances across a concentration gradient.

Other proteins are also present in the membrane. Receptor proteins are discussed further under the heading of *Cell Communication*, while recognition proteins are included with *Cell Differentiation*. Some membrane proteins are enzymes. As discussed in Chapter 3, the proper functioning of mitochondria and chloroplasts relies on arrays of enzymes, such as ATP synthase, embedded in their membranes.

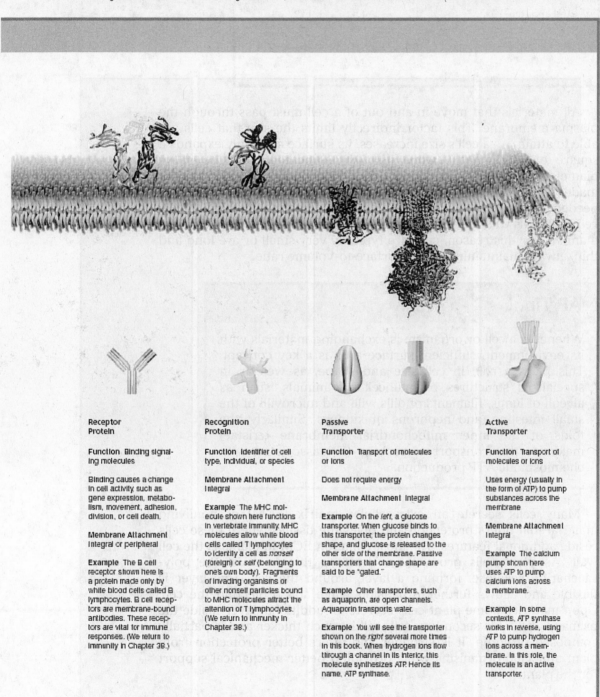

Receptor Protein

Function Binding signaling molecules

Binding causes a change in cell activity, such as gene expression, metabolism, movement, adhesion, division, or cell death.

Membrane Attachment Integral or peripheral

Example The B cell receptor shown here is a protein made only by white blood cells called B lymphocytes. B cell receptors are membrane-bound antibodies. These receptors are vital for immune responses. (We return to immunity in Chapter 38.)

Recognition Protein

Function Identifier of cell type, individual, or species

Membrane Attachment Integral

Example The MHC molecule shown here functions in vertebrate immunity. MHC molecules allow white blood cells called T lymphocytes to identify a cell as *nonself* (foreign) or *self* (belonging to one's own body). Fragments of invading organisms or other nonself particles bound to MHC molecules attract the attention of T lymphocytes. (We return to immunity in Chapter 38.)

Passive Transporter

Function Transport of molecules or ions

Does not require energy

Membrane Attachment Integral

Example On the *left*, a glucose transporter. When glucose binds to this transporter, the protein changes shape, and glucose is released to the other side of the membrane. Passive transporters that change shape are said to be "gated."

Example Other transporters, such as aquaporin, are open channels. Aquaporin transports water.

Example You will see the transporter shown on the *right* several more times in this book. When hydrogen ions flow through a channel in its interior, this molecule synthesizes ATP. Hence its name, ATP synthase.

Active Transporter

Function Transport of molecules or ions

Uses energy (usually in the form of ATP) to pump substances across the membrane

Membrane Attachment Integral

Example The calcium pump shown here uses ATP to pump calcium ions across a membrane.

Example In some contexts, ATP synthase works in reverse, using ATP to pump hydrogen ions across a membrane. In this role, the molecule is an active transporter.

Surface-to-Volume Ratio			
Diameter (cm)	2	3	6
Surface area (cm²)	12.6	28.2	113
Volume (cm³)	4.2	14.1	113
Surface-to-volume ratio	3:1	2:1	1:1

All materials that move in and out of a cell must pass through the plasma membrane. This factor indirectly limits the size that cells are able to attain. As a cell's size increases, its surface area only expands a square of its diameter, while its volume increases a cube of its diameter. If a cell becomes too large, its plasma membrane has inadequate surface area to accommodate the required transport needed to sustain such a large volume. Furthermore, once inside of the cell, materials will not be able to be distributed in a timely and efficient manner. For this reason, cells are typically very small or are long and thin, always maintaining a high surface-to-volume ratio.

AP Tip

Whenever a cell or organism is exchanging materials with its environment, sufficient surface area is a key concept. This plays a role in cell size and shape, as well as in specialized structures of multicellular animals, such as alveoli of lungs, filaments of gills, villi and microvilli of the small intestine, and nephrons of kidneys. Similarly, the folds of the inner mitochondrial membrane (cristae) maximize the transport of protons (H^+) associated with chemiosmotic ATP production.

Many cells secrete an extracellular matrix (ECM) of nonliving material that offers protection and gives the tissues where these cells reside additional features. The most common ECM in plants is the cell wall. As plant cells grow, they secrete a thin layer of the poly-saccharide cellulose, forming a layer around the cell. This layer is flexible and allows further expansion while still protecting the cell. Upon maturity, some plant cells secrete an additional layer inside the primary wall. This secondary cell wall is much thicker and is partially composed of lignin. It is stronger and offers better protection from plant-attacking organisms while providing better mechanical support for the plant.

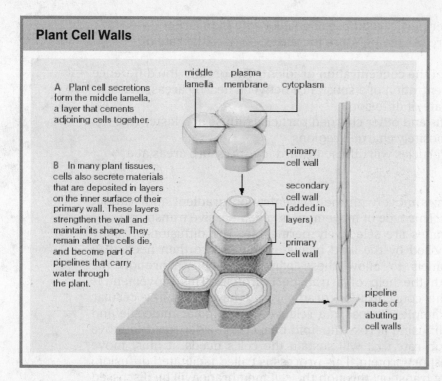

Plant Cell Walls

A Plant cell secretions form the middle lamella, a layer that cements adjoining cells together.

B In many plant tissues, cells also secrete materials that are deposited in layers on the inner surface of their primary wall. These layers strengthen the wall and maintain its shape. They remain after the cells die, and become part of pipelines that carry water through the plant.

middle lamella / plasma membrane / cytoplasm

primary cell wall

secondary cell wall (added in layers)

primary cell wall

pipeline made of abutting cell walls

In fungi, the ECM also forms a cell wall, but it is composed mostly of the polysaccharide chitin. In animals, the ECM is composed of carbohydrates and proteins. It does not form a cell wall, but it does help hold tissues together and provides structural support. Bone, for example, is mostly ECM composed of the fibrous protein collagen that is hardened by mineral deposits.

Prokaryotic cells are typically surrounded by a cell wall composed of peptidoglycan, a polymer of cross-linked peptides and polysaccharides. The wall is rigid, providing excellent support, but permeable, allowing materials to pass through it easily. Some bacteria surround their wall with a slime layer called a capsule. It is composed of a sticky polysaccharide that allows it to adhere to smooth surfaces. This covering also protects it from predators and environmental toxins, as well as disguises it from a host's immune system.

Cells are not isolated and routinely interact with each other. Some cell junctions allow communication between adjacent cells; these will be discussed under the heading "Cell Communication." Two types of junctions are used to hold animal cells together. Adhering junctions are very strong. They link cells to each other or to the ECM. Tight junctions are not nearly as strong, but they offer a watertight seal between adjacent cells. They are especially important in the organs of our digestive tract. These junctions prevent the digestive juices from leaking and damaging our internal organs.

PASSIVE AND ACTIVE TRANSPORT
Enduring Understanding 2.B

Diffusion is the random movement of particles from high to low concentrations. The difference in concentration between two adjacent areas is called a concentration gradient. The rate of diffusion varies and is influenced by five factors, shown on page 102.

1. Size: Smaller particles diffuse at a faster rate than larger ones.
2. Temperature: As temperature increases, so does the rate of diffusion.
3. Steepness of the concentration gradient: The greater the difference in the concentration of a substance between nearby areas, the faster the rate of diffusion.
4. Charge: Ions and other charged particles diffuse at a faster rate toward oppositely charged regions.
5. Pressure: Particles will diffuse toward low-pressure areas at a faster rate.

Many particles move with the concentration gradient and without the use of ATP. This type of movement is called passive transport.

Cell membranes are selectively permeable. The diffusion of many particles is blocked by the lipid bilayer. Proteins are then needed to serve as channels to allow these particles to pass through the membrane with the help of a transport protein. This movement is always with the concentration gradient and never requires cellular energy. For example, glucose is a relatively large polar molecule and has difficulty diffusing across the lipid bilayer. In order for it to move at a fast enough rate that will sustain the cell's needs, it must move through a transport protein. This process is called facilitated diffusion. Water's passive transport through the cell membrane will be discussed separately, within the *Osmosis* section of this chapter.

Active transport occurs when solutes are moved across the membrane, against the concentration gradient. In this case, a transport protein pumps the substance from lower to higher concentration using cellular energy, usually in the form of ATP. One common type of active transport proteins are the calcium pumps found in our muscle cells. These transporters use energy to pump calcium ions back into a storage chamber, against the concentration gradient, allowing the muscle to relax.

A cotransporter is a protein that employs active transport to simultaneously move two different substances in opposite directions across a membrane. The sodium-potassium pump uses energy to push sodium ions out of the cell and potassium ions into the cell. Both ions are moved from lower to higher concentration.

In some cases, membraneous sacs called vesicles are used to move very large molecules across the membrane. Vesicles can merge with the membrane, and in doing so, transport their contents across it. In exocytosis, large materials are transported out of the cell. The process begins as a vesicle buds from a Golgi body and moves towards the cell's surface. The vesicle will then merge with the plasma membrane, turning inside out and expelling its contents.

A cell can obtain large particles in an opposite process called endocytosis. When certain substances concentrate near the outer surface of the cell, the plasma membrane begins to fold inward. This movement continues until a vesicle forms on the inside of the cell. In receptor-mediated endocytosis, this process is initiated when a specific particle binds to a specific protein on the surface of the plasma membrane. This contact stimulates a cascade of events inside of the

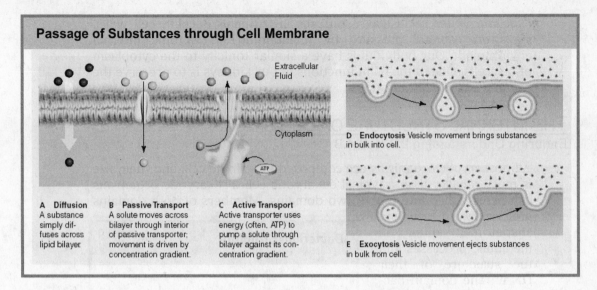

Passage of Substances through Cell Membrane

Extracellular Fluid

Cytoplasm

ATP

A Diffusion A substance simply diffuses across lipid bilayer.

B Passive Transport A solute moves across bilayer through interior of passive transporter; movement is driven by concentration gradient.

C Active Transport Active transporter uses energy (often, ATP) to pump a solute through bilayer against its concentration gradient.

D Endocytosis Vesicle movement brings substances in bulk into cell.

E Exocytosis Vesicle movement ejects substances in bulk from cell.

cell, triggering it to engulf the particles. When an entire cell or cell fragment is engulfed, it is referred to as phagocytosis. Some of our white blood cells remove bacteria and viruses through this process. Protists, like the amoeba, feed using this phagocytosis.

OSMOSIS

Enduring Understanding 2.B

One molecule that is constantly moving in and out of a cell is water. Osmosis is the diffusion of water across a selectively permeable membrane. Tonicity is the relative concentration of solutes on either side of a membrane. A hypotonic solution has a lower concentration of dissolved materials or solutes. A solution with a higher concentration of solutes is hypertonic. If the solute concentration is equal on both sides of a membrane, the solution is isotonic.

Water potential is the tendency of water to move from high to low potential. When the tonicity is changed, the water potential also changes. If a cell were placed in a hypertonic solution, it would have a higher concentration of water (higher water potential) than that solution. It is then likely to shrivel as water moves out in an attempt to seek equilibrium. Conversely, the same cell would swell (due to its low water potential) if it were placed in a hypotonic environment. In an isotonic solution the size of the cell would remain constant. Although water would still be moving in both directions across the membrane, no net change would result.

The cells of different groups of organisms have adopted various strategies in order to cope with the relentless movement of water. Bacteria, fungi, and plants all tend to live in hypotonic environments, and their cell walls help them battle the constant influx of water. The rigid outer covering prevents these cells from expanding to the point that they would burst, and hydrostatic or turgor pressure results, countering the effect of osmosis. Many plants rely on turgor pressure to remain stiff and upright; without it they wilt.

Some protists without cell walls, such as the amoeba and paramecium, have an organelle called a contractile vacuole which is used to maintain osmotic balance. This structure is like a bilge pump, expelling water as fast as it diffuses in. Animals, lacking cell walls, stave off osmotic pressure by maintaining an isotonic internal environment. Our body fluids have a similar tonicity to the cytoplasm of our cells. One of the main functions of our kidneys is to preserve the osmotic balance of our bodies.

THE INTERNAL STRUCTURE OF CELLS

Enduring Understanding 2.B, 4.A, 4.B

All prokaryotic organisms are composed of a single cell, and their size is much smaller than a typical eukaryotic cell. Prokaryotic organisms can be classified into one of two domains. Members of both domains are similar in size and shape, but differ in metabolic processes and the structure of their DNA. The domain bacteria is the more familiar of the two and includes the bacteria that we use to make yogurt and the ones that make us ill. The domain archaea tend to thrive in hostile environments, so we don't encounter them as often. The structure of archaean DNA has some similarities to eukaryotic DNA, and therefore these organisms are considered more closely related to our cell type.

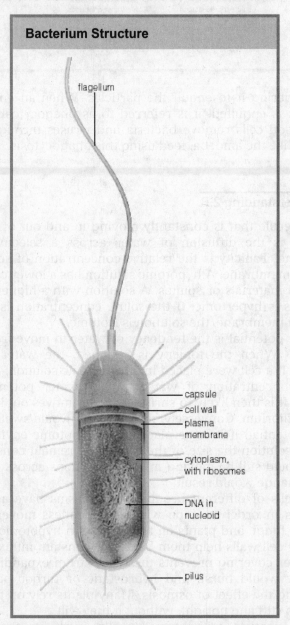

Bacterium Structure

flagellum

capsule
cell wall
plasma membrane
cytoplasm, with ribosomes
DNA in nucleoid
pilus

Although prokaryotic cells are relatively simple, they still possess a variety of structures that help them survive. In some bacteria, the typical peptidoglycan cell wall is surrounded by a slime layer, called a capsule. Composed of a sticky polysaccharide, it allows the cell to adhere to smooth surfaces; it also protects the cell from predators, environmental toxins, and a host's immune system. One or more flagella, used for locomotion, extends beyond the cell wall. Also projecting from the surface are protein filaments called pili. These structures help bacteria stick to or move across different surfaces. In some cells, specialized pili are adapted to facilitate the exchange of genetic material with another cell; these are referred to as sex pili.

The genetic material of prokaryotes is different from that of eukaryotic cells. Bacteria have a single chromosome composed of circular pieces of DNA, while eukaryotic cells have multiple linear chromosomes. In addition, many prokaryotes have small auxiliary pieces of DNA called plasmids. Plasmids only contain a few genes, but offer the host unique features, like resistance to antibiotics.

Plant and Animal Cell Components

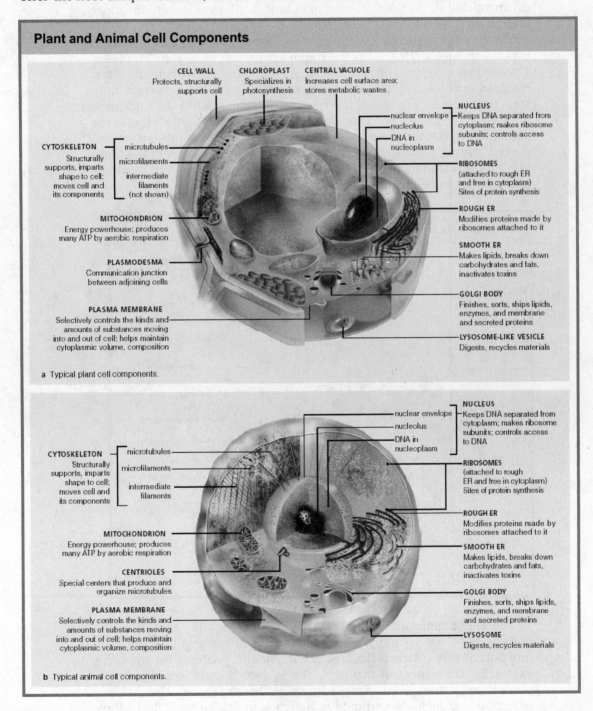

a Typical plant cell components.

b Typical animal cell components.

Eukaryotic cells are larger and much more complex than prokaryotic cells. Their DNA is usually contained within a membrane, forming a structure called the nucleus. In addition, membranes surround other areas, compartmentalizing various parts of the cell. All of these regions enveloped by membranes are called organelles. Although their size is typically less than 500 micrometers in diameter, they are too large to function efficiently without a high level of organization. Organelles partition the cytoplasm so that the chemical reactions of life can be isolated by space and time. The concentration of chemicals in a reaction and the timing of events can be more effectively controlled within organelles.

Of all of the organelles, none is more important than the nucleus. It isolates the cell's DNA from the harsh environment of the cytoplasm. The nuclear envelope, or membrane, is composed of two lipid bilayers. Nuclear pores span this envelope, selectively allowing certain substances to move in or out of the nucleus. Located within the nucleus is at least one nucleolus. This dense, irregular region is where the subunits of the ribosomes are assembled. These subunits are transported through nuclear pores to the cytoplasm, where ribosomes serve as a workbench for polypeptide formation. The major contents of the nucleus are the thread-like chromosomes.

Components of Nucleus

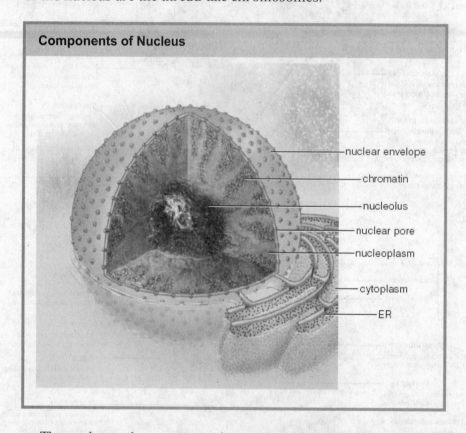

- nuclear envelope
- chromatin
- nucleolus
- nuclear pore
- nucleoplasm
- cytoplasm
- ER

The endomembrane system is a series of structures that links the nuclear envelope to the plasma membrane of eukaryotic cells. The function of this system is to produce lipids and proteins for the cell's use or for the export of proteins. The system begins with the endoplasmic reticulum (ER). This organelle extends from the nuclear envelope and forms a continuous network of folded sacs and tubes.

Some of the ER has ribosomes attached to its surface and is referred to as rough ER. The rough ER is associated with the formation of polypeptides that will be used for secreted proteins, membrane proteins, and lysosomes. Smooth ER lacks ribosomes; it produces lipids.

Budding from the rough ER are small saclike organelles called vesicles. These spherical structures transport substances from one organelle to another, or to the plasma membrane for export. Many of the vesicles deliver their contents to another organelle in the endomembrane system, the Golgi body. This structure resembles a stack of pita bread and is where polypeptides and lipids can receive their final alterations to become functional molecules. After these modifications are complete, the molecules are packaged again into vesicles that bud from the Golgi bodies. Many merge with the plasma membrane in exocytosis. Lysosomes are vesicles that remain within the cell; they contain strong digestive enzymes and recycle worn out cellular components. Lysosomes also function in apoptosis, or programmed cell death.

The mitochondrion takes energy stored in carbohydrates and other organic molecules and converts it into ATP energy. Chloroplasts are the sites of photosynthesis. In both of these organelles, compartmentalization resulting from inner membranes is critical to energy transfer. Both of these organelles have bacteria-like characteristics, such as their own DNA and ribosomes, and are likely to have evolved through the process of endosymbiosis, as discussed in Chapter 1. The structure and function of these eukarotic organelles are discussed in detail in Chapter 3.

One of the largest organelles is the central vacuole found in plant cells. It stores water, ions, amino acids, sugars, pigments, poisons, and wastes. It can occupy as much as 90 percent of a cell's interior volume. Because this organelle has low metabolic requirements, its presence allows plant cells to exceed the surface-to-volume restriction that limits the size of most cells. Smaller vacuoles may function in digestion (e.g., the food vacuole formed when an amoeba engulfs another organism by endocytosis) or the release of cellular waste products.

Organelles of Eukaryotic Cells

Name	Major Function
Nucleus	Protecting, controlling access to DNA
Endoplasmic reticulum (ER)	Routing, modifying new polypeptide chains; synthesizing lipids
Golgi body	Modifying new polypeptide chains; sorting, shipping proteins and lipids
Vesicles	Transporting, storing, or digesting substances in a cell
Mitochondrion	Transferring energy from organic compounds (e.g., sugars) to ATP
Chloroplast	Transferring light energy into bonds of organic compounds (e.g., sugars)
Lysosome	Intracellular digestion
Vacuole	Storage

Even though many cells have an external cell wall for support, all eukaryotic cells have an internal interconnected network of protein fibers called the cytoskeleton. The largest components of the cytoskeleton are the microtubules. As their name implies, they are small, tubular structures composed of repeating subunits of the protein tubulin. They form the internal scaffolding that helps a cell maintain its shape and hold some organelles in place. They are also responsible for the movement of chromosomes during cell division and of organelles throughout the cytosol.

Microfilaments are the smallest members of the cytoskeleton. They form a cross-linking mesh of fibers that reinforces the plasma membrane. The interaction of the microfilaments actin and myosin is largely responsible for muscle contractions. Intermediate filaments are the most stable parts of the cytoskeleton. They form a layer on the inner side of the nuclear envelope, providing it with support.

Microtubules also build eukaryotic flagella and cilia, two structures associated with cell movement. The microtubules form an array in which they slide back and forth, resulting in a whip-like movement that propels the cell. Prokaryotic flagella lack the arrayed microtubule arrangement.

CELL DIFFERENTIATION
Enduring Understanding 2.E, 4.C

Each cell in an animal's body is the descendant of the fertilized egg from which it started. As a result, every somatic cell in its body contains the same genetic information. (Egg and sperm cells, as discussed under the *Meiosis and Sexual Reproduction* section, will have half of that genetic information.) Yet, some somatic cells are pancreatic cells while others are white blood cells. How do cells with the same genetic information end up performing such different functions? The answer is differentiation. Differentiation is the expression of different subsets of genes by different types of cells. The group of genes a cell uses determines what proteins are present and thereby what type of cell it becomes. For example the protein hormone insulin is produced by certain pancreatic cells and protein antibodies are produced by certain white blood cells. Similarly, between different people the proteins on the cell surface can vary, leading to the need for blood typing before transfusions and tissue typing before organ transplants. Furthermore, antibodies of different shapes, corresponding to different antigens, are produced by different white blood cells based on which gene components are used and in what order.

THE CELL CYCLE
Enduring Understanding 3.A

Prokaryotic cells reproduce asexually, simply by making a copy of their circular chromosome and dividing their cytoplasm. This process is called prokaryotic or binary fission. With their nucleus and multiple chromosomes to divide and their ability to reproduce sexually, asexually or both, the eukaryotic cell cycle is more complicated.

In eukaryotic organisms, a chromosome is a linear double-stranded DNA molecule. The number and size of chromosomes differ among organisms, but before a cell reproduces the chromosomes are duplicated. Each duplicated chromosome consists of two double-stranded DNA molecules known as sister chromatids, attached at a centromere. For most of a cell's lifetime, DNA is stored as chromatin, an uncondensed form. As the cell begins to reproduce, the DNA molecules and the histones around which each is wrapped coil tightly, becoming highly condensed to enable accurate and quick nuclear division. Each of these condensed structures is an individual chromosome.

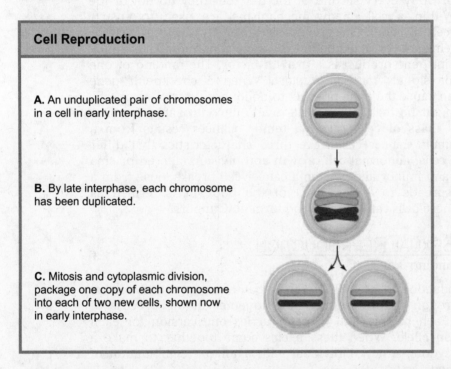

Cell Reproduction

A. An unduplicated pair of chromosomes in a cell in early interphase.

B. By late interphase, each chromosome has been duplicated.

C. Mitosis and cytoplasmic division, package one copy of each chromosome into each of two new cells, shown now in early interphase.

The eukaryotic cell cycle is a series of phases that divides a parent cell into two genetically identical daughter cells. The process of cell division is used by a cell for growth, repair, and cell replacement. It is also used by some organisms for asexual reproduction. The cell cycle starts with interphase, which consists of three phases. In the first, the cell grows. Next, it synthesizes DNA, replicating its chromosomes. Then it prepares for division. Mitosis is division which results in the production of two genetically identical nuclei. When cytokinesis occurs at the end of mitosis, the identical nuclei are distributed into two cells, which start the cycle again in interphase. Within multi-cellular organisms, specialized cells can enter an extended stage where they do not proceed with the cell cycle. Such a cell can continue the cell cycle when given appropriate cues. Mitosis is a continuous process involving several key events:

1. The replicated chromosomes condense, and microtubules which will aid their movement assemble in the cytoplasm.
2. The nuclear membrane disintegrates, allowing pairs of microtubules to attach to the chromosomes.
3. The chromosomes are aligned along one plane.

4. The sister chromatids separate and move to opposite sides of the cell.
5. The two separated sets of chromosomes decondense and are surrounded by newly formed nuclear envelopes.

The process of cytokinesis or cytoplasmic division differs for animals and plants. In animal cells, a contractile ring divides the cytoplasm and pinches the two new cells apart. In plant cells, a cell plate forms and expands as a cross wall between the two nuclei. In both cases, the two daughter cells are genetically identical.

The cell cycle is a highly regulated process. Millions of cells are made by your body every second of the day, but they do not divide randomly. Within a cell, many mechanisms are used to ensure appropriate cell division. Checkpoints are used by the cell cycle to ensure problems are corrected before the cycle continues. An example of a checkpoint gene product is a growth factor. The binding of one growth factor signals mitosis to start. When a checkpoint gene mutates, it can cause the gene product to no longer function properly. One result might be that the cell will divide uncontrollably, forming an abnormal mass of cells called a tumor. Cancer results from a malignant tumor. Cancer cells have three characteristics that differ from normal cells: abnormal cell growth and division, altered plasma membranes, and immortality. When a cancer cell breaks loose from a tumor and spreads to a new area of the body, it is termed as metastasis. These cells can colonize and form new tumors.

MEOISIS AND SEXUAL REPRODUCTION
Enduring Understanding 3.A

Sexual reproduction in animals involves gametes (eggs and sperm) produced through meiosis and coming together in the process of fertilization. Each haploid (1n) gamete carries one version for each gene called an allele. When these alleles come together to make a diploid (2n) zygote, a new individual with a unique combination of alleles is formed.

While mitosis maintains the chromosome number, meiosis halves the chromosome number. In animals, this creates haploid germ cells or gametes from a diploid parent cell. The process takes place in highly specialized reproductive organs. In most animals, sperm originate in the male testis and eggs are produced in the female ovary. When these two haploid gametes come together in the process of fertilization, the original diploid number of chromosomes is restored in the resulting zygote. This zygote undergoes mitosis and cell differentiation as it becomes a multicellular organism.

In plant sexual reproduction, the diploid (sporophyte) generation produces haploid spores, rather than gametes, through the process of meiosis. These spores undergo mitosis, resulting in a multicellular haploid stage (gametophyte) which produces haploid gametes by mitosis. When these join in fertilization to form a diploid zygote, the cycle begins again.

Diploid cells that undergo meiosis first complete the interphase events of the cell cycle, including DNA replication. Then, two

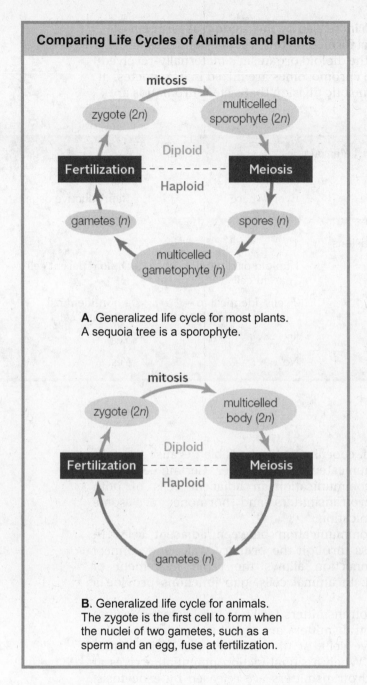

Comparing Life Cycles of Animals and Plants

A. Generalized life cycle for most plants. A sequoia tree is a sporophyte.

B. Generalized life cycle for animals. The zygote is the first cell to form when the nuclei of two gametes, such as a sperm and an egg, fuse at fertilization.

consecutive nuclear divisions result in four haploid nuclei. The process of meiosis is similar to mitosis with a few significant differences:

1. In mitosis, individual replicated chromosomes line up along one plane, whereas in the first meiotic division, homologous pairs of replicated chromosomes line up. In each pair, one homolog was inherited from the diploid organism's mother; the other of the same size and shape was inherited from its father.
2. Another difference is that soon after the pairs form, crossing over occurs between homologous chromosomes, allowing for the exchange of alleles. This exchange of heritable information increases genetic variation in gametes.

3. Genetic variation is also increased by the random assortment of homologs into the nuclei formed by the first division. Thus, there is a high probability that the diploid organism's maternally-received and paternally-received chromosomes are mixed in its gametes. It is not until the second meiotic division that sister chromatids are separated.

Comparison of Mitosis and Meiosis		
Characteristic	**Mitosis**	**Meiosis**
Location in Organism	Everywhere	Reproductive organs
Number of DNA Replications	1	1
Number of Cytoplasmic Divisions	1	2
Starts with	Haploid or diploid parent cell	Diploid parent cell
Ends with	2 cells, identical to parent and each other	4 non-identical haploid cells
Crossing Over Occurs	No	Yes
Genetic Variation Increases	No	Yes

CELL COMMUNICATION
Enduring Understanding 3.D

In a multicellular organism, coordination is possible because the cells of the organism can communicate with each other. Certain cell-to-cell junctions facilitate this communication in adjacent cells of both animals and plants. Neurotransmitters and hormones are some chemicals used for communication.

Cell junctions allow communication between adjacent cells. In plants, plasmodesmata pass through the primary walls and connect bordering cells. This connection allows the rapid movement of materials from cell to cell. In animal cells, gap junctions provide a similar function.

Like cell junctions, neurotransmitters facilitate local communication with adjacent cells. Neurotransmitters are signal molecules stored in vesicles in a neuron (nerve cell), at the terminal end of its output extension, called an axon. When a signal (action potential) arrives at the axon terminal, the neurotransmitters are released by exocytosis. These chemicals cross the synapse (space between neuron and its target cell: another neuron or a muscle cell, for example) and bind to a receptor on the membrane of the target cell. When this binding occurs, the receptor protein's ion channel opens, and ions flow by facilitated diffusion into the target cell. The effect on the target cell varies depending on its identity and the proportion of excitatory and inhibitor neurotransmitters binding to its surface.

Neurotransmitters must be removed from a synapse for effective communication to continue. They might diffuse away, be actively transported back into the neuron, or be broken down by enzymes released into the synapse. If the neurotransmitter is allowed to accumulate in the synapse, skeletal paralysis, headaches, and even death can occur. Certain drugs function by mimicking or inhibiting neurotransmitters. Examples include the stimulant caffeine, the depressant ethanol, and the analgesic codeine.

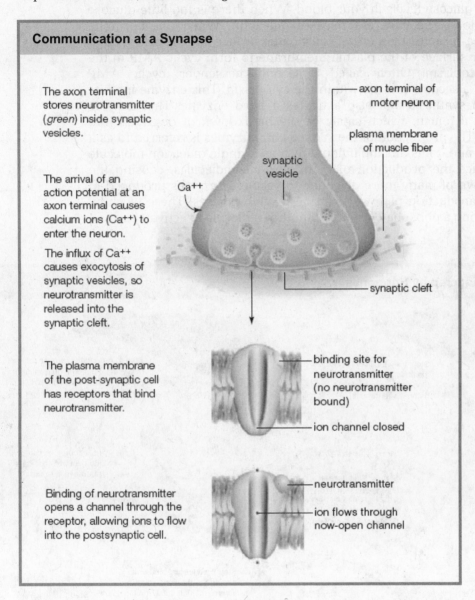

Communication at a Synapse

The axon terminal stores neurotransmitter (*green*) inside synaptic vesicles.

The arrival of an action potential at an axon terminal causes calcium ions (Ca⁺⁺) to enter the neuron.

The influx of Ca⁺⁺ causes exocytosis of synaptic vesicles, so neurotransmitter is released into the synaptic cleft.

The plasma membrane of the post-synaptic cell has receptors that bind neurotransmitter.

Binding of neurotransmitter opens a channel through the receptor, allowing ions to flow into the postsynaptic cell.

axon terminal of motor neuron

plasma membrane of muscle fiber

synaptic vesicle

Ca⁺⁺

synaptic cleft

binding site for neurotransmitter (no neurotransmitter bound)

ion channel closed

neurotransmitter

ion flows through now-open channel

Hormones produced by animal endocrine gland cells travel long distances through the blood for communication with target cells of various types located at a distance within the body. Hormones which are steroid molecules, such as cortisol, function differently from those which are amino acid based molecules. This is directly related to the composition of the plasma membrane, as steroids are lipid soluble and easily diffuse across it. Hormones based on amino acids or amino acid chains cannot pass through the membrane due to their size and polarity.

Most amine hormones and all peptide and protein hormones (consisting of amino acid chains) bind to receptor proteins on the surface of the target cell. The receptor proteins are shape-specific, so only cells with the receptors will recognize and bind to the hormone, also called a ligand. This binding causes the receptor's shape to change, starting the process of signal transduction. In signal transduction, a magnified pathway of chemical reactions occurs inside the cell. One example of this process involves the hormone glucagon, which helps regulate glucose levels in your blood. When there is too little glucose in the blood, the pancreas releases glucagon. When this hormone binds to a receptor on a target cell's outer surface, ATP is catalyzed at the inner surface of the plasma membrane to form cyclic AMP in the cell's cytoplasm. Often called a second messenger, cyclic AMP activates a second enzyme within the cytoplasm. This enzyme inhibits glycogen synthesis, but also activates a third enzyme. That enzyme activates a fourth, which catalyzes the breakdown of glycogen into glucose. The production of the subsequent enzymes is referred to as a cascade, and it has an amplifying effect, as a single glucagon molecule can induce the production of many enzyme molecules, causing the breakdown of many more glycogen molecules. Enzymes produced in signal transduction pathways can be protein kinases. These work by transferring a phosphate group to another molecule to activate it.

Responses Triggered by Hormones

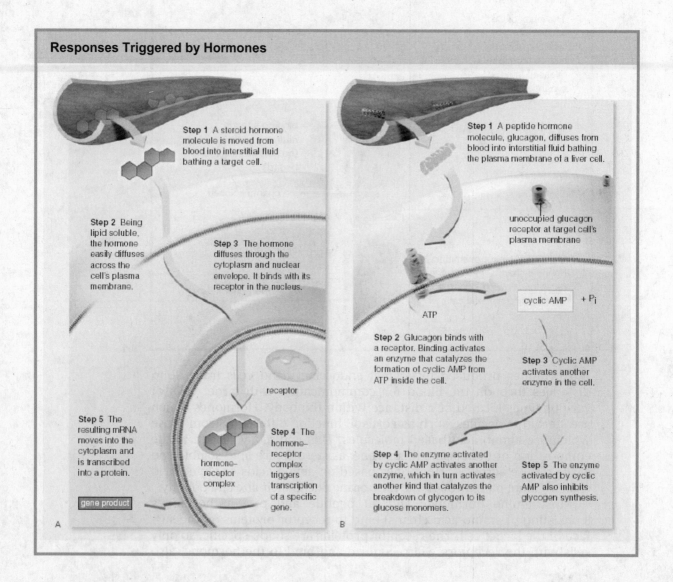

Step 1 A steroid hormone molecule is moved from blood into interstitial fluid bathing a target cell.

Step 2 Being lipid soluble, the hormone easily diffuses across the cell's plasma membrane.

Step 3 The hormone diffuses through the cytoplasm and nuclear envelope. It binds with its receptor in the nucleus.

Step 5 The resulting mRNA moves into the cytoplasm and is transcribed into a protein.

gene product

receptor

hormone–receptor complex

Step 4 The hormone–receptor complex triggers transcription of a specific gene.

A

Step 1 A peptide hormone molecule, glucagon, diffuses from blood into interstitial fluid bathing the plasma membrane of a liver cell.

unoccupied glucagon receptor at target cell's plasma membrane

cyclic AMP + Pi

ATP

Step 2 Glucagon binds with a receptor. Binding activates an enzyme that catalyzes the formation of cyclic AMP from ATP inside the cell.

Step 3 Cyclic AMP activates another enzyme in the cell.

Step 4 The enzyme activated by cyclic AMP activates another enzyme, which in turn activates another kind that catalyzes the breakdown of glycogen to its glucose monomers.

Step 5 The enzyme activated by cyclic AMP also inhibits glycogen synthesis.

B

Many steroid hormones diffuse through both the plasma membrane and the nuclear envelope. Inside the nucleus, the hormone binds to a receptor. The hormone/receptor complex then triggers transcription of a specific gene. Some cells have receptors for steroid hormones in their plasma membrane. Rather than affecting gene expression, they can affect the permeability of the membrane to certain ions or can act by means of a second messenger, as the amino acid-based hormones do. When steroid hormones act in this way, the cell's response is faster than when the hormone directly affects gene expression.

AP Tip

Students are not expected to know all possible examples of cell communication. However, signal transduction is an important concept, and more detailed knowledge of at least one example is expected. This would include the normal functioning of a signal transduction pathway and change expected due to the presence of other molecules such as certain drugs or other chemicals that would mimic or inhibit the normal communication between cells.

CELL-CELL INTERACTIONS AND FITNESS
Enduring Understanding 4.B

Interactions between cells of multicellular organisms as well as interactions between unicellular organisms in a population can be evolutionarily beneficial to the organism. In a multicellular organism, the death of certain cells can be of benefit under some circumstances. For example, infected cells can be destroyed by the immune system, leading to the improved health of the organism. Also, the death of some cells during development, by apoptosis, can result in helpful structures such as five separate fingers. Similarly, in multicellular organisms somatic cells might not be involved in the production of offspring, but the cooperation of all the organism's cells can ensure that their genetic material is passed on to offspring

Cooperation within populations of unicellular organisms can benefit the individual members; this could even resemble interactions between cells of multicellular organisms. When individual slime mold cells congregate for migration and reproduction, cyclic AMP both acts as the communication signal for gathering and affects gene expression.

Multiple-Choice Questions

1. All of the following are part of the endomembrane system typical of most eukaryotic cells EXCEPT
   (A) vesicles.
   (B) the endoplasmic reticulum.
   (C) mitochondria.
   (D) Golgi bodies.

Use the following information to answer questions 2 and 3:

A bag of dialysis tubing is partially filled with a solution containing 0.2 M maltose, 0.2 M sucrose, and 0.2 M glucose. A beaker contains a solution of 0.4 M lactose and 0.2 M galactose. The bag is permeable to water, glucose, and galactose, but not to any of the other substances.

2. Which of the following will occur when the bag is immersed in the beaker?
   (A) plasmolysis only
   (B) diffusion and plasmolysis
   (C) diffusion only
   (D) osmosis only

3. A net movement of which substances will occur when the bag is immersed in the beaker?
   (A) Maltose and sucrose will move out, and lactose will move in.
   (B) Water and glucose will move out, and galactose will move in.
   (C) Water will only move out.
   (D) Glucose will move out, and galactose will move in.

4. A major distinction between active and passive transport is
   (A) active transport is the movement of water and passive is the movement of all other substances.
   (B) active uses a transport protein, while passive does not.
   (C) active moves particles against the concentration gradient, while passive moves particles with the concentration gradient.
   (D) a transporter protein can change shape in active transport, but not in passive.

5. Which of the following is in correct order of the cell cycle?
   I.   Cytokinesis
   II. Two identical daughter cells
   III. DNA replication
   IV. Chromosomes aligned along a plane
   V.   Disintegration of the nuclear membrane

   (A) III, V, IV, I, II
   (B) III, V, I, II, IV
   (C) III, IV, V, I, II
   (D) V, III, IV, I, II

6. Centromeres uncouple and chromatids are separated from each other.
   (A) This statement is true of mitosis.
   (B) This statement is true of meiosis I.
   (C) This statement is true of mitosis and meiosis I.
   (D) This statement is true of mitosis and meiosis II.

7. Which of the following is NOT involved in cell communication?
   (A) cyclic AMP
   (B) tight junctions
   (C) plasmodesmata
   (D) steroid hormone

8. All of the following are reasons why a neuron, a cell of an endocrine gland, and a muscle cell of one animal differ EXCEPT
   (A) different genes active in their nuclei.
   (B) different genes present in their nuclei.
   (C) different receptor proteins in their plasma membranes.
   (D) different enzymes active in their cytoplasm.

9. An animal's gametes are
   (A) produced by meiosis.
   (B) produced by mitosis.
   (C) produced by fertilization.
   (D) genetically identical to its other cells.

10. Neurotransmitters are released into a synapse by which organelle and process?
    (A) endoplasmic reticulum; active transport
    (B) Golgi body; facilitated diffusion
    (C) lysosome; phagocytosis
    (D) vesicle; exocytosis

11. The cytoskeleton consists of
    (A) microtubules, microfilaments, and intermediate filaments.
    (B) phospholipids, collagen, and glycoproteins.
    (C) phospholipids, cholesterol, and proteins.
    (D) cellulose, chitin, or peptidoglycan, depending on the type of cell.

12. Which of the following is found in all prokaryotic and eukaryotic cells?
    (A) nucleus
    (B) flagellum
    (C) ribosome
    (D) mitochondrion

13. A cancer cell must have a malfunction related to proteins which
    (A) control the cell cycle.
    (B) act as receptors for hormones.
    (C) actively transport ions out of the cell.
    (D) catalyze the breakdown of neurotransmitters.

14. Signal transduction pathways are involved in which of the following?
    (A) active transport to keep Na⁺ ions more concentrated outside a neuron
    (B) cell communication via a peptide hormone and a second messenger
    (C) the production of new nuclear membranes during mitosis and meiosis
    (D) the movement of a protein from ribosomes on the ER to the Golgi apparatus

15. Steroid hormones can enter a cell and bind to a receptor molecule inside its nucleus. This is different from how neurotransmitters and peptide hormones function because
    (A) steroid hormones must bind to this second messenger molecule, while the others do not.
    (B) steroid hormones affect eukaryotic cells, while the others affect prokaryotic cells.
    (C) steroid hormones are lipids which can pass through phospholipid bilayer membranes.
    (D) steroid hormones do not have to pass through cell walls, while the others do.

Grid-In Question

1. A student examined a prepared slide of some HeLa cells. These cells, descendant from a cancer tissue sample from Ms. Henrietta Lacks, were stained so that the student could identify which cells were undergoing mitosis and which were in interphase. The student tallied the cells in both these parts of the cell cycle and identified 311 cells in interphase and 18 cells in various stages of mitosis. If the HeLa cell cycle is presumed to last 20.1 hours, for how many minutes, to the nearest tenth of a minute, does mitosis last?

Free-Response Questions

MULTI-PART QUESTION

1. All life on earth is composed of cells. They vary in size, shape, and complexity.
   (a) Describe THREE similarities common in all cells.
   (b) Discuss the major factor that limits the size that a typical cell can attain.
   (c) Describe TWO levels of organization associated with eukaryotic cells. Explain how this organization allows these cells to function more efficiently.

SINGLE-PART QUESTION

2. Describe two different types of communication between adjacent animal cells.

Answers

MULTIPLE-CHOICE QUESTIONS

1. **C.** Mitochondria are found in all eukaryotic cells; they are not part of the system that builds proteins and lipids (*Biology*, 12th ed., page 66/13th ed., page 66).

2. **C.** Both glucose and galactose will seek equilibrium as they diffuse through the tubing. Both solutions are isotonic (*Biology*, 12th ed., page 88/13th ed., pages 90–91).

3. **D.** The only sugars small enough to pass through the tubing are glucose and galactose. They will both seek equilibrium as they diffuse through the tubing (*Biology*, 12th ed., page 88/13th ed., pages 90–91).

4. **C.** Active transport moves a substance from low to high concentration, against the gradient (*Biology*, 12th ed., page 84/13th ed., pages 92–93).

5. **A.** DNA replication occurs in interphase, which precedes mitosis. The nuclear membrane must disintegrate before the chromosomes can attach to microtubules for alignment. After chromosome separation, cytokinesis or cytoplasmic division occurs, producing two identical daughter cells (*Biology*, 12th ed., pages 146–149/13th ed., pages 178–182).

6. **D.** In mitosis, chromosomes line up and sister chromatids are pulled apart by spindle fibers. In meiosis I, homologous pairs of chromosomes are separated, but in meiosis II, chromosomes are separated in the same method as mitosis (*Biology*, 12th ed., pages 146–147/13th ed., pages 198–199).

7. **B.** Tight junctions seal cells together tightly so fluid cannot pass through them. Hormones are chemical messengers by which cells communicate; cyclic AMP is a second messenger acting within cells after a hormone binds to a receptor on the cell surface. Plasmodesmata are channels that connect plant cells across their cell walls. (*Biology*, 12th ed., pages 70–71, 600–601/13th ed., pages 71, 588–589).

8. **B.** All somatic cells of a multicellular organism are identical, having been produced by mitosis (*Biology*, 12th ed., pages 142, 230/13th ed., pages 164, 178).

9. **A.** In animals, egg and sperm cells (gametes) are produced by meiosis, a nuclear division which halves the chromosome number (*Biology*, 12th ed., page 156/13th ed., page 191).

10. **D.** When an action potential arrives at an axon terminal, vesicles move to the plasma membrane and release the neurotransmitters they contain by exocytosis (*Biology*, 12th ed., page 560/13th ed., page 548).

11. **A.** Microtubules, microfilaments and intermediate filaments are protein structures found within the cytoplasm which function in organization and aid in movement within the cell or of the cell (*Biology*, 12th ed., page 72/13th ed., page 68).

12. **C.** Ribosomes are found in the cytoplasm of all cells. Membrane-bound organelles such as the nucleus or mitochondrion are found only in eukaryotic cells. Flagella are different in prokaryotes and eukaryotes and are not found in all cells (*Biology*, 12th ed., pages 56–63/13th ed., pages 58–69).

13. **A.** Cancer cells can result when checkpoint genes mutate and their protein products involved in the cell cycle no longer work properly (*Biology*, 12th ed., pages 150–151/13th ed., pages 184–185).

14. **B.** In signal transduction a signal received by a cell is changed into a different form that affects a target cell's behavior (*Biology*, 12th ed., page 600/13th ed., page 588).

15. **C.** Lipid soluble steroid hormones can pass easily through the plasma membrane (*Biology*, 12th ed., pages 600–601/13th ed., pages 588–589).

GRID-IN QUESTION

1. **66.0 (minutes)**

   (20.1 hours × 60 minutes × 18 mitosis cells) / (311 + 18 total cells).

   (*Biology*, 12th ed., page 144/13th ed., page 178).

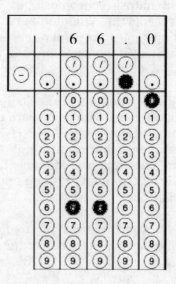

FREE-RESPONSE QUESTIONS

MULTI-PART

1. (a) Regardless of their size, shape, or complexity, all cells have three common similarities. First, cells are surrounded by a plasma membrane. This structure envelops the cell contents and serves as a boundary between the cell and its environment. Typically the membrane is composed of a phospholipid bilayer. These molecules are arranged with their hydrophobic fatty acid tails sandwiched between the hydrophilic phosphate heads. Embedded within it are proteins that give it unique features. This membrane is selectively permeable and regulates the movement of particles across it.

A second similarity is that all cells contain DNA. In eukaryotic cells it is housed within a double-membrane sac called the nucleus. In prokaryotes it is located in a central region called a nucleoid, but a membrane does not envelop it. A third similarity that all cells share is cytoplasm. This gelatinous material is a mixture of water and many metabolically important ions and compounds. Suspended within this solution are ribosomes. These small bodies aid in protein production.

(b) The major factor that limits cell size is its surface-to-volume ratio. As a cell grows, its volume increases by a cube of its diameter. At the same time, a cell's surface area only increases by a square of its diameter. This discrepancy leads to an inadequate movement of materials across the cell's membrane. A large cell simply doesn't have enough surface area to bring in all of the materials needed to accommodate its large size. Wastes will also encounter the same difficulty leaving the cell.

(c) Organelles represent an internal level of organization found in eukaryotic cells. Most of these structures are membrane-bound and carry out specialized functions within the cell. Some organelles are organized into systems. The endomembrane system is a series of organelles that lead to the efficient production of lipids and proteins. Another level of organization that eukaryotic cells exhibit is multicellularity. The cells of multicellular organisms tend to be specialized and can therefore carry out fewer tasks more effectively.

Organization is the key to efficiency at the cellular level. By compartmentalizing the cytoplasm into organelles, a cell can have better control over its metabolism. Certain materials can be concentrated in an organelle, increasing their rate of interaction. Isolating components in separate organelles can allow for better control of the timing of reactions. When organelles are grouped in systems, they can perform with the efficiency of an assembly line. In multicellular organisms, cells specialize and only carry out specific tasks. By only having a few functions, cells can then perform them more efficiently (*Biology*, 12th ed., pages 56–73/13th ed., pages 54–72).

SINGLE-PART

2. The cytoplasm of adjacent animal cells might be connected by gap junctions. These are channels through the membranes of the two cells. Chemicals produced in one cell can pass directly into the adjacent cell. Heart muscle cells can contract as a unit because signal molecules can pass easily between the cells. Neurotransmitters are polypeptides released by an axon terminal into the synaptic cleft, the intracellular space between a neuron and its target cell. The neurotransmitter binds to receptor proteins on the surface of the target cell, causing an ion channel to open. Ions flow into the target cell. When a threshold level is reached, the target cell will respond (*Biology*, 12th ed., pages 71, 560–561/13th ed., pages 71, 548–549).

Note: Other possible answers exist, including discussion of the interactions between antigen-presenting cells and T cells of the immune system (*Biology*, 12th ed., pages 672–673/13th ed., pages 664–665).

5

GENETICS

BIG IDEAS 3, 4

DNA is the molecule of heredity, passing genetic information from one generation to the next. Held within the DNA code are the instructions responsible for assembling proteins that catalyze reactions, regulate metabolism, help cells communicate, and protect the body against foreign invaders. For diploid organisms that reproduce via meiosis and fertilization, probability can be used to predict many genetically determined traits of offspring. The expression of genes, however, can be influenced by environmental factors.

KEY TERMS

activator	genetic code	mutation
allele	genotype	nondisjunction
anticodon	heterozygous	nucleotide
codominance	homozygous	pedigree
conjugation	incomplete dominance	phenotype
dihybrid cross	independent assortment	plasmid
DNA		probability
DNA ligase	intron	promoter
DNA polymerase	karyotype	Punnett Square
dominant	lysogenic pathway	recessive
epistasis	lytic pathway	regulator protein
exon	messenger RNA	repressor
gene	monohybrid cross	reverse transcriptase
gene expression	multiple alleles	ribosomal RNA (rRNA)

RNA interference
  (RNAi)
RNA polymerase
segregation
semiconservative
  replication

sex chromosome
transcription factor
transduction
transfer RNA (tRNA)
transformation

translation
transposable elements

KEY CONCEPTS

▪ The discovery of DNA as the hereditary molecule was the result of the collaboration of many scientists.

▪ DNA replication occurs before mitosis or meiosis. The process requires the assistance of different enzymes and proteins. After the process, the DNA is checked for errors. Uncorrected errors are known as mutations.

▪ DNA dictates the sequence of amino acids in proteins. The process leading from DNA to proteins consists of two parts: transcription and translation. RNA is involved in both of these processes.

▪ Cells do not continuously make all of the proteins their genes encode. Prokaryotes and eukaryotes have different methods to control protein synthesis.

▪ The expression of genes does not always follow the patterns discovered by Gregor Mendel.

▪ Gene expression can be affected by other genes' products or by environmental factors.

▪ Genes on different chromosomes are randomly assorted into gametes independently of how other genes are assorted.

▪ Mutations, horizontal gene transfer, independent assortment of chromosomes during meiosis, and crossing over contribute to genetic variation.

▪ DNA can be manipulated by scientists in techniques collectively known as genetic engineering.

▪ Viruses reproduce inside of host cells by using the cell's ribosomes.

For a full discussion of cells, see *Biology*, 12th ed., Chapters 11–16 and 21/13th ed., Chapters 8, 9, 10, 13, 14, 15, and 20.

DNA AND RNA TRANSMIT GENETIC INFORMATION
Enduring Understanding 3.A

The discovery of DNA as the hereditary molecule was the result of the collaboration of many scientists over more than a century. Key contributions include:

▪ Experimentation by Frederick Griffith on mice injected with strains of Streptococcus pneumoniae, which demonstrated that the hereditary material of deadly bacteria could be absorbed and used by previously harmless bacteria. Replication is said to be semiconservative because each of these double helixes has half of the original and half new DNA.

▪ Experimentation by Oswald Avery and Maclyn McCarty with those same bacterial strains, which demonstrated that nucleic acids must have been what changed the bacteria. They did this by removing the carbohydrates and enzymatically destroying the lipids and proteins of the dead harmful cells.

■ Experimentation by Alfred Hershey and Martha Chase using bacteria and bacteriophages (viruses that infect bacteria), which showed that the DNA of the virus was what entered the cells. They grew bacteriophages in cell cultures provided with specific sulfur or phosphorus isotopes. Because sulfur content is high in proteins and phosphorus content is high in nucleic acids, analysis of whether these isotopes wound up inside or outside subsequently infected cells showed that the bacteriophages had injected DNA into the bacteria.

■ Analysis by Erwin Chargaff of the nucleotide composition of DNA, which showed 1:1 ratios of adenine and thymine and of cytosine and guanine in all cells, even when the ratio of adenine to guanine differs between species.

■ Analysis by Maurice Wilkins and Rosalind Franklin using x-ray diffraction, which led to specific calculations of the molecular geometry of DNA. Access to their work, especially Franklin's images and calculations, fueled model-building by James Watson and Francis Crick. Their accurate model of the double helix not only adhered to the data they obtained, but also suggested how DNA could act as a template for copying during cell reproduction, ensuring that the hereditary information could be preserved across generations.

As discussed in Chapter 2, both DNA and RNA are polymers of nucleotides. They differ structurally in terms of the sugar component of the nucleotides (deoxyribose or ribose), by one of their nitrogen bases (thymine or uracil), and in terms of the number of strands that make up one molecule (two or one). One key insight of Watson and Crick was that the two DNA strands are antiparallel, arranged in opposite directions.

Prior to reproduction, a cell will replicate the DNA of its chromosomes (or chromosome, for a prokaryotic cell) so that each daughter cell will

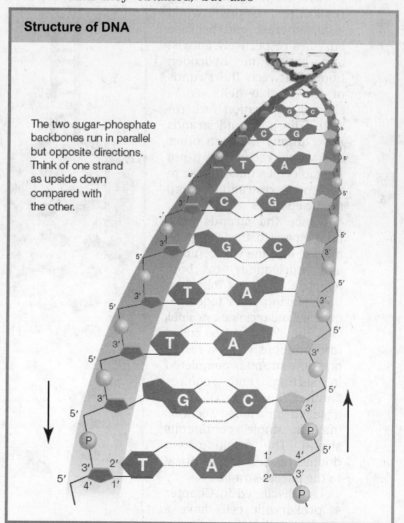

Structure of DNA

The two sugar–phosphate backbones run in parallel but opposite directions. Think of one strand as upside down compared with the other.

contain a complete set of DNA from the parent cell. DNA replication is a series of steps that begins with the unwinding and separating of the DNA helix, exposing the nitrogen bases of each strand. By the end of DNA replication, two identical strands of DNA have been produced. The production of these two DNA molecules is said to be semi-conservative, as each molecule contains one old strand that acted as the template and one newly assembled strand.

Numbering the carbon atoms in nucleotides allows us to keep track of each strand. A chain of nucleotides will have an unbounded 3' carbon atom at one end and an un-bounded 5' carbon at the other end. Double-stranded DNA has one chain of nucleotides running from 3' to 5' and an adjoining strand running from 5' to 3'. The structure is therefore de-scribed as antiparallel.

More specifically, DNA replication begins when topoisomerase and helicase enzymes respectively untwist and break the hydrogen bonds between the strands of the double helix. A Y-shaped, replication fork re-sults. The unwound strands have affinity for each other and would recombine if not for molecules that adhere to each opened strand, keeping them separate.

Once the strands have been separated, the DNA poly-merase enzyme will begin to add nucleotides to both template strands following base pairing rules (adenine-thymine and guanine-cytosine). Only the 3' end can be added to continuously. As a result, one new strand is completed in sections and requires another enzyme, DNA li-gase, to join those sections into a single continuous strand. The resulting two double helixes are identical to the parent strands.

As discussed in Chapter 4, prokaryotic cells have a single circular chromosome,

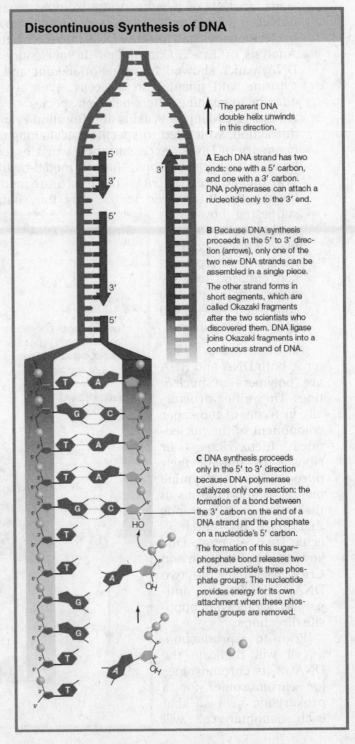

Discontinuous Synthesis of DNA

The parent DNA double helix unwinds in this direction.

A Each DNA strand has two ends: one with a 5' carbon, and one with a 3' carbon. DNA polymerases can attach a nucleotide only to the 3' end.

B Because DNA synthesis proceeds in the 5' to 3' direc-tion (arrows), only one of the two new DNA strands can be assembled in a single piece.

The other strand forms in short segments, which are called Okazaki fragments after the two scientists who discovered them. DNA ligase joins Okazaki fragments into a continuous strand of DNA.

C DNA synthesis proceeds only in the 5' to 3' direction because DNA polymerase catalyzes only one reaction: the formation of a bond between the 3' carbon on the end of a DNA strand and the phosphate on a nucleotide's 5' carbon.

The formation of this sugar–phosphate bond releases two of the nucleotide's three phos-phate groups. The nucleotide provides energy for its own attachment when these phos-phate groups are removed.

while eukaryotic cells have multiple linear chromosomes. For replication purposes, the significance of this is that prokaryotic replication has one starting place, while eukaryotic chromosomes have multiple starting places. Smaller pieces of circular DNA, called plasmids, can be found in prokaryotes, eukaryotes, and viruses. These are replicated independently of the chromosome and can be involved in horizontal gene transfer, as discussed in the section *Genetic Variation*.

While the hereditary information of cells is DNA, the hereditary information of viruses can be DNA or RNA. Certain RNA viruses, called retroviruses, inject not only RNA into a host cell, but also the enzyme reverse transcriptase. This enzyme catalyzes the production of DNA from the viral RNA, and this DNA can insert into the host cell's DNA. Once there, the viral DNA can be expressed by the cell, resulting in the formation of new viruses. The genes of other RNA viruses can be expressed directly from the RNA. The production of DNA by means of the enzyme reverse transcriptase by retroviruses violates what is known as the "central dogma," or the idea that DNA is transcribed into RNA, which then is translated to form a polypeptide. Viruses are discussed further in a later section.

GENE EXPRESSION
Enduring Understanding 3.A, 3.B

The sequence of DNA bases contains the information to construct proteins. Proteins determine our traits, but how do cells make the jump from a chain of nucleotides to proteins? Converting the base pair order into protein begins with the process of transcription. Enzymes within the nucleus use DNA as a template for the production of a complementary strand of RNA.

In translation, the information carried by RNA is read by the ribosome and used to assemble amino acids in the order dictated by the original DNA sequence. As amino acids are added to the growing polypeptide, the protein will fold into its desired shape.

In eukaryotic cells, chromosomes containing DNA are separated from the cytoplasm by the nuclear envelope; however, ribosomes reside in the cytoplasm. Thus, transcription is a simpler process which can be coupled with translation in prokaryotic cells. Transcription in all cells begins with the enzyme RNA polymerase binding to a specific region of bases on the DNA chain known as a promoter. Once attached, RNA polymerase moves along the DNA chain in the 3' to the 5' direction, thus assembling the RNA in the 5' to 3' direction. As it moves, RNA polymerase unwinds the DNA helix in order to "read" the base sequences. While separated, free RNA nucleotides are added to the exposed DNA bases. Nucleotides are paired following the base pair rulings with the exception that uracil is paired with DNA's adenine because RNA does not contain thymine. When RNA polymerase reaches the end of the gene, both this messenger RNA (mRNA) chain and the DNA helix are released. The result is a copy of the DNA sequence encoded as complementary mRNA. (*Note:* All forms of RNA are transcribed from the DNA in this fashion; however,

RNA Transcription

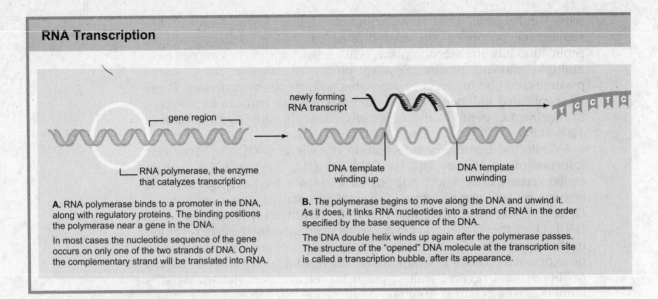

gene region

newly forming RNA transcript

RNA polymerase, the enzyme that catalyzes transcription

DNA template winding up

DNA template unwinding

A. RNA polymerase binds to a promoter in the DNA, along with regulatory proteins. The binding positions the polymerase near a gene in the DNA.

In most cases the nucleotide sequence of the gene occurs on only one of the two strands of DNA. Only the complementary strand will be translated into RNA.

B. The polymerase begins to move along the DNA and unwind it. As it does, it links RNA nucleotides into a strand of RNA in the order specified by the base sequence of the DNA.

The DNA double helix winds up again after the polymerase passes. The structure of the "opened" DNA molecule at the transcription site is called a transcription bubble, after its appearance.

forms other than messenger are not subsequently translated into an amino acid sequence.)

In eukaryotes, introns are sections of non-coding sequences of DNA. The mRNA copies of introns are snipped out, leaving just the coding sequences called exons. These exons can be linked together in order or rearranged and then spliced together. Rearrangement of exons allows for one gene to code for many different polypeptides. In addition, a modified guanine cap is added to the 5' end of the mRNA, and a tail sequence of multiple adenines, known as a poly-A tail, is added to the 3' end.

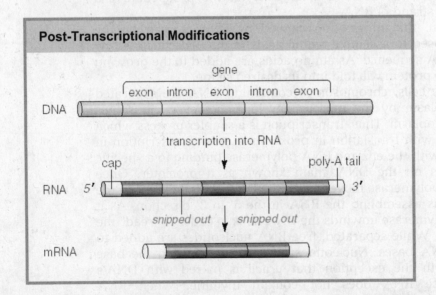

The function of mRNA is to bring a copy of DNA's information to the ribosome. During translation, mRNA bases are read in groups of three called codons. As illustrated on the next page, each codon is associated with a specific amino acid; this association is known as the

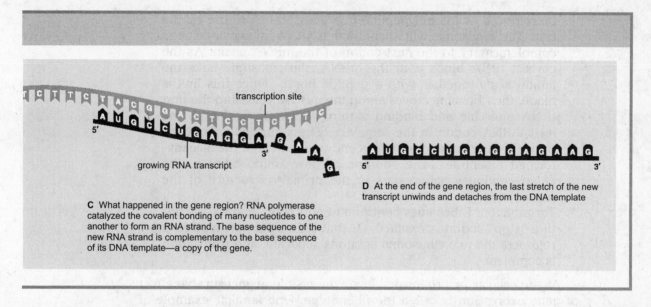

C What happened in the gene region? RNA polymerase catalyzed the covalent bonding of many nucleotides to one another to form an RNA strand. The base sequence of the new RNA strand is complementary to the base sequence of its DNA template—a copy of the gene.

D At the end of the gene region, the last stretch of the new transcript unwinds and detaches from the DNA template

genetic code. This code can be found in charts such as the one depicted below. As it shows, some amino acids are associated with more than one codon.

Other forms of RNA play a role in gene expression. Ribosomal RNA (rRNA) combines with protein to form both the large and small subunits of a ribosome. The rRNA is responsible for constructing the peptide bond that links amino acids together during translation. Transfer RNA (tRNA) binds to a specific amino acid and has along one of its loops a special sequence of three RNA bases, called an anticodon. tRNA anticodons are complementary to mRNA codons, and the amino acid attached to tRNA corresponds to the genetic code. A fourth type of RNA, microRNA, is very short in length and is involved in one form of eukaryotic gene control called RNA interference, discussed later in this chapter.

Converting the codons from the mRNA chain into functioning proteins is the multi-step process called translation. These steps, in sequence, are grouped as initiation, elongation, and termination.

▪ Initiation: Taking place in the cytoplasm, the small ribosomal subunit binds with the mRNA molecule. Next, the large subunit binds to the cluster.

▪ Elongation: The initiator tRNA carries with it the amino acid methionine. As a result, the first amino acid in the new polypeptide will be methionine; however, this amino acid can

Genetic Code

first base ▼	second base				third base ▼
	U	**C**	**A**	**G**	
U	UUU UUC phe / UUA UUG leu	UCU UCC UCA UCG ser	UAU UAC tyr / UAA STOP UAG STOP	UGU UGC cys / UGA STOP / UGG trp	U C A G
C	CUU CUC CUA CUG leu	CCU CCC CCA CCG pro	CAU CAC his / CAA CAG gln	CGU CGC CGA CGG arg	U C A G
A	AUU AUC ile / AUA / AUG met	ACU ACC ACA ACG thr	AAU AAC asn / AAA AAG lys	AGU AGC ser / AGA AGG arg	U C A G
G	GUU GUC GUA GUG val	GCU GCC GCA GCG ala	GAU GAC asp / GAA GAG glu	GGU GGC GGA GGG gly	U C A G

be removed as the polypeptide is processed before use by the cell. The ribosome will then bind a tRNA molecule that is complementary to the next codon of the mRNA chain. As the correct tRNA binds with the mRNA, the ribosome links the amino acids together with a peptide bond. Once this link is made, the ribosome moves along the mRNA, releasing the first tRNA molecule and binding a third tRNA, according to the next mRNA codon in the sequence. The amino acid from the third tRNA is bonded to the second amino acid of the already-formed dipeptide. The addition of new amino acids to the chain continues and results in the primary structure of the polypeptide.

▪ Termination: Ribosomes continue to add new amino acids until a "stop" codon is reached. At that point, the polypeptide is released; the two ribosomal subunits separate; and translation is complete.

At the cellular or organismal level, the visible or measurable effect of gene expression is called the phenotype. One familiar example of this is human ABO blood type. Different forms, or alleles, of the ABO gene exist. This gene codes for an enzyme that catalyzes the production of a certain plasma membrane glycolipid. The allele designated A codes for a different, but functional, version of the enzyme than the B allele; the O allele produces an inactive form of the enzyme. The A and B versions of the enzyme produce slightly different forms of the glycolipid. If a person receives a blood transfusion containing cells with glycolipids of the different form, his or her body's immune system reacts to their foreign shape and attacks those cells.

THE CHROMOSOMAL BASIS OF INHERITANCE
Enduring Understanding 3.A

As chromosomes are assorted into gametes and gametes join during fertilization, alleles of the genes located on those chromosomes are passed from parent to offspring. A diploid organism has pairs of chromosomes and, on them, pairs of alleles that influence its phenotype. When pairs of homologous chromosomes are split during meiosis (as discussed in Chapter 4), so only one of each pair is in a gamete, allele pairs are also split. If a parent is heterozygous, having two different alleles for a gene, each gene has an equal probability of being in a given gamete. Because homologous pairs of chromosomes align independently of one another, alleles of genes located on non-homologous chromosomes assort independently of each other into gametes. These principles of segregation and independent assortment pertaining to heredity were first described by Gregor Mendel. Further research has shown that if genes are on the same chromosome, however, their alleles can move to a gamete as a unit. The closer together two genes are located, the greater the probability is that the alleles on that one chromosome will be passed to the same gamete. Only if crossing over, or the exchange of DNA between two, usually homologous, chromosomes, occurs between the two gene loci, can those alleles assort independently and be passed to different cells during gamete formation.

AP Tip

Some terms used in modern genetics include:

Genes refer to segments of DNA that code for traits. Genes are passed on from parents to offspring. Each gene is found at a specific location on a specific chromosome, known as its locus.

Mutation refers to any permanent change in the sequence of nucleotides in a molecule of DNA. The vast majority of mutations are harmful to the organism, but sometimes may lead to an alternative functional gene.

Different forms of the same gene are known as *alleles*.

Heterozygous describes individuals that have different forms of the same gene for a trait. Organisms with the same form of a gene are homozygous for that trait.

Alleles that are expressed in the presence of other alleles are dominant. Those alleles that are not expressed or masked are recessive.

Genotype refers to the combination of alleles an organism has for one or more traits. The alleles are written as letters; a dominant allele is usually represented by a capital letter (A) and a recessive allele by the lower case form of the same letter (a). A heterozygote might have the genotype Aa, while AA and aa are homozygous genotypes for one trait.

Phenotype refers to the expressed trait. How the phenotype is expressed is a combination of the genotype and the environment.

Generations are designated by a P for parent and F for filial (offspring). In addition, a number placed after the F specifies the filial generation (F1, F2, etc.).

Sex chromosomes refers to chromosomes that are different in males and females. In humans these are the X and Y chromosomes. All other chromosomes are *autosomes*. In humans these have designated numbers 1–22.

A close examination of data concerning genetic traits, such as Mendel did with the pea plants he studied, can lead to a determination of the pattern of inheritance associated with each trait. A pedigree, or diagram of phenotypes for a trait within a family, can also be used to determine the pattern of inheritance of that trait. These data analyses can be used to determine:

- whether an allele is dominant, recessive, incompletely dominant, or co-dominant with respect to another allele.
- whether an allele is sex-linked, or located on one of the chromosomes for which its inheritance determined whether the individual is male or female.

■ whether two genes assort independently or are linked on the same homologous chromosome.

If two organisms' genotypes, or allele combinations, are known, the probability of their having an offspring with a specific allele combination can be mathematically determined. One tool for doing this is a Punnett square. A Punnett square puts the letters representing alleles (for one trait) or allele combinations (for two or more traits being examined at one time) for one parent along the top of a square and those for the second parent along the left side of that square. The letters from the top of the column and side of the row are combined in each square to a possible offspring genotype. The proportion of boxes indicates the probabilities of each type of offspring the parents could have, barring unpredictable mutations. The following Punnett square illustrates a monohybrid cross, in which two parents which are heterozygous (Aa) for one trait. Even though A is dominant in terms of gene expression, it has an equal probability of being passed on via the parent's gamete as a result of meiosis.

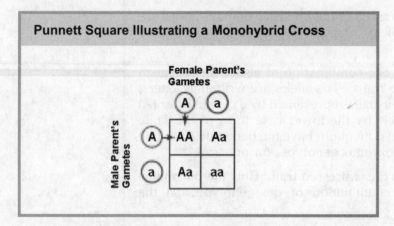

Punnett Square Illustrating a Monohybrid Cross

If the parents in this case were both heterozygous carriers of the auto-somal recessive Tay-Sachs disease, they would have a 25% chance of having a child who would die at a young age from this genetic disease.

The next Punnett square illustrates a cross, in which two traits are examined. One parent is heterozygous for both traits (IiGg), while the other is homozygous for the dominant form of one trait and the recessive form of the other (IIgg). Note that the gametes for the

Punnett Square Illustrating Cross of Two Traits

	IG	Ig	iG	ig
Ig	IIGg	IIgg	IiGg	Iigg
Ig	IIGg	IIgg	IiGg	Iigg
Ig	IIGg	IIgg	IiGg	Iigg
Ig	IIGg	IIgg	IiGg	Iigg

heterozygous parent consist of either the I or i allele and either the G or g allele. Because segregation occurs during meiosis, the gametes contain only one allele for each trait.

AP Tip

The proportion of offspring phenotypes produced in one particular (dihybrid) cross is significant: 9 dominant for both alleles; 3 dominant for the first allele only; 3 dominant for the second allele only; and 1 recessive for both alleles. When this ratio of offspring is seen, both parents were likely heterozygous for both traits.

A karyotype is another tool geneticists use to determine the nature of a genetic disease. This shows the paired chromosomes of a cell of an individual, lined up by size and location of the centromere. In some cases, a disease results when one gamete formed by nondisjunction either contains both members of a homologous pair of chromosomes or is missing one chromosome. In humans, who normally have 23 pairs for a total of 46 chromosomes, a person with this type of genetic disorder might have 45 or 47 chromosomes. Most cases of Down syndrome are the result of Trisomy 21, where the person has three copies of the small chromosome designated #21. In other cases, a disease might be the result of a chromosomal mutation, occurring when a large piece of a single chromosome has been omitted or duplicated. The changed length of the chromosome is visible in a karyotype.

AP Tip

When dealing with more than two traits, it can be more convenient to make a separate Punnett square for each trait. The probabilities can then be multiplied. For example, to determine the probability of getting an offspring with the genotype EeFFGgHH from parents with the genotypes EeFfggHH and EeFfGgHh, you can multiply the probability of getting Ee times the probability of getting FF times the probability of getting Gg times the probability of getting HH: $1/2 \times 1/4 \times 1/2 \times 1/2 = 1/32$. This method takes less effort than building a 16x16 Punnett square. Probabilities can likewise be multiplied to analyze the probability that a parent will pass to an offspring a certain combination of alleles. For example, EeFfGgHh has a 1/16 chance of passing on e, f, G, and H to an offspring ($1/2 \times 1/2 \times 1/2 \times 1/2$).

While dominant and recessive traits were identified by Mendel, other patterns of inheritance have since been discovered. These include, but are not limited to:

- multiple alleles (such as the three alleles of the ABO blood types).

- codominance (as when a person with blood type alleles A and B produces both types of glycoproteins).
- incomplete dominance (as seen in certain flowers when the heterozygote produces a smaller amount of the dominant pigment, making it pink, rather than red or white).
- Y-linked traits (expressed only in males of fruit flies or humans).
- X-linked traits (where a recessive allele is always expressed in male fruit flies or humans, which have only one X chromosome, while females have two X chromosomes. One form of color blindness in humans occurs more frequently in males due to this pattern of inheritance).
- epistasis (as when the recessive form of one gene makes a Labrador retriever yellow, no matter whether another of its genes would otherwise have made it black or brown).
- mitochondrial inheritance (where the gene is in the DNA of the mitochondria of a cell; a person inherits mitochondria maternally, from the cytoplasm of an egg; a plant's chloroplasts similarly have genes which are passed on independently of the nuclear genes).
- polygenic inheritance (as seen in traits such as human height, where numerous genes interact, resulting in continuous variation and a range of phenotypes).

AP Tip

When analyzing a pedigree to determine the mode of inheritance of a trait, look for the following clues:

- X-linked—Afflicted individuals are usually only male. Transmission of the trait is always through the mother.
- Autosomal dominant—Afflicted offspring will have an afflicted parent. Two normal parents will not have afflicted offspring. If one parent is afflicted, 50 percent of offspring will be afflicted.
- Autosomal recessive—Afflicted individuals can be of either sex. Afflicted individuals do not necessarily have afflicted parents. The parents are, however, carriers of the trait.

THE ENVIRONMENT AND GENE CONTROL
Enduring Understanding 3.B, 4.A, 4.C

Environmental factors such as temperature and a variety of chemicals can affect gene expression. In turn, variation in gene expression between cells in an organism's body leads to their differentiation into a variety of tissue and organs during development or even within an adult body.

One enzyme that affects melanin pigment production in hair-producing cells of a Himalayan rabbit or Siamese cat is heat sensitive. The cooler extremities of the animal's body, such as its ears, feet, and tail, tend to produce black hair as a result of this enzyme's function, while warmer parts of its body will be covered in light-colored hair. If an ice pack is applied to a normally light-colored area of skin, newly produced hair in that area will be black.

Some chemicals influence gene expression because they can bind to regulatory sequences of DNA to control transcription. For example, transcription factors can affect the binding of RNA polymerase to the promoter sequence of a gene. A regulatory gene is DNA that encodes a protein or RNA sequence that acts to regulate another gene. An example of this would be a bacterial gene that encodes a protein that binds to DNA near another gene, preventing RNA polymerase from transcribing that gene. RNA interference (RNAi) occurs when microRNA molecules are expressed. If these micro RNA molecules have a complementary sequence to another RNA transcript in a cell, they bind to it, forming double-stranded RNA that is destroyed by enzymes. Thus, RNAi can regulate gene expression after transcription of a gene has occurred.

In bacteria and viruses, positive and negative control mechanisms regulate gene expression. This allows some gene products to be made only at certain times. Regulator proteins can be turned off by a repressor or on by an inducer; when this molecule binds to the protein, the protein's shape is changed, affecting its ability to bind to DNA and block RNA polymerase. (*Note:* The binding site for the regulator protein, the "operator," is near the RNA polymerase binding site, the "promoter," for one or several genes; the arrangement of these sites together on the chromosome is referred to as an "operon.") Other regulatory proteins can bind to DNA to stimulate transcription or bind to repressors, inactivating them. These mechanisms are evolutionarily beneficial because the cell is not using energy to make proteins when they are not needed. Other genes are continuously expressed, as their products, such as those encoding ribosomal parts, are vitally important.

Eukaryotic gene expression is complex. Transcription factors are molecules that can act as activators and increase gene expression, or as repressors and decrease gene expression. Different transcription factors can act in concert, such that the relative combination of activators and repressors present can determine the amount of gene product made by a given cell. Molecules involved in gene expression can be produced within a cell; like hormones, can be produced by other cells of the body; or, like pheromones in animals or ethylene gas in plants, can be produced by other organisms. Genes involved in development can affect gene expression; *Hox* genes and morphogens are examples of this.

GENETIC VARIATION
Enduring Understanding 3.C

Changes in genes can result in phenotypic changes. A change in a DNA sequence might not have an effect; this can happen when a nucleotide is changed without causing a change in the amino acid sequence of the encoded polypeptide. This type of change is a neutral mutation. Other mutations can be positive or negative, depending on the effect on the protein made or the amount of protein produced. As discussed in Chapter 1, the resulting way in which any mutation affects the organism's ability to survive and reproduce can be beneficial or detrimental, or it will have no effect.

Mutations arise as errors during DNA replication or when the cell is exposed to harmful environmental conditions such as radiation or chemicals. While DNA repair mechanisms exist, not all mistakes are corrected. In addition, errors during mitosis or meiosis can occur, affecting phenotype. These can result in polyploidy or in changes of chromosome number, as with nondisjunction leading to Down syndrome/Trisomy 21. When mutations are environmentally caused, they occur at random. Only after subsequent gene expression can the effect be determined to be neutral, beneficial, or detrimental. Pesticides are harmful and can even have mutagenic effects; however, the evolution of a pesticide-resistant gene is not directed by pesticide. Instead, the application of pesticide selects for any organism with an allele conferring resistance, no matter the origin of that allele.

Mutations are not the only means by which genetic diversity can arise in organisms. Bacteria have several mechanisms by which they can obtain DNA and thus increase their genetic diversity. These involve the lateral or horizontal transmission of DNA by transformation (absorption of DNA from the environment, especially in times of stress); by transduction (when DNA is carried from one bacterium to another by means of a virus); by conjugation (when a plasmid is passed directly from one cell to another); or by transposition (the movement of DNA segments, called transposable elements, from one place to another within the organism's genome).

Non-mutational genetic variation in eukaryotes can arise through sexual reproduction. During meiosis, both crossing-over and the random alignment and assortment of chromosomes can cause combinations of genes in an organism's offspring that did not exist in either of its parents. Furthermore, fertilization can produce an organism with different new allele combinations.

GENETIC ENGINEERING
Enduring Understanding 3.A

Biologists have developed a variety of tools for manipulating DNA. These techniques have allowed for the production of genetically modified foods and the use of bacteria to produce human gene products such as insulin.

A recombinant DNA is a hybrid molecule consisting of DNA from more than one source. The DNA can be from a different part of the organism's genome or from a different organism altogether. Scientists have used restriction enzymes to integrate new sections of DNA into existing strands. Restriction enzymes occur naturally in bacterial cells and restrict the growth of viral particles by chopping viral DNA into small pieces. These enzymes are identified by the sequence of DNA that they recognize and cut. For example, the restriction enzyme EcoRI will cut when it encounters the DNA sequence GAATTC. Some of these enzymes leave single-stranded tails, called "sticky ends" on DNA fragments. By matching the sticky ends of DNA from different sources, scientists can "paste" desired segments of DNA into a host. DNA fragments isolated by restriction enzymes can be inserted into plasmids (small circular pieces of DNA) by cutting the plasmid and the desired segment of DNA with the same restriction enzyme. When mixed with the enzyme DNA ligase, the fragment and plasmid DNA can be linked. Bacteria mixed with the integrated plasmids can absorb the plasmids by transformation; they can then pass copies of the recombinant plasmid to subsequent generations. The genes of the desired segment will be expressed when other plasmid genes are expressed. If a gene for insulin is inserted next to a plasmid gene conferring antibiotic resistance, when the bacteria are exposed to the antibiotic, they will produce insulin. If the desired gene comes from a eukaryotic cell, in this case, any introns first must be removed for a functional protein to be produced. This can involve using the viral enzyme reverse transcriptase to produce DNA from cytoplasmic messenger RNA for insulin.

Gel electrophoresis and PCR can be used to isolate and then make multiple copies of a particular DNA sequence. Gel electrophoresis uses an electrical charge to push DNA fragments through a gel-like material. Larger fragments migrate through the gel at a slower rate and end up closer to the starting point. Smaller fragments, on the other hand, are able to quickly migrate through the gel and will travel farther than larger fragments in the same amount of time. PCR, or polymerase chain reaction, is a hot-cold cycling process that can make a huge amount of DNA from trace amounts. These techniques can be used in tandem both prior to genetic engineering and in forensic DNA fingerprinting.

VIRUSES
Enduring Understanding 3.C

Viruses are extremely small, noncellular infectious particles that can only survive inside a host cell. Viruses require host cells to reproduce and metabolize. The structure of viruses is genetic material (DNA or RNA) surrounded by a protein coating. Viruses do not have a cell membrane or ribosomes. They have a number of different ways to carry out their life cycle, but most follow five basic steps:

1. Attachment: the virus binds to the host cell.
2. Injection: the virus injects its genetic material into the host cell.
3. Replication: the viral genes hijack the host cell and direct the host cell to replicate the viral genetic material and viral proteins.
4. Assembly: new viral particles are assembled in the host cell.
5. Release: new viral particles are released from the host cell.

Viruses come in a variety of structures. For example, HIV is a retrovirus that uses reverse transcriptase to transcribe its RNA to DNA after injecting itself into the host. Once the viral RNA is transcribed into DNA, the viral DNA integrates into the host cell's DNA. When the host cell replicates, the viral DNA is transcribed along with the host's genome. Most animal viruses have a membrane made from the host cell membrane when the virus is assembled by the host cell. Bacteriophages, viruses which infect bacterial cells, have two possible replication pathways. The lytic pathway causes the host cell to burst or lyse after the new viruses have been made. In the lysogenic pathway, the viral DNA integrates into the host cell; it is replicated and passed on when the host cell replicates. Depending on where the viral

DNA has entered the host's genome, it can affect the expression of a host's genes. Eventually the lysogenic virus will enter the lytic pathway.

Viruses accumulate mutations in the same manner as their host cells, but they lack error-checking mechanisms and can change at a faster rate. A cell infected by multiple, related viruses can produce viruses with new genetic combinations; this is one way in which new flu viruses evolve and a reason why new flu vaccines are offered every year. When viral mutations accumulate quickly, as in HIV, the development of a vaccine can be a challenge.

Multiple-Choice Questions

1. Which of the following DNA sequences would be considered complementary to the DNA strand 5'-TACGAA-3'?
    (A) 5'-CGTAGG-3'
    (B) 5'-ATGCTT-3'
    (C) 3'-TACGAA-5'
    (D) 3'-ATGCTT-5'

2. All of the following are post-transcriptional modifications of eukaryotic mRNA EXCEPT
    (A) Introns are removed.
    (B) Exons can be spliced.
    (C) Peptide bonds are formed.
    (D) A modified guanine "cap" is added.

3. A fruit fly with the four genes AABbCCDd undergoes meiosis. If all four genes assort independently, what fraction of the gametes formed will have a dominant allele for all four traits?
    (A) 0
    (B) 1/16
    (C) 1/8
    (D) 1/4

4. Your mother has blood type B, and your father has blood type A. You learn that you have blood type O. What does this tell you?
    (A) You cannot be the biological child of these two people because it is impossible for them to produce a child with blood type O.
    (B) Both of your parents were heterozygous for the *ABO* gene.
    (C) Type O blood must be caused by an interaction between the A and B alleles.
    (D) The allele for type O blood is dominant to both the A and B alleles.

Use the following to answer Questions 5–7. These terms may be used once, more than once, or not at all.
(A) epistasis
(B) codominance
(C) polygenic inheritance
(D) segregation

5. A cow has genetic information to express both brown and white fur, resulting in a roan, with splotches of brown and white.

6. Through experimentation it was discovered that chickens have two genes that code for the shape of their comb. Depending on the interaction of the products of those two genes, chickens can express four different comb shapes.

7. A parent is heterozygous for sickle shaped red blood cells. The gametes this individual would produce either contain a normal red blood cell gene or a sickle cell shape gene, but not both.

8. Molecules which bind to regulatory proteins to prevent gene transcription are
(A) repressors.
(B) promoters.
(C) exons.
(D) inactivators.

9. Which of the following statements is false?
(A) A virus can increase variation by carrying DNA from one cell to another.
(B) Reverse transcriptase enzyme from some viruses is used to genetically engineer human insulin.
(C) Restriction enzymes are used by bacteria as a defense against viruses.
(D) Lysogenic viruses do not need to be inside a host cell in order to replicate.

10. Which of the following best describes RNA interference (RNAi)?
(A) RNAi occurs when certain proteins block RNA polymerase to prevent transcription.
(B) RNAi involves microRNA molecules binding to complementary pieces of messenger RNA.
(C) RNAi is a common type of gene control in prokaryotic cells.
(D) RNAi is the process used by viruses to ensure a cell's ribosomes make only viral proteins.

11. Which of the following scientists helped to experimentally demonstrate that DNA is the hereditary molecule of cells?
(A) Chargaff
(B) Franklin and Wilkins
(C) Hershey and Chase
(D) Watson and Crick

12. Horizontal gene transfer
    (A) is common among prokaryotic organisms.
    (B) can involve the transfer of a plasmid.
    (C) is one way for disease-causing bacteria to become antibiotic resistant.
    (D) all of these are correct.

13. PCR is important in genetic engineering because it
    (A) makes many identical copies of a DNA sequence in a short time.
    (B) separates DNA fragments by their size, helping form a DNA fingerprint.
    (C) cuts DNA at specific nucleotide sequences before a DNA fingerprint can be made.
    (D) makes intron-free copies of a eukaryotic gene using messenger RNA.

14. Protein synthesis in prokaryotes differs from protein synthesis in eukaryotes because
    (A) translation can begin before transcription finishes in a prokaryotic cell.
    (B) transcription begins at the promotor in prokaryotes, but at a replication origin in eukaryotic cells.
    (C) prokaryotes use RNA polymerase, while eukaryotes use DNA polymerase.
    (D) prokaryotes use uracil, while eukaryotes use thymine.

Use the following table to answer question 15.

first base ▼	second base				third base ▼
	U	C	A	G	
U	UUU phe	UCU	UAU tyr	UGU cys	U
	UUC phe	UCC ser	UAC tyr	UGC cys	C
	UUA leu	UCA ser	UAA STOP	UGA STOP	A
	UUG leu	UCG	UAG STOP	UGG trp	G
C	CUU	CCU	CAU his	CGU	U
	CUC leu	CCC pro	CAC his	CGC arg	C
	CUA	CCA	CAA gln	CGA	A
	CUG	CCG	CAG gln	CGG	G
A	AUU	ACU	AAU asn	AGU ser	U
	AUC ile	ACC thr	AAC asn	AGC ser	C
	AUA	ACA	AAA lys	AGA arg	A
	AUG met	ACG	AAG lys	AGG arg	G
G	GUU	GCU	GAU asp	GGU	U
	GUC val	GCC ala	GAC asp	GGC gly	C
	GUA	GCA	GAA glu	GGA	A
	GUG	GCG	GAG glu	GGG	G

15. If a bacterial gene has the sequence 3'-TACGGACTCCCTCGAAAT-5',
the polypeptide it will make will have the sequence
(A) his - arg - leu - ser - thr.
(B) met - pro - glu - gly - ala.
(C) tyr - gly - leu - pro - arg - asn.
(D) ile - ser - arg - glu - ser - val.

Grid-In Question

1. Two Wisconsin Fast Plants are crossed. One has the recessive dwarf trait, but the normal pigment anthocyanin, while the other has the recessive anthocyaninless trait, but is of normal height. Their offspring consist of 89 plants of normal height and pigment; 93 anthocyaninless plants; 96 dwarf plants; and 94 anthocyaninless, dwarf plants. A student proposes that the parent plants' genotypes must have been ddAa for the dwarf parent and Ddaa for the anthocyaninless parent. Calculate, to the nearest 0.01, the Chi-Square value that would be used to confirm this hypothesis.

Free-Response Questions

MULTI-PART QUESTION

1. While Gregor Mendel described how the inheritance of certain traits worked in pea plants, other patterns of inheritance are described as non-Mendelian.
   (a) Identify three examples of traits that are inherited by different non-Mendelian patterns in eukaryotic organisms. Explain how each differs from Mendelian inheritance.
   (b) Identify and explain one means by which prokaryotic cells perform lateral gene transfer.

SINGLE-PART QUESTION

2. Restriction enzymes have been used to genetically engineer human insulin and in forensic DNA fingerprinting. Some restriction enzymes cut straight across a DNA strand and do not produce "sticky ends." Explain how the lack of "sticky ends" affects the enzyme's role in these two technologies.

Answers

MULTIPLE-CHOICE QUESTIONS

1. **D.** The DNA molecule consists of two parallel strands of DNA running in opposite directions. Nucleotides follow the base pair rules: A pairs with T and C pairs with G (*Biology*, 12th ed., page 207/13th ed., page 139).

2. **C.** Peptide bonds form during translation (*Biology*, 12th ed., page 220/13th ed., page 156).

3. **D.** The law of independent assortment states that genes are sorted into gametes independently of each other. Analyze each gene individually. Homozygous dominant gene pairs (in this case AA and CC) have a 100 percent chance of passing on the dominant allele. Heterozygous gene pairs (Bb and Dd) have a 50 percent chance of passing on the dominant allele. Probability rules allow us to multiply the individual probabilities of passing on the dominant alleles to calculate the combined probability of passing on all four dominant alleles together: $1/1 \times 1/2 \times 1/1 \times 1/2 = 1/4$. So, 1/4 of the gametes will be homozygous dominant for all four traits (*Biology*, 12th ed., page 174/13th ed., pages 208–209).

4. **B.** The *O* allele of the *ABO* gene is recessive to the A and B forms. If both parents are heterozygous, each can pass the *O* allele on to a child (*Biology*, 12th ed., page 176/13th ed., page 210).

5. **B.** Two different alleles of a gene are both fully expressed in the cow, with neither being dominant nor recessive (*Biology*, 12th ed., page 176/13th ed., page 210).

6. **A.** Epistasis occurs when one gene is influenced by the interactions of another gene's products (*Biology*, 12th ed., page 177/13th ed., page 211).

7. **D.** During segregation alleles of homologous chromosomes separate and enter different gametes (*Biology*, 12th ed., page 173/13th ed., page 207).

8. **A.** One type of regulatory protein in eukaryotic cells is called a repressor; this molecule binds to DNA and stops transcription (*Biology*, 12th ed., page 230/13th ed., page 164).

9. **D.** All viruses must reproduce inside of a host cell. Lysogenic viruses do not reproduce immediately, but their DNA inserts into a host cell's chromosome and will be copied along with that chromosome if still there when the host cell reproduces (*Biology*, 12th ed., pages 336–337/13th ed., page 326).

10. **B.** RNA interference involves the enzymatic destruction of mRNA molecules which have formed base pairs with bits of microRNA (*Biology*, 12th ed., page 231/13th ed., page 165).

11. **C.** Alfred Hershey and Martha Chase used isotopes of phosphorus and sulfur to determine that DNA, but not most of the protein, of bacteriophages enters the host cell (*Biology*, 12th ed., page 205/13th ed., page 137).

12. **D.** Horizontal gene transfer in prokaryotes involves conjugation, transduction, or transformation (*Biology*, 12th ed., pages 340–341/13th ed., page 333).

13. **A.** PCR uses heat tolerant DNA polymerase and cycles of heating and cooling to make many copies of a DNA sample, which can then be used, for example, in bacterial transformation or gel electrophoresis (*Biology*, 12th ed., pages 244–245/13th ed., page 238–239).

14. **A.** Because prokaryotic cells do not have membrane-enclosed nuclei, transcription and translation both occur in the cytoplasm (*Biology*, 12th ed., page 222/13th ed., page 157).

15. **B.** RNA polymerase adds mRNA nucleotides in the 5' to 3' direction (*Biology*, 12th ed., page 219/13th ed., pages 152–153).

Grid-In Question

1. 0.28

   Total offspring = 372. These parents would produce offspring in a 1:1:1:1 ratio, so there would be 372/4 = 93 expected of each offspring phenotype actually observed.

   $$X_2 = \frac{\Sigma (o - e)^2}{e}$$

   $X_2 = (89 - 93)^2/93 + (93 - 93)^2/93 + (96 - 93)^2/93 + (94 - 93)^2/93$ is the correct set-up used to calculate the Chi-Square value.

   (*Biology*, 12th ed., pages 174–175/13th ed., pages 208–209).

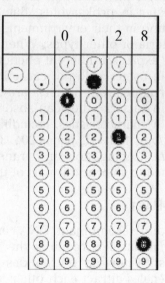

FREE-RESPONSE QUESTIONS

MULTI-PART

1. (a) Pink flower color in snapdragons, red-green color blindness in humans, and coat color in Labrador retrievers show non-Mendelian inheritance patterns. Pink flower color is the phenotype that results from incomplete dominance in the heterozygote flower. Its allele for red pigment is functional, but less pigment is produced than in homozygous red flowers because its second allele does not produce any. The traits Mendel studied had alleles that were either completely dominant or recessive. The gene for red-green color blindness is located on the X chromosome. This means that males need only one recessive, mutated allele to be color blind, while females would need two copies of the allele. Mendel's pea plants do not have different combinations of chromosomes for males and females. Coat color in Labrador retrievers does not give the expected 9:3:3:1 ratio when two heterozygous for both of the coat color genes are crossed. The 9:3:4 ratio results from epistasis, where the recessive form of one gene negatively affects the production of either black or brown hair encoded by the other gene. Genes for the traits Mendel studied did not interact in this way. (*Biology*, 12th ed., pages 176–178, 190–191/13th ed., pages 210–211, 224–225). (*Note:* Other non-Mendelian traits could also be discussed, including, but not limited to, codominance, pleiotropy, multiple alleles, and polygenic inheritance.)

   (b) Transformation is one type of lateral or horizontal gene transfer in prokaryotes. Bacteria can absorb DNA that is free-floating in their environment. The origin of this DNA can be dead bacteria of other types. When the bacteria absorb this DNA, they may express a different phenotype as a result. For example, rough-strain bacteria do not cause infected mice to die. However, when the rough-strain bacteria are exposed to DNA from dead smooth-strain bacteria, they can absorb the DNA and acquire the smooth-strain characteristics, including the ability to kill mice they infect. (*Biology*, 12th ed., pages 204, 340–341/13th ed., pages 136–137, 333). (*Note:* Conjugation and transduction could alternatively be discussed to answer this part of the question.)

SINGLE-PART

2. Making recombinant DNA, as was done to genetically engineer human insulin, requires the use of enzymes that create "sticky ends." Unpaired nucleotides at the resulting cut ends of DNA molecules attract each other (when cut by the same enzyme), and hydrogen bonds form between them. If the ends of the DNA were blunt, they would not easily form new bonds. On the other hand, DNA with blunt ends will still be able to migrate during gel electrophoresis; "sticky ends" are not a factor influencing their movement (*Biology*, 12th ed., pages 242, 247/13th ed., pages 236–237, 240).

6

ORGANISMS

BIG IDEAS 2, 4

Organisms respond to environmental changes through physiological and behavioral mechanisms. Organisms also respond to internal changes using positive and negative feedback.

KEY TERMS

antigen	humoral response	open circulatory system
apoptosis	immune response	pathogen
b-cell	inflammation	phagocyte
biological clock	innate immune system	pheromones
circadian rhythm	macrophage	photoperiod
closed circulatory system	memory cell	phototropism
	microRNA	positive feedback
homeostasis	negative feedback	T-cell
homeotic genes	nonspecific immunity	transcription factors
hormone		

KEY CONCEPTS

- ▦ Organisms use feedback mechanisms to regulate growth and development.
- ▦ Vertebrate immune systems are designed to defend against specific and nonspecific invaders.
- ▦ Organisms have a variety of mechanisms for obtaining nutrients and eliminating wastes.
- ▦ Animals and plants use signals to communicate with their own species.

145

- Plant development is regulated by genetics that code for the production of hormones and other signaling molecules.
- Plant development is influenced by environmental stimuli such as the amount of light, day length, seasonal and temperature changes, or changes in the availability of water and nutrients.

For a full discussion of organisms, see *Biology,* 12th ed., Chapters 15, 27, 31, and 38/13th edition, Chapters 10, 30, 37, and 40.

FEEDBACK MECHANISMS
Enduring Understanding 2.C

Negative feedback is a common form of control for organisms. This is where the product of a stimulus leads to the dampening of the stimulus. For example, the parathyroid gland produces parathyroid hormone which is responsible for regulating the amount of calcium in the blood. If too much calcium is determined to be in the blood, the glands will stop producing parathyroid hormone. Another example is how animals prevent overheating on a hot day. Receptors sense the increase in temperature and trigger changes that affect the whole body. Blood flow shifts from the core to the skin in order to maximize the heat available to dissipate to the surroundings. Glands in the skin increase their secretion of sweat which evaporates and helps cool the body surface. Once the body temperate decreases, the responses are reversed and homeostasis is maintained. Plants also use negative feedback pathways to limit water loss during photosynthesis. Under dry conditions, some plants will open their stomata at night to fix and store carbon dioxide as organic molecules. During the day, the stomata are closed, and the carbon dioxide needed for photosynthesis is released from the organic molecules made during the night.

Positive feedback mechanisms are also used by organisms, although less commonly than negative feedback. In positive feedback, a stimulus causes a response, which then causes the intensity of the stimulus to increase. For example, when a woman is giving birth, muscles in her uterus contract and force the fetus against the wall of the uterus. The resulting pressure on the uterine wall induces secretion of the hormone oxytocin, which causes stronger contractions. As contractions get more forceful, the pressure on the uterine wall increases, causing a positive feedback cycle that continues until the baby is born.

Both positive and negative feedback mechanisms are critical to an organism's ability to maintain a constant internal environment and to respond to external stimuli. When changes occur to the mechanisms of feedback, it often causes harmful results. One example is diabetes mellitus, a metabolic disorder where cells do not take up glucose properly. The hormones responsible for maintaining the proper levels of glucose in the blood are insulin (decreases blood sugar) and glucagon (increases blood sugar). Insulin stimulates muscle and fat cells to take up glucose and then activates enzymes that make protein and fat. It also discourages the metabolism of fat and proteins. Insulin is made by beta cells that in Type 1 diabetes are wrongly identified by the immune system as foreign and are thus destroyed. As a result of too little insulin, excessive fat and proteins break down causing serious effects on the body.

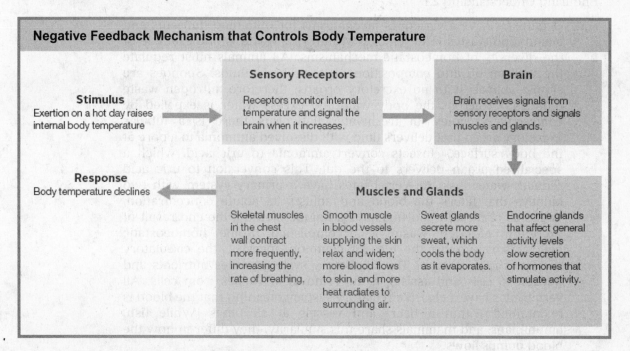

Negative Feedback Mechanism that Controls Body Temperature

Stimulus
Exertion on a hot day raises internal body temperature

Sensory Receptors
Receptors monitor internal temperature and signal the brain when it increases.

Brain
Brain receives signals from sensory receptors and signals muscles and glands.

Response
Body temperature declines

Muscles and Glands

Skeletal muscles in the chest wall contract more frequently, increasing the rate of breathing.

Smooth muscle in blood vessels supplying the skin relax and widen; more blood flows to skin, and more heat radiates to surrounding air.

Sweat glands secrete more sweat, which cools the body as it evaporates.

Endocrine glands that affect general activity levels slow secretion of hormones that stimulate activity.

RESPONSE TO THE EXTERNAL ENVIRONMENT
Enduring Understanding 2.C

Many organisms respond to changes in the environment through behavioral and physiological mechanisms. In plants, the environmental stimuli range from gravity and light to touch and mechanical stress. All are known as tropisms. Plants that grow toward the light have a positive phototropism. There is a cascade of events that occurs in plants in response to blue light. This causes the plant hormone auxin to function as an internal molecular signal which elongates cells on the shaded side of the plant more than the light side. The difference causes the entire structure to bend toward the light and results in maximum exposure of light to the leaves for photosynthesis.

Also connected to the sun is the idea of a photoperiod, or an organism's response to the amount of light relative to the amount of night. Long-day plants only bloom when the hours of darkness are below a critical value, and short-day plants only bloom when the hours of darkness are greater than the critical value. For example, irises will only flower when the night length is less than 12 hours, whereas chrysanthemums will only flower when night length is greater than 12 hours. Animals also respond to external stimulus through physiological changes. One example is how animals respond to heat or cold stress. When animals become too hot, widening of blood vessels in the skin occurs and, in some species, sweating or panting. This allows for the heat to dissipate from the body. When animals encounter cold, they respond by redistributing blood flow, fluffing hair or fur, and shivering. All of these responses decrease heat loss.

HOMEOSTATIC MECHANISMS
Enduring Understanding 2.D

Organisms have a variety of mechanisms for obtaining nutrients and eliminating wastes. The removal of nitrogen waste is one example of the diversity of homeostatic mechanisms. All animals must regulate the amount of, and composition of, their body fluids. Sponges are simple animals with no excretory organs; therefore, nitrogen waste diffuses out across the body wall, and excess water is expelled by contractile vacuoles. In freshwater flatworms there is a tubular excretory organ that delivers fluid with dissolved ammonia to a pore at the body surface. Insects convert ammonia to uric acid, which a specialized organ delivers to the gut. This conversion to uric acid reduces water loss. All vertebrates have a urinary system with two kidneys that filters the blood and adjusts its solute concentration. While all of these organisms have a unique method, the end result of excreting nitrogen waste is accomplished. Some homoeostatic mechanisms support the idea of common ancestry; the circulatory system is one example. The circulatory system carries nutrients and oxygen to cells and assists in the removal of wastes from cells. All vertebrates have a closed circulatory system, meaning that the blood is maintained within a heart and vessels at all times. While fish, amphibians, and mammals share this similarity, they differ in how the blood pumps flows.

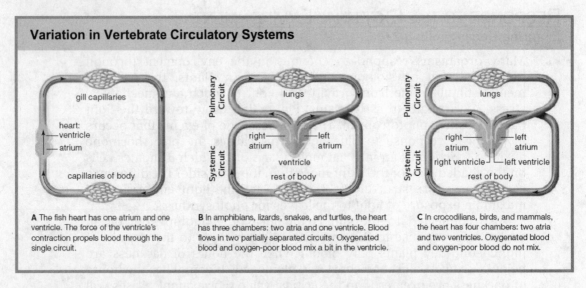

Variation in Vertebrate Circulatory Systems

A The fish heart has one atrium and one ventricle. The force of the ventricle's contraction propels blood through the single circuit.

B In amphibians, lizards, snakes, and turtles, the heart has three chambers: two atria and one ventricle. Blood flows in two partially separated circuits. Oxygenated blood and oxygen-poor blood mix a bit in the ventricle.

C In crocodilians, birds, and mammals, the heart has four chambers: two atria and two ventricles. Oxygenated blood and oxygen-poor blood do not mix.

These differences have evolved over millions of years. In fish, the heart has two chambers (one atrium and one ventricle). Blood flows through one circuit. It picks up oxygen in the capillary beds of the gills and delivers it to capillary beds in all body tissue. In amphibians, the heart has three chambers (two atria and one ventricle). Blood flows along two partially separated circuits. The force of one contraction pumps blood from the heat to the lungs and back. In mammals the heart has 4 chambers (two atria and two ventricles). The blood flows through two fully separated circuits. In one circuit blood flows from the heart to the lungs and back, and in the second circuit the blood flows from the heart to all body tissue and back.

DISRUPTIONS TO HOMEOSTASIS
Enduring Understanding 2.D

Organisms are affected by disruptions to their homeostasis. These disruptions can be at a molecular, cellular, or ecosystem level. Disruptions on a molecular and cellular level affect the health of an organism. For example, when an organism reacts to a harmless substance and stimulates an immune response, this is harmful to homeostasis. Sensitivity to an allergen is called an allergy. The first exposure to an allergen stimulates the immune system to make a protein, which triggers an immune cell to release histamine, which initiates inflammation. If this reaction occurs in the lining of the respiratory tract, the airway can become constricted and a large amount of mucus is secreted. When disruptions occur within ecosystems, the balance between species can be altered. Invasive species can greatly affect native communities. In the 1800s, for example, rabbits were introduced to Australia where they have no natural predators. Rabbits displaced livestock, ate all of the vegetation, and greatly reduced natural wildlife. The rabbits also dug burrows which undermined the soil and set the stage for widespread erosion. The addition of invasive species to an ecosystem can have drastic affects on the balance of life. Ecosystem disruption is also discussed in Chapter 7.

CHEMICAL DEFENSE
Enduring Understanding 2.D

Animals and plants have chemical defenses to fight against foreign invaders such as viruses, bacteria, fungi, parasites, and other pathogens. The vertebrate immune system has a nonspecific and specific defense to protect against pathogens. The nonspecific immunity, or innate immune system, is a set of general defenses against a fixed number of antigens. It acts when a microbe makes it past the first line of defense (skin and mucus). Humans have a host of nonspecific defenses that will prevent a pathogen from getting a hold in the body but are not specific to the antigen. These nonspecific second lines of defense mechanisms include phagocytes, or white blood cells, that engulf and digest foreign invaders. Examples of phagocytes include macrophages, neutrophils, and natural killer cells. The inflammatory response is another nonspecific defense mechanism, which is activated by tissue damage to a specific area. Symptoms of inflammation include redness, warmth, pain, and swelling.

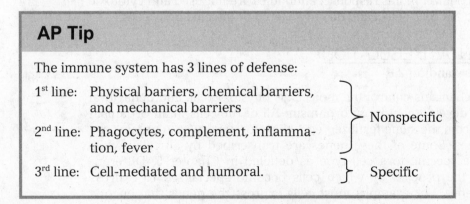

AP Tip

The immune system has 3 lines of defense:

1st line: Physical barriers, chemical barriers, and mechanical barriers
2nd line: Phagocytes, complement, inflammation, fever   } Nonspecific

3rd line: Cell-mediated and humoral.   } Specific

Pathogens that survive the nonspecific immune response are targeted specifically by the third line of defense, or specific immune response. The mammalian immune system is made up of two types of specific responses: cell mediated and humoral. These two arms of adaptive immunity work together to maintain the health of an organism. The humoral response activates B-cells (a type of lymphocyte) which produce antibodies. Antibodies are proteins that can bind to a specific antigen receptor. Recognition of the antigen begins when a macrophage, B-cell, or dendritic cell presents the foreign antigen by engulfing the invader, digesting the particle, and then presenting the antigen on the cell surface. Helper T-cells then bind with the presented antigen and signal the production of more T- and B-cells. The B-cells then make antibodies specific to the antigen presented. Memory B- and T-cells also form during the humoral response and persist long after the initial infection ends. If the same antigen enters the body at a later time, these memory cells will initiate a secondary response.

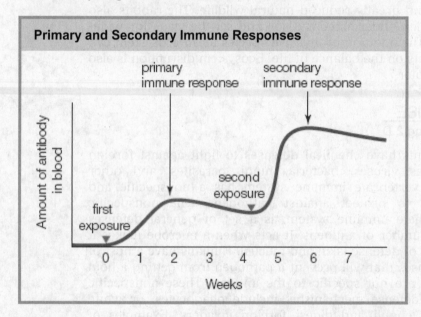

In the secondary response, larger populations of effector cell clones form much more quickly than they did in the primary response, thus more antibodies can be produced in a shorter time. In the cell mediated response, cytotoxic T-cells target intracellular pathogens which B-cells cannot recognize. In this response, antibodies are not used and cytotoxic T-cells and NK cells detect and destroy altered or infected body cells.

DEVEOPMENTAL REGULATION
Enduring Understanding 2.E

Many mechanisms control the molecular, physiological, and behavioral events of development in an organism. All of the cells in an organism descend from the same fertilized egg, therefore every cell contains the same genes. Some of these genes are transcribed by all cells, while others are specific to a cell type as detailed in Chapter 5. Differentiation is the process by which cells become specialized to express certain genes. For example, most cells express the genes that encode for the enzymes in glycolysis but only red blood cells use the genes that code for globin chains to make hemoglobin. Cells rarely use more than ten percent of their genes at any one time. Which genes are expressed at any given time depends on conditions in the cytoplasm, the type of cell, and other factors. Regulatory proteins such as activators and repressors are called transcription factors. When and how fast a gene is transcribed depends on which transcription factors are bound to the DNA. One example of a master gene found in most eukaryotic organisms is the homeotic genes. These genes control formation of specific body parts during embryonic development. Homeotic genes encode for transcription factors with a homeodomain that can bind to a promoter or other DNA sequence. Localized expression of homeotic genes in the tissue of a developing embryo gives rise to details of the adult body plan. Products of these homeotic genes form in specific areas of the embryo. The different products cause cells to differentiate into tissues that form specific structures such as the head. Depending on where these concentration gradients fall within the embryo, cells suppress or activate other master genes. The products of these genes then create gradients which affect other genes, and then the process continues throughout development.

Development of an embryo into the body of an organism is controlled layer after layer by master genes. The failure of any master gene to function properly results in a drastically altered body plan. In fruit flies, for example, a mutation in the transcription of the antennapedia gene in the embryonic tissue of the head causes legs to form on the head. The products of master genes diffuse outward, and concentration gradients for these products develop along the head to tail and dorsal to ventral axes.

Antennapedia Gene

Mutation in transcription (left); normal (right)

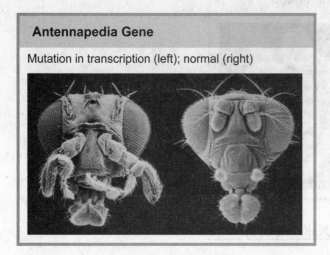

Another way that organisms genetically regulate development is the use of microRNAs. MicroRNAs inhibit translation of other RNA. Part of a microRNA folds back on itself and forms a small double-stranded RNA. By a process called RNA interference, any double-stranded RNA is cut up into small bits that are taken up by special enzyme complexes. These complexes destroy every mRNA in a cell that can base pair with the bits. Therefore, the expression of a microRNA complementary in sequence to a gene inhibits the expression of that gene.

Genetics and the environment both play a role in coordinating growth and development in plants as well as animals. Seed germination, root and shoot development, flowering, fruit formation, senescence, and dormancy all work together to establish patterns of plant development. Germination is the process in which the seed is no longer dormant. It is triggered by water moving into the seed and activating enzymes so that the stored starches are hydrolyzed and can be used by the seed. Once this happens, the seed splits and oxygen can enter. The use of sugar and oxygen starts aerobic respiration, and the meristem cells in the embryo begin to divide rapidly. Seed dormancy is a climate-specific adaptation that allows germination to occur when conditions in the environment are most likely to support the growth of a seedling. For example, plants that are native to colder regions are dispersed in autumn. If the seeds germinated immediately, they would not survive the cold winter. Instead, the seeds stay dormant until spring, when milder temperatures and longer day length are more suitable for tender seedlings.

Apoptosis, or the death of programmed cells, also plays an important part in normal development. As part of animal development, many cells self-destruct at a specific time. Apoptosis often starts when certain molecular signals attach to receptors at the cell surface. A chain of reactions leads to the activation of self destruction. An example of apoptosis in normal development is in the formation of hands. Each hand starts as a paddle structure and apoptosis occurs in vertical rows until individual fingers form. When the cells do not die on cue, the paddle does not split properly.

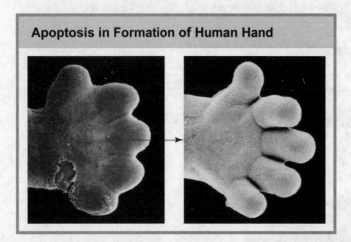

Apoptosis in Formation of Human Hand

COORDINATION OF PHYSIOLOGICAL EVENTS
Enduring Understanding 2.E

In plants and animals, physiological events are triggered by environmental signals. As previously discussed, phototropism (a plant's response to light) and photoperiodism (a plant's response to the change in the length of night) are examples of an external stimulus causing a reaction by the plant. In animals, pheromones are used as chemical signals to alter behavior. The honeybee alarm pheromone is an example of when a pheromone is secreted, which causes a behavioral change such as attacking a predator. This type of coordinated response to an environmental stimulus often evolves in a population as it increases fitness.

Some signals are internal and are not dictated by external cues. The biological clock, an internal mechanism that governs timing of rhythmic cycles, is one example. A cycle of activity that starts new every twenty four hours is called a circadian rhythm. This is present in all eukaryotes. In bacteria, quorum sensing is used to communicate between organisms of the same and different species using chemical messengers secreted from the cell. Bacteria have receptors in the plasma membrane that can identify species specific signals and interspecific signals. This allows bacteria to turn on genes together and thus make a much larger host sick.

INTERACTIONS BETWEEN PARTS OF ORGANISMS
Enduring Understanding 4.A

Organisms have interactions between organs that allow for essential biological activities. Two such organs are the kidney and the bladder. The urinary system is responsible for monitoring and adjusting the composition and volume of extracellular fluid. The system consists of a pair of kidneys and ureters, along with a urinary bladder and one urethra. Kidneys work to remove nitrogenous waste and regulate the chemical composition of the blood. All but about 1% of the blood that enters the kidney is returned into the bloodstream. The small leftover amount is termed urine and consists of un-reclaimed water and solutes. Urine is transported from the kidney via ureters and is temporarily held in a muscular sac, the bladder, before it exits the body through the urethra.

Systems can be intricately connected, such as the respiratory and circulatory systems. The pulmonary circuit is a short loop that oxygen-ates blood and releases carbon dioxide. Beginning in the right atrium, oxygen poor blood is moved into the right ventricle. The right ventricle contracts, moving blood through the pulmonary artery to the lungs where gas exchange occurs, releasing CO2 and picking up O2. Oxygenated blood returns to the left atrium of the heart via the pulmonary vein.

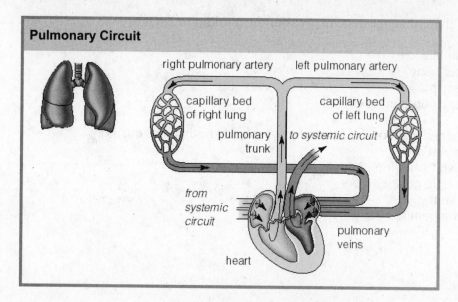

Pulmonary Circuit

right pulmonary artery left pulmonary artery

capillary bed of right lung capillary bed of left lung

pulmonary trunk *to systemic circuit*

from systemic circuit

pulmonary veins

heart

> ## AP Tip
>
> You are not responsible for the specifics of the excretory, circulatory, or respiratory system but do need to understand how organs interact within organisms. These are provided as an example of this interaction.

The systemic circuit moves oxygen-rich blood to the cells of the body, releasing oxygen and picking up carbon dioxide. The pathway begins with oxygen-rich blood in the left atrium. The left atrium moves blood into the left ventricle, where it is pumped out of the heart through the aorta. The aorta branches off into arterioles, finally delivering oxygen- rich blood to the capillaries. Once depleted of its oxygen, the blood passes from venules to veins and enters the heart in the right atrium to begin the process all over again.

Multiple-Choice Questions

1. All of the following are nonspecific immune responses EXCEPT
   (A) neutrophils.
   (B) blood clotting proteins.
   (C) T-cells.
   (D) fever.

2. If a plant only blooms when it gets more than 12 hours of sunlight, it is considered to be
   (A) a long day plant.
   (B) a short day plant.
   (C) a long night plant.
   (D) biennial.

3. Proteins that influence gene expression by binding to DNA are called
   (A) promoters.
   (B) master gene.
   (C) transcript.
   (D) transcription factors.

4. Master genes that control formation of specific body parts during development are
   (A) pattern formation genes.
   (B) homeotic genes.
   (C) knockout genes.
   (D) operon genes.

5. Humoral responses work against _____ while cell mediated responses work against _____.
   (A) extracellular pathogens; cancerous and intracellular pathogens
   (B) intracellular pathogens; cancerous cells
   (C) cancerous cells; intracellular pathogens
   (D) virus infection cells; parasitic pathogens

6. A scientist observed a plant growing toward a window. The cells appear to be elongated on the shaded side of the plant. This response is called
   (A) thigmotropism.
   (B) gavitropism.
   (C) phototropism.
   (D) photoperiodism.

7. What process is used to form hands from paddle-like forms?
   (A) transformation
   (B) transcription
   (C) apoptosis
   (D) passive transport

8. The heart is responsible for pumping blood throughout the body. The respiratory system is responsible for oxygenating the blood and removing the carbon dioxide. This interaction is an example of
   (A) organisms interacting with the environment.
   (B) organisms in the same population interacting.
   (C) organs interacting within a body.
   (D) organs interacting between species.

9. Which of the following is NOT an example of a stimulus causing a cellular response in the same organism?
   (A) The plant hormone gibberellin stimulates cell division in the stem tip and young leaves.
   (B) The animal hormone prolactin targets mammary glands and stimulates milk production after childbirth.
   (C) The plant hormone ethylene stimulates ripening in fruit.
   (D) Pheromones are secreted from an animal and help indicate social behavior.

10. In *Drosophilia* an experiment was done where the gene for wings was knocked out. Which of the following does this experiment show?
    (A) mutations can cause abnormal development
    (B) normal regulated development
    (C) apoptosis
    (D) signal transduction

11. MicroRNA is important in gene control because
    (A) it inhibits translation of other RNA molecules.
    (B) it inhibits post transcriptional modifications.
    (C) it activates protein processing.
    (D) it enhances different chromosomes.

12. Humans can make about 2.5 billion unique antigen receptors. The diversity arises by genes encoding for the receptors. This is an integral part of what type of immunity?
    (A) adaptive immunity
    (B) inflammation
    (C) complement
    (D) innate immunity

13. The presence of a closed circulatory system in all vertebrates shows
    (A) acquired characteristics.
    (B) common ancestry.
    (C) common diversity.
    (D) coevolution.

14. All organisms must secrete nitrogenous waste. In birds the waste is in the form of uric acid, in sponges it diffuses out of the body, in humans it is urea, and in flatworms ammonia. This shows what concept?
    (A) common ancestry
    (B) common diversity
    (C) unity of homeostatic mechanisms
    (D) diversity of homeostatic mechanisms

15. Where on this graph would memory B- and T-cells be quickly making effector cells to secrete antibodies?

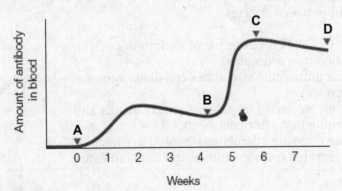

    (A) A
    (B) B
    (C) C
    (D) D

Grid-In Question

1. A bacteria strain is susceptible to antibiotics, meaning 50% of the population dies each day starting Day 2 and every day thereafter. All bacteria double in population every 24 hours. Antibiotics are metabolized in the body in 24 hours. After 24 hours there are no antibiotics left in your body. If you have 130 bacteria in your body and start your antibiotics on Day 0 but skip it on Day 4 how many bacteria will be present on Day 10?

Free-Response Questions

MULTI-PART QUESTION

1. Feedback mechanisms are vital to an organism's survival. Receptors detect stimuli and send signals to the brain. Signals cause effectors to respond.
   (a) Discuss the difference between positive and negative feedback.
   (b) Choose an example of positive feedback and explain the mechanism.

SINGLE-PART QUESTION

2. Explain the process of seed germination and what environmental factors influence the timing and coordination of this process.

Answers

MULTIPLE-CHOICE QUESTIONS

1. **C.** Nonspecific immune system response includes physical, chemical, and mechanical barriers that prevent pathogens from entering the body as well as innate immunity that is activated after tissue damage (*Biology*, 12th ed., page 667/13th ed., page 650).

2. **A.** A long day plant like the iris requires less than 12 hours of night in order to bloom. More hours of darkness than that and it won't bloom. Short day plants and long night plants are basically the same thing and need a light length that exceeds more than 12 hours. Biennials and perennials only bloom after exposure to cold temperatures (*Biology*, 12th ed., pages 532–533/13th ed., pages 516–517).

3. **D.** Regulatory proteins that can both activate and repress gene expression are transcription factors. Transcription factors bind to promoters and through transcription make a transcript (*Biology*, 12th ed., pages 230–231/13th ed. pages 164–165).

4. **B.** Homeotic genes encode for transcription factors that can bind to a promoter in specific cells and determine the body parts in a developing embryo (*Biology*, 12th ed., page 234/13th ed., page 166).

5. **A.** Humoral immune responses produce B-cells which produce antibodies that can bind to specific antigen bearing particles. Cell mediated immune responses do not involve antibodies but can detect and destroy altered or infected cells (*Biology*, 12th ed., page 667/13th ed., page 660).

6. **C.** Light streaming in from one direction causes a stem to curve toward its source. The response is termed phototropism. Gravitropism is a plant's response to gravity, thigmotropism is a plant's response to touch, and photoperiodism is a plant's response to

length of night (*Biology*, 12th ed. pages 530–532/13th ed., pages 514–515).

7. **C.** Apoptosis is the process of programmed cell death where specific cells die in response to a specific signal. A chain of reactions leads to the activation of self destructive enzymes which kills the cell (*Biology*, 12th ed., page 470/13th ed., page 757).

8. **C.** The circulatory and respiratory systems work together to deliver oxygen and remove carbon dioxide from the body. This is an example of organs within a body working together to meet biological necessities (*Biology*, 12th ed., page 638/13th ed., page 628).

9. **D.** Hormones interact with cells as a signal and cause a cellular response within a cell. Pheromones diffuse through water or air and bind to target cells in other individuals (*Biology*, 12th ed., pages 602–603/13th ed., pages 780–781).

10. **A.** In this experiment a gene was knocked out causing an abnormal phenotype. This type of mutation is an example of a defective gene causing abnormal development (*Biology*, 12th ed., page 234/13th ed., pages 302–303).

11. **A.** MicroRNA inhibit translation of other RNA molecules by binding to a complementary sequence to a gene and inhibit the expression of the gene (*Biology*, 12th ed., page 231/13th ed., page 165).

12. **A.** Adaptive immunity tailors the immune defense against specific pathogens, whereas innate immunity is a fast general defense against infection (*Biology*, 12th ed., page 660/13th ed., page 650).

13. **B.** A closed circulatory system is found in annelids (segmented worms) and all vertebrates. This shows common ancestry among all vertebrates. In a closed circulatory system the blood remains in vessels (*Biology*, 12th ed., page 639/13th ed., page 628).

14. **D.** While keeping the solute composition constant is an important aspect to all organisms, the way in which they carry out the function can be very different. Therefore, the different compounds used to excrete nitrogen waste are an example of diversity in homeostatic mechanisms (*Biology*, 12th ed., pages 722–723/13th ed., pages 716–717).

15. **C.** After the secondary exposure of an antigen, memory cells will initiate a secondary response in which effector cells form much more quickly than they did in the primary response and more antibodies can be produced to avoid illness (*Biology*, 12th ed., page 671/13th ed., page 661).

GRID-IN QUESTION

1. 2

Day	0	1	2	3	4	5	6	7	8	9	10
Bacteria strain	130	260	130	65	32.5	65	32.5	16.25	8.125	4.06	2

130 × 2 = 260
260/2 = 130
130/2 = 65
65/2 = 32.5
35 × 2 = 65
65/2 = 32.5
32.5/2 = 16.25
16.25/2 = 8.125
8.125/2 = 4.06
4.06/2 = 2

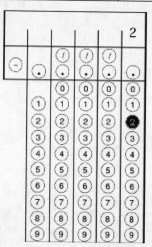

(*Biology*, 12th ed., page 346/13th ed., page 277).

FREE-RESPONSE QUESTIONS

MULTI-PART

1. (a) Positive feedback sparks a chain of events that intensify changes from the original condition. With a positive feedback mechanism, detection of a change leads to a response that intensifies the change. In negative feedback mechanisms, receptors detect a change, then effectors respond and reverse the change. This mechanism is vital to homeostasis. For example, this feedback mechanism keeps the internal body temperature constant, despite changes in the temperature of the surroundings.

    (b) One example of positive feedback is in the nervous system. Gated sodium channels open in an accelerating way after the threshold potential is reached. As sodium starts to flow in, it makes the neuron cytoplasm more positive so more sodium channels open and more sodium flows into the neuron. Another example is when women give birth. When muscles in the uterus contract, they force the fetus against the wall. The resulting pressure on the uterine wall induces secretion of a signaling molecule that causes stronger contractions until the baby is born (*Biology*, 12th ed., pages 466–467 and 558/13th ed., pages 536 and 546).

SINGLE-PART

2. Temperature and water availability determine when seed germination occurs. Germination is the process by which a seed begins growth. It is triggered by water seeping into the seed. Water activates an enzyme that starts to hydrolyze stored starches into sugar monomers. It also swells tissues inside the seed, so the seed coat splits open and oxygen enters. The embryonic plant begins to grow (*Biology*, 12th ed., page 524/13th ed., pages 496–497).

ECOLOGY

BIG IDEAS 2, 3, 4

If John Donne had been an ecologist, his famous poem might have started, "No organism is an island entire of itself." This chapter discusses the ways in which organisms interact with each other and with their environments. Categories of organization in ecology include:

1. *Population:* All the individuals of one species in one area at one time.
2. *Community:* The interaction of multiple populations in a given area.
3. *Ecosystem:* The interaction of a community with the abiotic (nonliving) factors of their environment.
4. *Biosphere:* The portion of the Earth where organisms live. This area includes the soil, air, and water. The biosphere is just a sliver when compared to the total mass of the Earth. For example, if you compared Earth to an apple, Earth's biosphere would be thinner than the apple's skin.

KEY TERMS

age structure diagram	competitive exclusion	ecosystem
biogeochemical cycle	consumer	energy
biomass	decomposer	eutrophication
biome	density-dependent factors	exponential growth
biosphere		food chain
biotic potential	density-independent factors	food web
carrying capacity		global climate change
commensalism	detritivore	habitat
community	ecology	innate behavior

161

interspecific competition	parasitism	resource partitioning
keystone species	pheromone	secondary succession
learned behavior	pioneer species	succession
limiting factor	predation	survivorship curve
logistic growth	primary producer	symbiosis
mutualism	primary productivity	trophic level
niche	primary succession	zero population growth

KEY CONCEPTS

▧ Population statistics are used to describe population size, density, distribution, and ages.

▧ Environmental factors cause population size to continually fluctuate.

▧ Animal behavior is influenced by both genetics and environmental factors.

▧ Animals use signals to communicate with other members of their own species.

▧ The characteristics of a community are influenced by the species in the habitat, how those species interact with each other, and how they interact with abiotic factors of their ecosystem.

▧ Raw materials cycle and energy is passed in one direction through trophic levels of an ecosystem.

▧ The biosphere is divided up into biomes based on amount of sunlight, moisture, and soil which affect characteristics of the dominant vegetation and other organisms that have evolved there.

▧ Human activity has influenced the biosphere.

For a full discussion of ecology, see *Biology,* 12th ed. Chapters 44–49/13th ed., Chapters 43–48.

POPULATION ECOLOGY

Enduring Understanding 2.D, 4.A, 4.C

Population ecology studies the distribution, density, and age structure of species as they are influenced by the resources and physical factors around them. Population sizes and distribution can be defined through the following demographics:

1. Population size (N) is the number of individual organisms in a population.
2. Age structure counts the number of individuals who fall into specific age parameters within a population. Often the parameters are grouped to reflect the following tiers: pre-reproductive, re-productive, and post-reproductive.
3. Population density describes how many individuals are located within a measured area (or volume) of habitat.
4. Population distribution details how individuals are located within their habitat. Individuals can be clumped together, dispersed uniformly, or dispersed randomly.

Population size is dynamic, increasing due to births and immigration, and decreasing due to deaths and emigration. During zero population growth, population sizes remain constant as the number of births equals the number of deaths in a given time period. Birth rates and death rates can be measured per capita (per individual).

Per capita growth rate (r) can be determined by subtracting a population's per capita death rate (d) from a population's per capita birth rate (b), so r = b - d. If r remains positive and consistent, then exponential growth will continue. In other words, the size of the population will increase by the same proportion in continuous time segments.

Population growth rate (G), or the percent change in population size over a given period of time, can be calculated by multiplying the per capita growth rate by the number of individuals, so G = rN.

If a population existed under perfect conditions—no predators, no disease, and plenty of resources (food, shelter, water, etc.)—the population would be able to attain its biotic potential, which is the maximum growth rate that a species can achieve. If its size were plotted over time, such a population would likely show a J-shaped curve, demonstrating its exponential growth. Populations, however, are usually unable to achieve their biotic potential because of limiting factors. Environmental factors such as food, minerals, territory, and predators influence population growth.

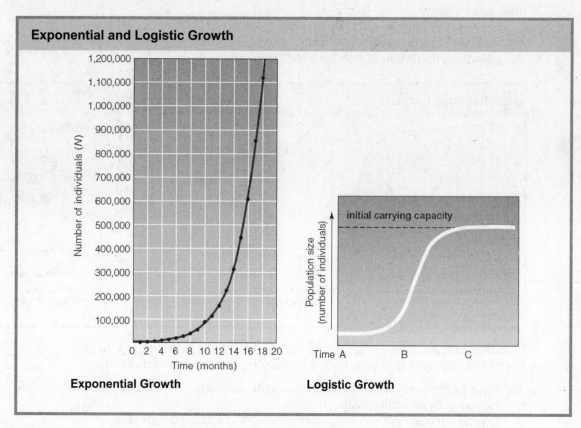

Exponential and Logistic Growth

Exponential Growth

Logistic Growth

Populations eventually reach a balance that takes into account all of the limiting factors in an environment. The carrying capacity of a population is the maximum number of individuals that an ecosystem can sustain. As resource availability determines population size, the pattern called logistic growth appears. Such a population's size, when plotted over time, would demonstrate an S-shaped curve; it could grow exponentially when the size was small, but it eventually would level off near the carrying capacity.

Limiting factors can be described as biotic or abiotic, and as density-dependent or density-independent. Biotic factors involve other organisms, including predators or parasites. Abiotic factors include nonliving aspects of the environment, including temperature and salinity. Density-dependent factors get worse as population density increases, as with disease or competition for limited resources. Density-independent factors are just as likely to affect populations that are spread thin as those that are crowded, as with temperature or salinity.

Changes in limiting factors can affect populations. Two examples of this include rampant population growth seen in invasive species which lack predators in a non-native environment, and populations shrinking in response to drought. Not all members of a population, however, respond equally to such changes. Genetic differences among organisms can mean that some members of a population can be better able than others to respond to drought or to survive when exposed to infectious disease.

When a population shrinks in size, genetic drift can occur, and some alleles disappear from the population. This loss of genetic diversity puts the population at risk for extinction.

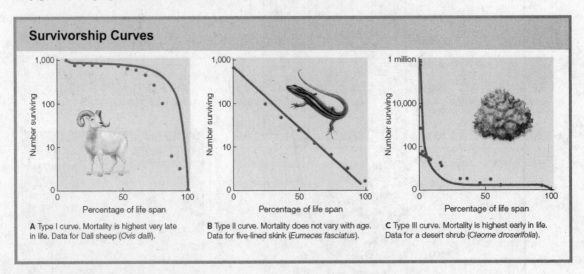

Survivorship Curves

A Type I curve. Mortality is highest very late in life. Data for Dall sheep (*Ovis dalli*).

B Type II curve. Mortality does not vary with age. Data for five-lined skink (*Eumeces fasciatus*).

C Type III curve. Mortality is highest early in life. Data for a desert shrub (*Cleome droserifolia*).

Survivorship curves display the mortality rates of individuals of a species at different points in their lifespan. Three common curves are:

1. Type I curves, representing species with individuals that have low mortality rates until advanced ages.
2. Type II curves, representing species with a constant death rate.
3. Type III curves, representing species with high mortality rates at a young age and lower mortality rates as the organisms reach adulthood.

Population density has influence on reproductive strategies as well. Species that inhabit areas of low density and take advantage of available resources to quickly produce offspring are classified as R-selected species. R-selected species reproduce at young ages, produce many small offspring, and invest few resources in parental care. R-selected species display J-shaped growth curves. K-selected species, on the other hand, reproduce later in life and produce fewer, but higher quality offspring. K-selected species maintain their population levels at or near the carrying capacity.

Age structure diagrams are a representation of the number of individuals of a species at different ages. Bars represent the number of organisms for each given age range. A line down the middle of the bars separates males on one side and females on another side. Younger individuals are located at the bottom of the graph, and older individuals are placed at the top. From the shape of an age structure diagram, the population growth rates can be determined. Age structure diagrams with bars of equal length are representative of populations experiencing zero population growth. If the bars form a pyramid, with the widest bar at the base, a positive growth rate is indicated; the wider the base, the faster the growth is occurring. If the pyramid is inverted, the population is experiencing negative growth.

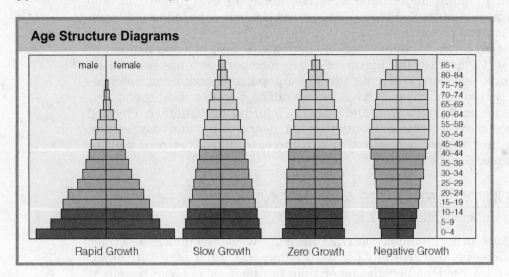

COMMUNICATION AND BEHAVIOR IN POPULATIONS
Enduring Understanding 2.E, 3.E, 4.B

A population is often a group of individuals of the same species that interact with each other, rather than a collection of isolated and independent individuals. Just as the different cells of a multicellular organism communicate and coordinate, so can the members of a population.

Communication among animals involves signals given by one individual that influence the behavior of other individuals in the population. These signals can take several distinct forms that correspond with several senses.

1. *Chemical communication:* Chemical signals produced by animals are called pheromones. When a dog sniffs at and urinates on

trees, fire hydrants, and the like, it is communicating with other dogs that have walked along the same route. Ants and termites sometimes follow trails to food set down by others.

2. *Auditory communication:* Some songs produced by birds are for attracting or keeping a mate. A prairie dog's whistle lets others know it has detected a predator.

3. *Visual communication:* Baby geese imprint upon a nearby moving object during a critical time shortly after hatching; they will follow what is moving, which would most naturally be a parent, but which could also be a person, such as the behavioral biologist Konrad Lorenz. A peacock's elaborate tail not only attracts a mate, but also indicates its health to the mate.

4. *Tactile communication:* A bee's waggle dance, performed within a dark hive, informs hive mates of both the distance and direction to a source of nectar.

The responses to signals an organism receives from other members of its population or from other environmental factors are either innate (inherited) or learned; however, frequently the organism's behavior results from a combination of genetics and experience. Both innate and learned components are critical to effective communication. A male songbird might have an innate ability to sing, but it can only produce the complex song of its species if it was exposed to that song at a critical period in its life.

Many forms of communication among members of a population can serve to increase the fitness of those members and are favored by natural selection. When members of a population communicate effectively, more of them survive to reproduce because they spend less energy on fighting with and possibly injuring one another. Physical aspects of the environment, such as temperature and day length, can also trigger behavior that can increase fitness, as discussed in Chapter 6.

COMMUNITY STRUCTURE AND BIODIVERSITY
Enduring Understanding 2.D, 2.E, 4.A, 4.B, 4.C

Species in a community interact in many ways. Symbiosis describes two species that live in close association with each other. At times, these interactions benefit one or both partners, or one can benefit at the other's expense. The three common symbiotic relationships are:

1. *Commensalism:* One species benefits from the relationship, and the other is neither harmed nor helped. For example, a tree can benefit a bird by providing a place for it to live. The tree, however, is neither helped nor harmed by this relationship.

2. *Mutualism:* Both species benefit from cooperating. For example, some species of fish hide among the tentacles of certain anemones (a thick coat of mucus coating the fish protects them from being stung). The anemone benefits when the symbiotic fish chase off fish of other species that feed on the anemone's tentacles. Some examples of mutualism have specific names: lichen are mutualistic relationships formed between a fungus and unicellular photoautotrophs (prokaryotic or eukaryotic) which survive better through cooperation than as separated species; and mycorrhizae are

mutualistic relationships formed between a fungus and a plant's roots, where the plant is able to form a more extensive root system even though it provides the fungus with nutrients.

3. *Parasitism:* One species benefits at the other's expense. For example, tapeworms residing in the digestive system of a human are provided nourishment and habitat by their host. Host, however, is denied nourishment as a result.

Direct Two-Species Interactions

Type of Interaction	Effect on Species 1	Effect on Species 2
Commensalism	Beneficial	None
Mutualism	Beneficial	Beneficial
Interspecific competition	Harmful	Harmful
Predation, hervivory, parasitism, parasitoidism	Beneficial	Harmful

Another form of interaction between two species is predation. Predators are free-living (so not symbiotic) organisms that hunt, capture, kill, and consume organisms of other species (prey). Predation can be seen when a pride of lions takes down a wildebeest for food. Some predators and their prey, such as the Canadian lynx and the snowshoe hare, exhibit coupled cycles of abundance: prey population size increases; predators increase due to food availability; prey numbers then decrease; predators decrease in response; and the cycle begins again. Different predator species respond differently to increases in prey density. This can depend on whether the predator switches among several species of prey and whether the predator species has a maximum rate at which individuals can eat and digest prey.

Different species of organisms living together in a habitat often compete for a limited supply of energy, nutrients, living space, and so on. Species have many ways of resolving the conflicts that arise from this competition. Competitive exclusion occurs when two species compete for the exact same resources. One is likely to outcompete the other and become more successful. When this happens, the other species can be eliminated. The biologist G. Gause

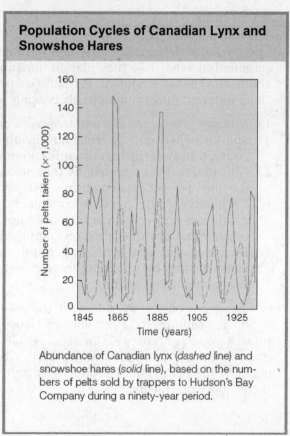

Population Cycles of Canadian Lynx and Snowshoe Hares

Abundance of Canadian lynx (*dashed* line) and snowshoe hares (*solid* line), based on the numbers of pelts sold by trappers to Hudson's Bay Company during a ninety-year period.

demonstrated this principle when he grew two species of *Paramecium* separately, and then together. Alone, both species were able to sustain populations at a carrying capacity. When grown together, however, they fiercely competed for the same provided bacterial food source, and one species was eliminated.

When two species in the same geographic area appear to compete for the same resources, resource partitioning can occur. In this case, the species can coexist because they occupy slightly different niches. A niche is the accumulation of all the interactions an organism has, both with other organisms and with its environment. Using different means of obtaining slightly different resources allows organisms to reduce competition and increases individual success. Resource partitioning can be observed in neighboring plants in a field; some species will send their roots deep in the soil to obtain water and minerals while others can have shallow root systems.

Species richness is one way of describing the composition of a community. Scientists examining species richness on islands have described two patterns. The distance effect indicates that islands of similar size will have less diversity the farther they are from a source of colonists. The area affect shows that islands at the same distance from a source of colonists have more diversity if they are larger in area.

While communities consisting of multicellular organisms are familiar, unicellular prokaryotes can form communities. Such communities exist, for example, in the extreme environments of Yellowstone National Park's hot springs.

ECOSYSTEMS

Enduring Understanding 2.A, 4.A

Energy flows through an ecosystem in one direction. Species can be classified by what role they play in moving energy from one place to another in the environment. Producers, consumers, and decomposers all fill different nourishment levels (trophic levels) within an ecosystem.

1. Primary producers are autotrophs, which are organisms that are able to obtain energy from non-living sources (like the sun) and convert that energy into organic compounds.
2. Consumers are heterotrophs that obtain energy and carbon from feeding on other organisms. Herbivores feed on producers. Carnivores feed on other consumers. Omnivores feed on both producers and consumers. Detritivores feed on small particles of organic matter rather than on complete organisms.
3. Decomposers are types of fungi and prokaryotes that are characterized by obtaining their energy and carbon from organic wastes and the remains.

Primary productivity refers to the rate at which an ecosystem's producers capture and store energy. Gross primary productivity is the total amount of energy captured, while net primary productivity measures the amount of energy stored. Gross primary productivity is equal to the net primary productivity and respiration (energy use) of the primary producers.

Ecological pyramids visually show the feeding relationship between trophic levels. The length of the bars indicates the amount of energy, biomass, or number of individuals at each trophic level. Food chains indicate the sequential movement of energy and organic nutrients from primary producers to organisms in higher trophic levels. Food webs illustrate the interconnected food chains in a particular ecosystem. As food energy passes from one trophic level to the next, some is converted to unusable forms, in accordance with the second law of thermodynamics (entropy). If less energy is available to producers, organisms at other trophic levels of that ecosystem are also affected.

Unlike energy, various elements undergo biogeochemical cycles, moving not only through increasing trophic levels, but also back into the abiotic environment. Chemical compounds containing these elements can act as abiotic limiting factors. For example, the amount of dissolved oxygen, nitrates, and phosphates can all act to determine the composition of an aquatic community.

AP Tip

The four major biogeochemical cycles are:

1. *Water cycle:* Processes include evaporation, transpiration, condensation, precipitation, cellular respiration, and photosynthesis. Abiotic water sources include the atmosphere (water vapor and clouds), oceans, lakes, and rivers.
2. *Carbon cycle:* Processes include cellular respiration, photosynthesis, combustion, and the dissolving of carbon dioxide in water where it reacts to form carbonic acid. Oxygen often cycles in conjunction with carbon. Abiotic reservoirs of carbon include fossil fuels, atmospheric carbon dioxide, and carbonate rocks.
3. *Nitrogen cycle:* Processes include nitrogen fixation, nitrification, ammonification, and denitrification. All of these processes are done exclusively by various types of prokaryotes, such as the nitrogen-fixing bacteria living symbiotically in the roots of leguminous plants (e.g., peas). The main abiotic reservoir of nitrogen is the atmosphere.
4. *Phosphorus cycle:* This cycle differs from the others in that it lacks an atmospheric component.

The terrestrial biosphere can be divided up into regions called biomes that have common characteristics. Biomes are characterized by soil type, temperature, and amount of rainfall. These abiotic factors affect the types of plants and, thus, animals that live there. The following list details characteristics of the major biomes.

Characteristics of Major Biomes

Biome	Precipitation	Temperature	Soil	Plants	Animals
Desert	Very dry	Hot or cold	Nutrient poor, somewhat salty	CAM and C4 plants	Adapted to conserve water
Chaparral	Dry	Hot summer, cool winter	Nutrient poor	Drought and fire-adapted plants	Drought and fire-ada[ted animals
Tundra	Dry	Cold	Permafrost	Lichens and shallow-rooted, low-growing plants and moss	Migrating animals
Conferous Forest	Adequate	Cool summers, cold winters	Nutrient poor, rocky soil	Conifers	Mainly herbivores with some carnivores
Temperate Deciduous Forest	Moderate	Warm summers, cold winters	Fertile soil	Shrubs, moss, fern, hardwood deciduous trees	Large diversity; includes deer, wolves, birds, and small mammals
Grassland	Minimal	Hot summers, cold winters	Fertile soil	C4 plants: perennial grasses and some flowering plants	Large diversity; many mammals, birds, insects, arachnids, etc.
Tropical Rain Forest	Abundant rain, high humidity	Continually warm	Nutrient poor, highly weathered heavily leached	Huge diversity	Huge diversity

AP Tip

Rather than memorizing the above table, be able to explain how the plants and animals characterizing each biome illustrate the influence of the abiotic factors of precipitation, temperature, and soil.

ECOSYSTEM DISRUPTIONS

Enduring Understanding 2.D, 4.A, 4.B, 4.C

A community can exhibit homeostasis and remain stable over time. Changes in biotic or abiotic aspects of the environment, however, can disrupt that homeostasis. These changes, such as global climate change, can be the result of natural geological or meteorological events or the result of human activities.

Smaller or fragmented habitats and other changes created by human activities can affect ecosystems. As the human population has expanded, land transformed for farming has eliminated habitats, leading to extinction of species; forests cut for wood and the building of roads have contributed to extinctions and increased runoff; compounds such as sulfates have been added to the atmosphere, where they combine with water to produce more acidic rainfall; and species released into new ecosystems have driven native species to extinction.

The introduction of a non-native species can be disruptive when that species experiences exponential growth in the absence of predators. Such an invasive species can cause native species' populations to plummet; both species on which it preys and species with which it competes for prey would be affected. Whether done accidentally or on purpose with good intent, humans have introduced non-native species to the environment which have had a huge impact on ecosystems. Kudzu was introduced to the United States to control erosion on slopes. While in its native Japan it is held in check by herbivores and pathogens, in the American Southeast it has grown and spread without control. Zebra mussels, native to Russia, have spread in the Great Lakes as cargo ships released ballast water and have spread as they out-competed native mollusk species.

A keystone species is one that has a greater effect on its community than its population size would suggest. For example, when the sea star *Pisaster ochraceus* preys upon mussels, other species with which the mussels compete are able to coexist with them. When the sea star is removed, competitive exclusion occurs and the mussels predominate. Thus, the removal of a keystone species can lead to a lack of diversity which puts the community at risk.

Natural disasters such as hurricanes, fires, floods, and volcanic eruptions can kill all or many members of a community. In the case of a lava flow, a new community might rebuild, starting with pioneer species such as lichen, which can start to slowly form new soil in that location; this is primary succession. If soil remains, secondary succession follows and is faster. A community undergoing succession will change over time because species that can disperse quickly (e.g., because its seeds or spores are propelled by wind) and arrive soon after the disruption may change the soil conditions, allowing other species to thrive years later. While scientists can predict that succession will occur after a disturbance, the order in which species arrive is affected by chance. Thus, the composition of the community over time is not predictable.

While not a natural disaster, El Niño events can affect a community. The changes in water temperature affect dissolved oxygen levels and can have an effect on aquatic food chains. In addition, changes in rainfall patterns can affect terrestrial plant growth. In the Galapagos Islands in an El Niño year, sometimes vines cover cacti, the effective beak size for survival in finches change, and the population size of fish eating blue-footed boobies may plummet.

Runoff water from agricultural fields and manicured lawns often carry excess nitrates and phosphates into lakes and rivers. The increase of nutrients, eutrophication, can cause an algal bloom, a rapid increase in population size of primary producers in those waters. When increased decomposition follows, dissolved oxygen levels can drop, leading to the death of many other organisms in the community.

Multiple-Choice Questions

1. Which organisms fill the role of decomposer in the environment?
   (A) plants and fungi
   (B) fungi and bacteria
   (C) bacteria and viruses
   (D) animals and bacteria

Use the following information to answer questions 2 and 3.

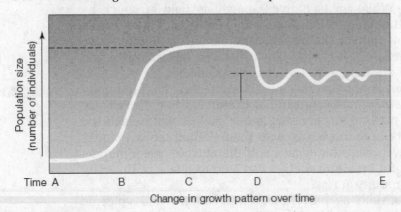

Change in growth pattern over time

2. Rapid growth of the population is occurring during which time interval?
   (A) A - B
   (B) B - C
   (C) C - D
   (D) D - E

3. Which is a likely cause for the changed position of the dotted line?
   (A) habitat destruction caused by a hurricane
   (B) removal of a predator species
   (C) increased food availability
   (D) removal of competitor species

4. Which of the following best illustrates a keystone species?
   (A) nutrias, which were brought to the USA to be grown for their fur
   (B) trout, which are highly sensitive to pollutants and low oxygen levels
   (C) sea stars, which maintain community biodiversity by preying on mussels
   (D) kudzu, which has spread through the American Southeast, due to lack of herbivores and pathogens

5. Following a volcanic eruption,
   (A) after a period of time, the same plant species will populate the area.
   (B) no plants will be able to grow for hundreds of years.
   (C) the order in which plant species repopulate follows a predictable pattern.
   (D) the first plant species to populate the area will likely include those with wind-dispersed seeds.

6. Which of the following illustrates mutualism?
   (A) Populations of Canadian lynx and snowshoe hares cycle in response to each other.
   (B) An eagle eats from a carcass after chasing away a fox.
   (C) A single moth species pollinates a single yucca plant species.
   (D) An orchid grows on a tree trunk.

7. A student observes that her dog sniffs and then urinates on the same multiple trees, but defecates at most once, and in different locations, when she takes him for a walk. She has also noticed that her neighbor's dog tends to urinate on the same trees as her dog. Which of the following is the most likely explanation for her dog's behavior?
   (A) When it urinates, the dog is leaving a chemical signal for other dogs; that chemical is not present in the dog's feces.
   (B) The dog has been taught when and where to urinate, but has not been taught where to defecate.
   (C) The dog is responding to a tactile signal when urinating; it is the texture of the tree bark that induces urination.
   (D) The dog probably has prostate cancer; the pressure on its bladder is increasing its need to urinate, but has no effect on its need to defecate.

8. If the biomass of the algae and pond plants in a pond is estimated to be 809 grams per square meter, which of the following actual biomass measurements most likely reflects the gar and bass, top predatory fish in the pond?
   (A) 1.5 grams/square meter
   (B) 11 grams/square meter
   (C) 37 grams/square meter
   (D) 809 grams/square meter

9. A student examines a pond within the confines of a local nature reserve and another pond on a local farm, less than a mile away. Both ponds are fed by natural springs and have about the same depth as well as surface area. She notices that the pond at the farm has thick mats of algae, while the pond at the nature preserve has more clear water and fish visibly present. What is the most likely cause of the difference between these two ponds?
   (A) Foxes are eating the fish at the farm; the nature reserve keeps out predators.
   (B) Some of the farmer's fertilizer could have accumulated in the pond, causing eutrophication.
   (C) The pond at the nature reserve gets more sunlight than the pond at the farm.
   (D) The pond on the farm has been exposed to less phosphates than the pond on the nature reserve.

10. Competition between two species
    (A) helps both species.
    (B) must lead to the elimination of one species in favor of the other.
    (C) is reduced if the species have slightly different niches.
    (D) helps one species and harms the other.

11. Which of the following does NOT describe chemoautotrophs?
    (A) They are prokaryotic organisms.
    (B) They are primary producers in some ecosystems.
    (C) They can be found in some extreme environments such as near hydrothermal vents.
    (D) They are best described as detritivores.

12. Which of the following would be a density-independent limiting factor for a population of little brown bats, *Myotis lucifugus*, in Vermont?
    (A) the number of caves in which it can hibernate
    (B) *Geomyces destructans*, the fungus that causes white nose syndrome
    (C) flooding in Vermont caused by Hurricane Irene
    (D) the size of the mosquito populations in a given summer

13. A biological supply company grows amoebae in cultures it sells to schools. These organisms reproduce only asexually, via the mitotic cell cycle. On Tuesday, a company employee places 18 amoebae in a culture jar with abundant food, water, and air above the water. When the teacher receives the culture on Thursday, she loosens the cap and aerates the culture. If the amoeba cell cycle lasts 36 hours, approximately how many amoebae, at most, should be in the culture jar when students examine the amoebae during a lab activity on the following Monday?
    (A) 85
    (B) 125
    (C) 275
    (D) 535

14. Which of the following is the best example of an innate behavior?
    (A) A mouse arrives at a slice of cheese faster the third time that it is placed in a maze than it did the first or second time.
    (B) A newly-hatched European cuckoo pushes other eggs out of its nest.
    (C) City pigeons do not fly away when people walk within a meter of them.
    (D) A blue jay avoids eating monarch and viceroy butterflies after eating one resulted in its frothing at the mouth.

15. Which of the following processes is least likely to affect carbon dioxide levels in the atmosphere?
    (A) ammonification
    (B) cellular respiration
    (C) burning of fossil fuels
    (D) photosynthesis

Grid-In Question

1. An ornithologist spreads mist nets in a state park to capture small birds. She collects, bands, and releases 18 chickadees. When she returns two weeks later, she collects 15 chickadees, six of which she had already banded. How large is the estimated size of the population in her study area?

Free-Response Questions

MULTI-PART QUESTION

1. Analyze the organization of an ecosystem by describing trophic levels. Include how trophic levels are divided, how energy flows through them, and the relationships between different levels.

SINGLE-PART QUESTION

2. With the best intentions, humans have been known to introduce a non-native species to other ecosystems on this planet, with sometimes devastating results. Identify one such species and describe how it has negatively impacted the ecosystem to which it was introduced.

Answers

MULTIPLE-CHOICE QUESTIONS

1. **B.** Decomposers are responsible for breaking down organic wastes into inorganic building blocks. Both bacteria and fungi serve this role (*Biology*, 12th ed., page 801/13th ed., page 840).

2. **B.** Rapid growth is occurring in this region of the graph with the greatest slope (*Biology*, 12th ed., page 802/13th ed., page 796).

3. **A.** Habitat destruction could lower the population's carrying capacity. The removal of a predator and increased food, however, would be expected to raise the population's carrying capacity (*Biology*, 12th ed., pages 802–803/13th ed., pages 796–797).

4. **C.** A keystone species helps maintain biodiversity. Without the presence of sea stars, mussels can drive other species to extinction by competitive exclusion (*Biology*, 12th ed., page 830/13th ed., page 822).

5. **D.** Typical pioneer species include annual flowering plants with wind-dispersed seeds. There is no one "climax community" for a given location. Random events can affect the order in which species arrive, and early arrivals can determine whether other species can become established (*Biology*, 12th ed., pages 828–829/13th ed., pages 820–821).

6. **C.** In mutualism, both species benefit. The moth pollinates the flower and her larvae develop in the fruit, but do not eat all of its seeds (*Biology*, 12th ed., page 819/13th ed., page 811).

7. **A.** The dog is sniffing to detect pheromones left by previous dogs and leaving its own chemical signal when it urinates (*Biology*, 12th ed., pages 598, 786–787/13th ed., pages 571, 780–781).

8. **A.** Primary producers have the greatest biomass in most ecosystems. Top predators typically have the least biomass (*Biology*, 12th ed., pages 844–845/13th ed., pages 834–835).

9. **B.** The addition of nutrients, especially phosphorus, can cause eutrophication and algal blooms. Subsequently low oxygen levels can make it impossible for fish and other animals to survive (*Biology*, 12th ed., page 857/13th ed., page 845).

10. **C.** Interspecific competition is harmful to both species and can lead to competitive exclusion, but could instead lead to resource partitioning (*Biology*, 12th ed., pages 818–821/13th ed., pages 810–813).

11. **D.** Chemosynthetic bacteria and archaea make their food using energy from chemicals such as those found at deep sea vents (*Biology*, 12th ed., page 884/13th ed., page 871).

12. **C** Natural disasters such as floods affect populations regardless of crowdedness (*Biology*, 12th ed., page 803/13th ed., page 797).

13. **C.** The population should double every 36 hours, and the six days from Tuesday through Monday consists of four 36-hour periods. Ideally, after the first of these periods, there would be $18 \times 2 = 36$ amoebae; after the second there would be $36 \times 2 = 72$ amoebae; after the third $72 \times 2 = 144$ amoebae; and after the fourth there would be 288 amoebae (*Biology*, 12th ed., page 801/13th ed., page 795).

14. **B.** An innate or instinctive behavior has not been learned or modified by the animal's previous experiences (*Biology*, 12th ed., pages 784–785/13th ed., pages 776–777).

15. **A.** Ammonification is a process in the nitrogen cycle. Burning of fossil fuels and cellular respiration both add carbon dioxide to the environment, while photosynthesis removes carbon dioxide from the environment (*Biology*, 12th ed., pages 850–855/13th ed., pages 838–842).

GRID-IN QUESTION

1. 45

   The percentage of marked recaptures is expected to be the same as the percentage of the population she originally banded. Thus, 6/15 = 18/x and x = (18×15)/6, or 45 chickadees.

   (*Biology*, 12th ed., page 799/13th ed., page 792).

FREE-RESPONSE QUESTIONS

MULTI-PART

1. Trophic levels refer to the hierarchy of feeding relationships within an ecosystem. When one organism consumes another organism, energy is transferred. Energy is transferred in a one way direction from non-living sources to producers to consumers and then to decomposers. Organisms that occupy the same trophic level are equal steps away from the energy input stage of the ecosystem. Producers are autotrophs or self-feeders that are able to obtain energy from non-living sources and form the base of the ecosystem. Obtaining energy is usually accomplished by photosynthesis, though some ecosystems are based on chemosynthetic organisms. Consumers are heterotrophs that obtain energy from consuming the tissue, wastes, or remains of other organisms. Decomposers are organisms that feed on organic wastes and break down complex molecules into useable forms for other organisms.

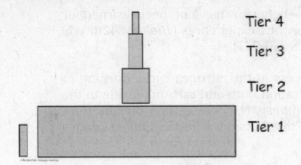

Trophic levels can be displayed in a visual form in the shape of a pyramid. Tier 1 represents the producers; Tier 2 represents the primary consumers (herbivores); Tier 3 represents secondary consumers; Tier 4 represents secondary consumers; and the bar to the side of Tier 1 represents decomposers. The size of the bar correlates with the amount of biomass or the amount of energy contained at each trophic level in a typical community. The energy at each trophic level decreases as some of it is changed to an unusable form, such as heat (*Biology*, 12th ed. pages 844–845/13th ed. pages 834–835).

SINGLE-PART

2. Kudzu is one well known example of an introduced species that became invasive. Brought to the United States because it was known to grow well on slopes in its native Japan, kudzu was planted to help control erosion. In the absence of the herbivores that feed on it in Japan and of the pathogens that usually affect it, however, kudzu has thrived and out-competed native species in the southeastern United States. It blankets many surfaces, from streambanks and trees to houses and telephone poles. It has deep roots and resists burning, so it is difficult to eradicate. Note: other examples exist, including rabbits in Australia and nutria in the United States; however, examples of invasive species that were not introduced for an intended benefit, such as zebra mussels in the Great Lakes, should not be used to answer this question (*Biology*, 12th ed., pages 831–833/13th ed., page 823).

Part III
Laboratory Review

NOTE TO STUDENTS

The AP Biology course requires teachers to engage their students in at least eight inquiry investigations, two for each Big Idea. The following lab descriptions and questions correlate with eight of the investigations included in the College Board's AP Biology Lab Manual. Teachers, however, may choose to conduct different inquiry and other investigations with their classes. When studying for the AP Biology Exam, you should focus on the nature of the questions within each lab described here, which focus on relevant concepts from the AP curriculum, experimental design, and on data manipulation and interpretation.

180

LABORATORY 1: POPULATION GENETICS AND EVOLUTION

BIG IDEA 1

OVERVIEW

This laboratory investigates the Hardy-Weinberg law of genetic equilibrium and studies the relationship between evolution and changes in allele frequencies. A computer/mathematical model was used to discover the Hardy-Weinberg equation and to build multi-generational simulations. The Hardy-Weinberg equation states that $p^2 + 2pq + q^2 = 1$ and $p + q = 1$, where p^2 represents the homozygous dominant individuals, $2pq$ represents the heterozygous individuals, and q^2 represents the homozygous recessive individuals.

The five criteria for the Hardy-Weinberg equation are:

1. Population size must be large.
2. There can be no gene flow.
3. There can be no mutations.
4. Mating must be random.
5. There can be no natural selection.

OBJECTIVES

After doing this laboratory you should be able to:

- Distinguish among dominant allele, homozygous condition, heterozygous condition, and recessive condition.
- Understand the equations as well as how different parameters change allele frequencies over multiple generations.
- Calculate the frequencies of alleles and genotypes in the gene pool of a population using the Hardy-Weinberg formula.
- Discuss natural selection and other causes of microevolution that can alter allelic frequencies in a population.
- Explain the effects on allelic frequencies of selection against the homozygous recessive condition.
- Apply conditions of Hardy-Weinberg equilibrium to populations, particularly how deviations from Hardy-Weinberg criteria relate to evolution.

181

QUESTIONS

1. If populations are rarely in genetic equilibrium, for what is the Hardy-Weinberg equation used?

2. In a population where natural selection favors the dominant condition and the homozygous recessive individuals never survive, what is the result of the selective pressures on this population?

3. Why is the heterozygous condition for sickle cell favorable against malaria?

4. In a population of 250 peas, 16% of the peas are homozygous recessive wrinkled and the rest are smooth.
   (a) How many peas are heterozygous for smooth peas?
   (b) What is the frequency of the dominant allele for smooth peas?

ANSWERS

1. The Hardy-Weinberg equilibrium is used to show that a population is undergoing evolution and to test whether evolution is occurring under specific circumstances. Because a natural population would always have changes in the allele frequencies and therefore not be in Hardy-Weinberg equilibrium, this shows evolution is occurring.

2. Over time, the homozygous recessive condition will be reduced. Because heterozygotes with the dominant trait survive, some of the recessive alleles will remain in the gene pool, but the number of individuals exhibiting the dominant phenotype will vastly outnumber the individuals exhibiting the recessive phenotype.

3. Heterozygote advantage maintains diversity within the gene pool. However, as in the case with sickle cell, the recessive allele carries the trait for immunity to malaria. Therefore, the individuals who are homozygous recessive don't get malaria but have sickle cell, and the homozygous dominant doesn't have sickle cell but is susceptible to malaria.

4. Using the equations $p^2 + 2pq + q^2 = 1$ and $p + q = 1$, you can figure out this problem. In order to figure out the frequency of the dominant allele, you need to calculate how many individuals are heterozygous and how many are homozygous dominant.

   (a) If 16% are homozygous recessive wrinkled, then $q^2 = 16\%$. The square root of $0.16 = 0.4$ and therefore $q = 0.4$. Because $p + q = 1$, $p = 1 - q$ or 0.6, the frequency of the heterozygote is $2pq$ or $2(0.4 \times 0.6)$ which $= 0.48$. Therefore the number of peas heterozygous for smooth peas is found by 250×0.48 which $= 120$.

   (b) Because $p = 0.6$, the dominant allele frequency is 60%. To understand why this works and to double check your work, do the following: p^2 or the frequency of homozygous dominant smooth is 0.36. The number of homozygous dominant individuals is 250×0.36 or 90. In order to find the allele frequency take 2×90, (180 dominant alleles) plus 1×120 for the dominant alleles in the heterozygotes (for number of heterozygotes see item a), for a total of 300 dominant alleles in the population. Because each individual has 2 alleles, there are a total of 500 alleles in the population. Therefore the frequency of the dominant allele in the population is 300/500 or 0.6 (60%).

LABORATORY 2: BLAST LAB

BIG IDEA 1

OVERVIEW

This laboratory activity investigates the use of the Basic Local Alignment Sequencing Tool (BLAST), an electronic comparative tool that is used to compare molecular data in order to create and interpret cladograms. This database is used by scientists to biochemically compare DNA nucleotide sequences and amino acid sequences of different species in order to draw conclusions about evolutionary history. A BLAST search is also useful to look at individuals from the same species to investigate how a defective gene differs from a normal functioning gene and to identify repeated genes in a genome.

OBJECTIVES

After doing this laboratory you should be able to:

- Propose a hypothesis and create a cladogram of evolutionary relationships based on morphological information.
- Interpret and draw conclusions from information provided by a BLAST search.
- Create a cladogram using comparative biochemistry information from a BLAST search.
- Use the BLAST program to answer questions about genes of interest.

QUESTIONS

1. Draw the most parsimonious cladogram that shows the following traits for each organism:

Organism	Presence of Wings	Circulatory System	Presence of Hair	Presence of Scales	Presence of Amniotic Egg	Limbs with 5 Digits
Insects	Yes	Open	No	No	No	No
Bats	Yes	Closed	Yes	No	Yes	Yes
Humans	No	Closed	Yes	No	Yes	Yes
Crocodiles	No	Closed	No	Yes	Yes	Yes
Turtles	No	Closed	No	Yes	Yes	Yes

The following is the amino acid sequence of mitochondrial b from twenty species. Use this information to answer questions 2 and 3.

```
    honeycreepers (10)...CRDVQFGWLIRNLHANGASFFFICIYLHIGRGIYYGSYLNK--ETWNIGVILLLTLMATAFVGYVLPWGQMSFWG...
          song sparrow...CRDVQFGWLIRNLHANGASFFFICIYLHIGRGIYYGSYLNK--ETWNVGIILLLALMATAFVGYVLPWGQMSFWG...
     Gough Island finch...CRDVQFGWLIRNIHANGASFFFICIYLHIGRGLYYGSYLYK--ETWNVGILLLTLMATAFVGYVLPWGQMSFWG...
             deer mouse...CRDVNYGWLIRYMHANGASMFFICLFLHVGRGMYYGSYTFT--ETWNIGIVLLFAVMATAFMGYVLPWGQMSFWG...
       Asiatic black bear...CRDVHYGWIIRYMHANGASMFFICLFMHVGRGLYYGSYLLS--ETWNIGIILLFTVMATAFMGYVLPWGQMSFWG...
             bogue (a fish)...CRDVNYGWLIRNLHANGASFFFICIYLHIGRGLYYGSYLYK--ETWNIGVLLLLVMGTAFVGYVLPWGQMSFWG...
                 human...TRDVNYGWIIRYLHANGASMFFICLFLHIGRGLYYGSFLYS--ETWNIGIILLLATMATAFMGYVLPWGQMSFWG...
     thale cress (a plant)...MRDVEGGWLLRYMHANGASMFLIVVYLHIFRGLYHASYSSPREFVWCLGVVIFLLMIVTAFIGYVLPWGQMSFWG...
          baboon louse...ETDVMNGWMVRSIHANGASWFFIMLYSHIFRGLWVSSFTQP--LVWLSGVIILFLSMATAFLGYVLPWGQMSFWG...
         baker's yeast...MRDVHNGYILRYLHANGASFFFMVMFMHMAKGLYYGSYRSPRVTLWNVGVIIFTLTIATAFLGYCCVYGQMSHWG...
```

2. How can these data be used to answer questions about species relationships?

3. Which species is the most closely related to honeycreepers and which species is least related to honeycreepers? How can you tell by looking at the data?

4. Every individual human is genetically different, therefore what kind of questions could be answered by biochemically comparing individuals of the same species?

ANSWERS

1.

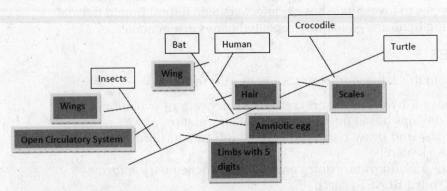

2. Comparing molecular data sequences such as the amino acid sequence of cytochrome b can be used to determine how closely related species are. Lineages that diverged long ago generally have more differences between their amino acids than do lineages that diverged more recently. In this example the differences in amino acids are shaded.

3. The honeycreepers and song sparrows differ in 3 amino acids indicating they are most closely related to each other. The Gough Island finch has 4 differences in the amino acid sequence making it the second most closely related species to the honeycreeper. Baker's yeast has 36 amino acid differences with the honeycreepers making it the least closely related. Therefore by comparing the number of differences in amino acids the relationship between species can be assessed.

4. Every human has a unique genome. Each individual is approximately 0.1% different from each other. BLAST comparisons can show the difference between individuals with a disease and a healthy individual. It can also show what genes are predominant in different regions and what genes are affected by a specific disease.

LABORATORY 3: OSMOSIS AND DIFFUSION

BIG IDEA 2

OVERVIEW

This laboratory investigates the processes of diffusion and osmosis using artificial and living membranes. In Part A, the effect of the surface-area-to-volume ratio on the rate of diffusion is tested using phenolphthalein agar blocks of different dimensions. Part B involves analyzing the movement of molecules into and out of dialysis tubing sacks filled with, and placed into, various solutions. Then, the visible effect of these solutions on plant cells is examined using light microscopes. Finally, water potential is measured in and compared between white and sweet potatoes.

OBJECTIVES

After doing this laboratory you should be able to:

- Explain how the surface-area-to-volume ratio is critical for cells to effectively exchange nutrients and wastes with their environment.
- Explain how a semi-permeable membrane can influence the diffusion of different sized particles.
- Distinguish between hypertonic, hypotonic, and isotonic solutions and be able to explain how these conditions would result in the movement of water in and out of cells.
- Design an experiment to determine the water potential of living tissue and analyze the results of such an experiment.
- Predict under which conditions plasmolysis would occur in plant cells.

QUESTIONS

1. Explain why a 0.9% sodium chloride solution is often administered intravenously to hospital patients. Explain the effects of an intravenous infusion of distilled water, rather than the 0.9% saline solution, on the patient's cells.

2. Describe four blocks of phenolphthalein agar, each with a volume of 64 cm³. Identify into which block of agar a vinegar solution would penetrate most thoroughly in ten minutes as well as the block that would have the greatest volume of pink phenolphthalein remaining at the end of ten minutes. Justify your answers mathematically and relate your predicted results to the surface area of your blocks.

185

3. How could you go about determining the water potential of a pear?

4. A student has estimated that a 0.5 M sucrose solution is isotonic to the sweet potatoes he has used in this lab investigation in class. He decides to examine the sweet potato cells under the microscope in class and puts a very thin slice of the sweet potato in a 0.4 M NaCl solution in preparing the slide. Is his estimate correct?

ANSWERS

1. A 0.9% NaCl solution must be isotonic to our tissues. Using an isotonic solution does not disrupt the water concentration within our cells. Distilled water, however, would be hypotonic relative to our tissues. Cells surrounded by this solution would swell and possibly burst.

2. The four blocks could be:

    (1) 4 cm × 4 cm × 4 cm
    (2) 2 cm × 8 cm × 4 cm
    (3) 1 cm × 8 cm × 8 cm
    (4) 1 cm × 1 cm × 64 cm

    If the vinegar could penetrate 0.4 cm in 10 minutes, then the volume unaffected by the vinegar would be:

    (1) (4 – 0.8) cm × (4 – 0.8) cm × (4 – 0.8) cm = 32.8 cm^3
    (2) (2 – 0.8) cm × (8 – 0.8) cm × (4 – 0.8) cm = 27.6 cm^3
    (3) (1 – 0.8) cm × (8 – 0.8) cm × (8 – 0.8 cm) = 10.4 cm^3
    (4) (1 – 0.8) cm × (1 – 0.8) cm × (64 – 0.8) cm = 2.5 cm^3

    Note: 0.8 is the sum of the affected portion from top and bottom, or from front and back, or from left and right sides of the block.

    Thus, of these four possibilities, block 4 is the one into which the vinegar would penetrate the most, and block 1 is the one that would have the most phenolphthalein at the end of ten minutes. This demonstrates the importance of surface area for the exchange of materials between a cell or organism and its environment. Block 1 has the least surface area, while block 4 has the most for the same volume of 64 cm^3.

    The surface areas of the blocks are:

    (1) 6 × (4 cm × 4 cm) = 96 cm^2
    (2) [2 × (2 cm × 8 cm)] + [2 × (2 cm × 4 cm)] + [(2 × 4 cm × 8 cm)] = 112 cm^2
    (3) [2 × (8 cm × 8 cm)] + [4 × (1 cm × 8 cm)] = 160 cm^2
    (4) [4 × (1 cm × 64 cm)] + [2 × (1 cm × 1 cm)] = 258 cm^2

3. To find the water potential of a pear or other plant material, one could start by cutting equal sized cubes of pear, such as 1 cm × 1 cm × 1 cm cubes. These could be weighed and then immersed for 24 hours into various concentrations of sucrose solutions, such as 0.0 M, 0.2 M, 0.4 M, 0.6 M, 0.8 M, and 1.0 M. When removed from the solutions, the cubes would be dried off, then weighed again. The percent change in mass of the cubes would be graphed as a function of the molarity. At some concentrations, such as 0.0 M, the

solution should be hypotonic to the pear, and the cubes should increase in mass; but at other concentrations, such as 1.0 M, the solution should be hypertonic to the pear, and the cubes should decrease in mass. Where the best-fit line crosses the X axis of the graph, the pear cubes should experience no change in mass. This value of molarity can be used to calculate the water potential of the pear, using the equations $\Psi = \Psi + \Psi s$ and $\Psi = -iCRT$. Because sucrose is a molecular compound, i would be 1.

4. The student failed to consider the fact that sodium chloride is an ionic compound while sucrose is a molecular compound. Sucrose does not separate or ionize in solution, while sodium chloride forms both sodium ions and chloride ions in water. Thus, the concentration of particles in the solution is higher in the 0.4 M sodium chloride solution than in the 0.5 M sucrose solution. As a result, while the water potential of the sweet potatoes is equal to that of the sucrose solution, it is greater than that of the sodium chloride solution, and the cells lose water, or plasmolyze.

LABORATORY 4: PHOTOSYNTHESIS

BIG IDEA 2

OVERVIEW

Conditions that can alter the rate of photosynthesis are investigated in this laboratory inquiry. One method suggested for use is an examination of the rate at which leaf disks float. The leaf disks are removed from a leaf using a straw; then a vacuum is made using a syringe, to eliminate any air existing inside the leaf disks. Finally, the disks are immersed in a solution containing sodium bicarbonate as a source of carbon dioxide. The disks can be exposed to various conditions, including various temperatures, pH, salinity, and light levels. As oxygen gas is produced as a byproduct of photosynthesis, the leaf disks begin to float. The rate of photosynthesis is measured as the number of disks floating over time.

OBJECTIVES

After doing this laboratory you should be able to:

- Design a controlled experiment to test a question and interpret data to draw conclusions.
- Explain how a variety of factors can influence the rate of photosynthesis.
- Demonstrate different rates of photosynthesis by manipulating a variable of your choice.
- Explain changes in photosynthesis rates caused by environmental conditions.

QUESTIONS

1. A student wrapped test tubes with screens to produce the following transmittance of light: 20%, 40%, 60% and 80%. Then she placed 10 leaf disks in each test tube. What results should she expect?

2. You notice that holly plants are evergreen broadleaf plants while lilacs are deciduous broadleaf plants. One question you ask is whether the optimum temperature for holly and lilacs is the same. How could you investigate this?

3. A student takes cuttings from her mother's African violet plant to make two genetically identical plants to give to her grandmothers when they visit at Thanksgiving. One grandmother lives in Shreveport, Louisiana, while the other lives in Tucson, Arizona. Both are at about 32 degrees latitude. When she visits both

188

grandmothers the following summer, she notices that the plant in Louisiana is faring much better than the plant in Arizona. What are three hypotheses she could give to explain her observations?

4. A student is testing the effect of pH on plant disks and found that none of the disks floated, even in his predicted "ideal" condition of pH 7. What are three possible design errors for which the student should check?

ANSWERS

1. The student should expect a direct relationship between the amount of light exposure and the rate of photosynthesis. This is because the higher the amount of light the more photosynthesis is occurring, and therefore the more oxygen is released. The 80% exposure leaf disks should have the highest rate at which they float, and the 20% exposure leaf disks should have the lowest rate.

2. A student could obtain leaf disks from both holly leaves and lilac leaves. Then he would set up test tubes at a variety of temperatures, such as 0°C, 10°C, 20°C, 30°C, and 40°C, put 10 leaf disks into each test tube, and measure the number of disks floating every minute for a total of 20 minutes of light exposure. Care would need to be taken to ensure that the temperature remained constant and was not influenced by heat from the light source used. This might be done using water baths and fluorescent lamps rather than incandescent ones. After determining at which tested temperatures the disks floated most quickly, the student could get closer to finding the optimum by checking every 4°C up to 8°C above and below the best temperature from the initial tests. Doing at least three trials of each temperature and averaging the rates would improve the reliability of the results. If there is a significant difference in temperature optimum for photosynthesis between the two types of leaves, the maximum average rate at which their disks float should occur at different temperatures.

Note: The temperature, number of leaf disks, and number of trials used in this answer are examples. Student answers will vary somewhat, though the use of multiple temperatures within a realistic range and the need for multiple leaf disks and multiple trials would be expected.

3. Possible hypotheses include, but are not limited to:

(a) The humidity in Louisiana is much higher than the humidity in Arizona, so the plant in Arizona is less able to perform photosynthesis.

(b) The plant in Louisiana is getting more sunlight than the plant in Arizona, so the plant in Arizona is less able to perform photosynthesis.

(c) The plant in Louisiana is at a lower altitude than the plant in Arizona, so the plant in Arizona is exposed to lower concentrations of carbon dioxide and is less able to perform photosynthesis.

(d) The plant in Louisiana was given fertilizer, but the plant in Arizona was not, so the plant in Arizona was less able to get other nutrients it needed for growth.

(e) The temperature in Louisiana is more constant than the temperature in Arizona, so the metabolism of the plant in Arizona was slower than the plant in Louisiana.

4. Among the errors the student could have made are:

(a) The temperature at which the student tested the leaf disks might have been too cold.

(b) The light might have been too far away from the test tubes the student used.

(c) If the student tested pH 2, pH 7, and pH 12, the optimum pH might have been pH 5 and the enzymes might have denatured at pH 7.

(d) The leaf disks might have dried out before they were used.

(e) The student might have forgotten to add the sodium bicarbonate to the solution.

(f) The student might have damaged the leaf disks when evacuating gases to make the disks sink.

LABORATORY 5: BACTERIAL TRANSFORMATION

BIG IDEA 3

OVERVIEW

In this investigation, students perform the techniques used to genetically engineer bacterial cells to have a gene for a specific trait that is new to them. *Escherichia coli* bacteria are made "competent" by being put in an environment that contains calcium chloride and then briefly "heat shocked" by being put at a temperature much hotter than the human colon, their usual habitat. Under this stress, the frequency at which they transform, or absorb DNA from their environment, increases, and multiple bacteria from the culture absorb plasmids. The plasmids contain a gene for antibiotic resistance. This can be the desired trait, or the plasmid might also contain a gene that confers to a colony a trait that can be visually detected, such as a certain color. The antibiotic resistance is the primary means of selecting for transformed cells. The presence of the color can be a double-checking indicator that transformation has occurred. Transformation efficiency can be calculated based on the number of transformed colonies that grow as compared to the estimated amounts of bacteria and plasmid that were combined and then spread on the culture plate.

A second component of this investigation asks students to apply a mutagen, such as ultraviolet radiation, to a bacterial culture and find evidence of a resulting mutation. The student then goes on to determine whether another environmental factor is mutagenic.

OBJECTIVES

After doing this laboratory you should be able to:

■ Explain the principles of bacterial transformation and its importance in bacterial evolution.
■ Explain how plasmid vectors are used to transfer genes.
■ Explain how antibiotic resistance is transferred between cells.
■ Explain how protein synthesis differs between prokaryotes and eukaryotes and how this affects the process used to genetically engineer bacteria to produce human proteins.

191

■ Explain the function of certain enzymes, especially reverse transcriptase, restriction endonucleases, and DNA ligase, which are used to make recombinant plasmids.

■ Explain what a mutagen is and how mutations are related to natural selection and evolution.

■ Design an investigation to determine whether an environmental factor can act as a mutagen.

Questions

1. As some restriction enzymes cut DNA, they cut directly across the two strands of DNA. Others cut between nucleotides at positions that are slightly askew, resulting in "sticky ends," with several unmatched nucleotides on one strand on each side of the cut. Why are restriction enzymes that produce blunt, rather than "sticky," ends of DNA not used for making recombinant DNA plasmids?

2. During the transformation process used in this investigation, plasmids with a gene for antibiotic resistance are used as a way to artificially select for the desired bacteria. How does this same process result in multiple drug resistant strains of bacteria in hospitals and other settings?

3. Calculate the transformation efficiency using the information and results provided below. Transformation efficiency is the number of antibiotic resistant colonies per microgram of plasmid used.
    ■ 0.12 ug/ul DNA plasmid concentration
    ■ 250 uL CaCl$_2$ transformation solution
    ■ 10 uL ampicillin resistance plasmid solution
    ■ 250 uL LB broth
    ■ 150 uL cell solution spread on agar
    ■ 85 colonies of transformed cells

4. Explain the use of reverse transcriptase by biologists who engineered bacteria that would make human insulin.

Answers

1. The purpose of using restriction enzymes that produce "sticky ends" in making recombinant plasmids is that these ends are capable of forming hydrogen bonds with other pieces of DNA that were cut with the same restriction enzyme. Then, DNA ligase can form more permanent phosphodiester bonds between the sugars and phosphates that make up the DNA "backbone." If the DNA is cut to form blunt ends, the resulting strands are more likely to remain separate, rather than recombining; no attractive hydrogen bonds form between the strands.

2. Bacterial transformation is a naturally occurring process of which biologists have taken advantage for the purposes of genetic engineering. Experimental work which led to the knowledge that DNA was the hereditary material included the discovery of bacterial transformation that changed a harmless, "rough" strain into a deadly "smooth" strain when the "rough" bacteria absorbed DNA from dead "smooth" bacteria in their environment. In a hospital environment, when patients are given antibiotics, bacteria that are not killed not only survive, but can get DNA from other

bacteria via transformation (or via transduction or conjugation, as discussed in Chapter 5). Thus, not only does the use of antibiotics select for antibiotic resistance, but also the capacity of bacteria to transform allows those surviving exposure to antibiotic "A" to absorb DNA from others that were killed by "A," but were resistant to antibiotic "B." These survivors and their descendants, as a result, can be resistant to multiple antibiotics.

3. The transformation efficiency is approximately 240 cells/ug of plasmid. 1.2 ug of plasmid DNA was used to transform the cells (0.12 ug/uL × 10 uL). Only 30% of the transformed cells were applied to the agar (150 uL of the 250 uL $CaCl_2$ solution combined with the 250 uL of LB broth). Thus, 0.36 ug of plasmid DNA should have been in cells applied to the agar. 85 colonies resulted from transformed cells, at an efficiency of 85 colonies (cells)/0.36 ug of plasmid DNA.

4. Nuclear genes of humans and other eukaryotes code for introns, segments of messenger RNA that are removed by enzymes before the mRNA leaves the nucleus so translation can occur. Prokaryotic (and eukaryotic mitochondrial) DNA does not code for introns. If the intron-coding segments of genes are transferred into bacteria, the resulting protein would have a different structure and would not function properly. Thus, biologists use cDNA, or DNA that is made from cytoplasmic messenger RNA through the use of the enzyme reverse transcriptase. This enzyme is found naturally in retroviruses and makes DNA from RNA. Because the cDNA is made using messenger RNA from the eukaryotic cytoplasm, it will not contain DNA that codes for introns.

LABORATORY 6: RESTRICTION ENZYME ANALYSIS

BIG IDEA 3

OVERVIEW

This investigation involves techniques used to fragment DNA and to separate the fragments by size. These techniques have been applicable not only to basic research, such as the Human Genome Project, but also to practical uses such as forensic DNA fingerprinting. Restriction enzymes (enzymes that cut DNA at specific nucleotide sequences) are applied to the DNA sample. Then, gel electrophoresis separates those fragments, with smaller fragments traveling further within an agarose gel (away from the negative electrode) than larger fragments. When a stain is applied, the DNA becomes visible as bands, for which distances can be measured from the well into which the DNA was placed. These distances can be compared to the distances traversed by DNA fragments of known size, and thus the sizes of unknown fragments can be interpolated.

OBJECTIVES

After doing this laboratory you should be able to:

- Explain how gel electrophoresis separates DNA molecules.
- Explain how restriction enzymes are used to create DNA fragments.
- Explain why the same DNA samples cut by different restriction enzymes or different DNA samples cut by the same restriction enzyme result in distinctly different patterns or "fingerprints."
- Determine the approximate sizes of DNA fragments by comparing their "fingerprint" to that made by DNA fragments of known size.
- Evaluate a DNA fingerprint to determine whether two samples could be from the same source.
- Explain the practical applications of gel electrophoresis and restriction enzymes.

194

QUESTIONS

1. The restriction enzyme EcoRI is applied to a sample of a specific plasmid. The restriction enzyme HindIII is then applied to a second sample of the same plasmid. Finally, the two restriction enzymes are both applied to a third sample of that plasmid. The digested plasmid samples are put into three separate wells of the same gel and undergo electrophoresis. What is the expected result if the plasmid has four recognition sites for EcoRI and two recognition sites for HindIII?

2. A student digests some DNA from a certain plasmid using three separate restriction enzymes that she has never before used on this plasmid. Then she uses gel electrophoresis to separate the DNA. When she applies the stain to the gel, she is surprised that she cannot see any distinct bands. She concludes that the restriction enzymes did not find any binding sites on the plasmid. Evaluate the validity of her conclusion.

3. How might restriction enzyme analysis be used to determine whether two men with the last name of Darwin are actually related to each other and to Charles Darwin?

4. A segment of DNA known to be 852 base pairs in length travels 3.6 cm during gel electrophoresis. A second segment that is 12,342 base pairs in length travels 1.2 cm during gel electrophoresis. A third fragment, of unknown size, travels 2.8 cm on the same gel. How might the size of this third be estimated?

ANSWERS

1. The EcoRI sample is expected to separate into four distinct bands. The HindIII sample is expected to separate into two distinct bands. Plasmids are small looped pieces of DNA, so the first cut will create one linear piece of DNA. A second cut will split this DNA into two pieces; a third cut will split one of those to form three pieces; and a fourth cut will, likewise, result in four pieces. The sample to which both enzymes were applied is expected to separate into six pieces because different enzymes will not have the same recognition sites and each enzyme will cut at its unique sequence. The relative locations of the sequences will determine the end results. Two possible outcomes exist:

   Case A: If the HindIII sites are between the same two EcoRI sites, three pieces of DNA will be the same as they were for EcoRI and will form similar bands, and the other three bands will be smaller than (and will travel further than) the fourth EcoRI alone band (see Figure 1 on the next page).

   Case B: If the HindIII sites are not between the same two EcoRI sites, two pieces of DNA will be the same as they were for EcoRI and will form similar bands. The other four bands will be two pairs that are smaller than (and will travel further than) the third and fourth EcoRI alone bands (see Figure 1 on next page).

Figure 1: Example of Gel Electrophoresis of Plasmid DNA cut by EcoRI and HindIII

| EcoRI Well | HindIII Well | EcoRI + HindIII Well (Case A) | EcoRI + HindIII Well (Case B) |

Note: Bands in Case A and Case B wells that are the same as EcoRI are marked with *.

2. If the student did not see any bands at all, she should not draw the conclusion that the enzymes were ineffective. If an enzyme did not make any cut, there should be a single band visible close to the well. Because of the phosphate groups, there are still negative charges that would cause the plasmid DNA to travel through the gel, but they would not be likely to travel far. However, if the gel was run for too long at a high voltage, the DNA could have traveled off the end of the gel so it was not visible. Similarly, if the electrodes were attached to the gel in reverse, the DNA could have traveled off the gel in the opposite direction of what would be expected. The wells are often located closer to one end of the gel, so this might have taken less distance and time to occur.

3. To determine the relatedness among males in a paternal line, one could apply restriction enzyme analysis to samples of the Y chromosome of the men. In this case, DNA samples should be obtained from both men as well as a living descendant of Charles Darwin who traces his ancestry to Darwin paternally for all generations. If the Y chromosome DNA from all three men is digested using the same restriction enzyme (or same combination of restriction enzymes) and the DNA fragments are separated using gel electrophoresis, then the resulting pattern of fragments, or fingerprints, can be compared. If either man is related paternally to Charles Darwin, his fingerprint should be the same as or very similar to Charles Darwin's known descendant's fingerprint (perhaps not identical if any mutations have occurred in the past several generations). If the fingerprints are the same, however, it is also possible that Charles Darwin is not the man's ancestor, but that both he and Charles Darwin share a common ancestor. If either man is unrelated to Charles Darwin, then his DNA fingerprint should be significantly different from Darwin's descendant's.

4. The fragments should be graphed using semi-log graph paper because they travel through the DNA at a rate that is inverse exponentially related to their size. Larger fragments are impeded by the agarose gel and do not travel very far in comparison to smaller fragments. When graphed on semi-log graph paper, the relationship between fragment length and distance is linear. A line can be drawn to connect the graphed points for the known fragments. Then, that line can be used to determine the approximate length of the third fragment based on the distance it traveled.

LABORATORY 7: TRANSPIRATION

BIG IDEA 4

OVERVIEW

This laboratory applies the concepts of diffusion and osmosis to the movement of water in a plant. The effect of environmental factors on transpiration rate is investigated, and possible adaptations plants have to minimize water loss explored. Based on the number and position of stomata, conclusions can be made about where plants live and the process of transpiration.

OBJECTIVES

After doing this laboratory you should be able to:

■ Design and carry out a controlled experiment that tests the effects of environmental conditions on the rate of transpiration.

■ Explain how different plants use adaptations to prevent excess water loss.

■ Apply the concept of water potential to guttation and transpiration, explaining how water moves from the roots to leaves.

■ Explain the importance of the characteristic properties of water to processes such as transpiration.

QUESTIONS

1. Form a hypothesis about the relationship of the following environmental conditions to the transpiration rate in plants.
   (a) Humid conditions
   (b) High light conditions
   (c) Very dry or windy conditions

2. Create a graph displaying the amount of transpiration and time with relations to the above variables.

3. Explain the role of water potential in the movement of water from soil through the plant and into the air.

4. What is the advantage of closed stomata to a plant when water is in short supply? What are the disadvantages?

ANSWERS

1. (a) In humid conditions, there is a decrease in the water potential gradient between the air leaf spaces and the surrounding air.

(b) In high light conditions, there is a decrease of water potential due to increased evaporation rates and an increase in transpiration rate due to an increase in photosynthesis.

(c) In very dry conditions, there is a decrease of water potential; therefore the rate of transpiration is increased.

2. The y-axis of the graph should be labeled with the dependent variable, water loss in mL/m^2. The x-axis should be labeled with time. The lines on the graph should indicate that the plant in the humid environment has the lowest rate of respiration or the lowest slope, where the plants in the light and dry/windy environment have a higher rate of respiration or a higher slope.

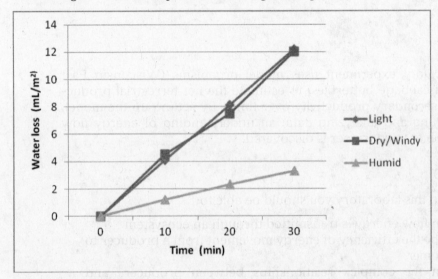

3. Water always moves from an area of high water potential (or high water concentration) to an area of low water potential (or low water concentration). In general, the water potential outside the roots is initially higher than the water potential in the root, and the water potential outside the leaf is lower than in the leaf. Therefore, as water enters the root through osmosis, the fluid in the plant is forced up due to increased positive pressure in the roots. At that point, evaporation at the leaf surface takes over, creating tension (negative pressure) which pulls the water up the xylem. The pull on the water is possible due to cohesion and adhesion. As water moves through the mesophyll cells by osmosis, it continues to move from areas of higher water potential to lower water potential until it reaches the air at the leaf's surface.

4. The advantage of closing stomata is it prevents water vapor from escaping. When the stomata of a plant are closed gas exchange cannot occur therefore limiting the rate of photosynthesis. This is a disadvantage to a plant as photosynthesis is the process by which plants make glucose. Without photosynthesis occurring, plants do not have enough glucose for cellular respiration to make the ATP necessary for growth and survival.

LABORATORY 8:
ENERGY DYNAMICS

BIG IDEA 4

OVERVIEW

This laboratory experiment uses model organisms (Wisconsin Fast Plants and cabbage butterflies) to estimate the net terrestrial productivity and secondary productivity over time. By setting up the model, and collecting and analyzing data, an understanding of energy flow from producer to consumer is discovered.

OBJECTIVES

After doing this laboratory you should be able to:

- Explain how energy is transmitted through an ecosystem.
- Describe the efficiency of energy movement from a producer to a consumer.
- Explain the complex relationships between producers and primary consumers.
- Use the terms autotroph, heterotroph, and decomposer to describe producers and consumers.
- Design and carry out an experiment based on personal research questions.

QUESTIONS

Use the following figure to answer questions 1–3.

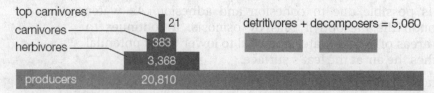

Energy pyramid for the Silver Springs ecosystem. The width of each tier in the pyramid represents the amount of energy that enters each trophic level annually, as shown in detail below.

1. This figure shows an energy pyramid from the Silver Springs ecosystem. Explain what each step represents and what happens as energy flows through an ecosystem.

2. When energy is transferred from one trophic level to the next, not all the energy moves through the ecosystem. Give 3 reasons why this is true.

3. Refer to the figure. What percent of energy is transferred from producers to the top carnivores?

4. Students in a biology class did an experiment to test the percentage of energy transferred from milkweed leaves to monarch butterfly larvae over a one-week period. Students massed the container with the leaves and larva every day and recorded the change in mass over the week period. What would be the control for this experiment? What variables would students need to make sure are held constant? What data calculation should be done in order to draw conclusions from the experiment?

ANSWERS

1. An energy pyramid illustrates how the amount of usable energy decreases as it is transferred through an ecosystem. The largest tier is always at the bottom, and the tiers decrease until the smallest amount of energy is available for the top consumer. This figure shows that producers or plants represent the most energy of the ecosystem. This is because plants are autotrophs and make their own food, using the process of photosynthesis. Producers set the energy level for an ecosystem. In this example the producers make 20,810 kcal of energy while only 3,368 kcal move to the primary consumers or herbivores. Only 383 kcal are available to secondary consumers or carnivores and only 21 kcal for the top carnivore.

2. The first reason is not all energy harvested by consumers is used to build biomass. Second, some of the energy is lost as heat during transfer. Third, few consumers specifically herbivores cannot digest cellulose.

3. $(21/20,810) \times 100 = 0.100\%$

4. The controlled experiment would be leaves with no monarch larva. The control must have everything remain constant except the presence of monarch larva. Variables that should remain constant in both the control and experimental setup include the container used, procedure for massing, time of day mass is taken, and environmental conditions of the room. To calculate the percentage efficiency, divide the mass of the larva and leaves at the end of 7 days from the mass of larva and leaves on day 0. The same calculation should be done for the control in order to draw conclusions about the amount of energy transferred.

Part IV
Practice Tests

Practice Test 1

AP BIOLOGY EXAMINATION
Section I: Multiple-Choice and Grid-In Questions
Time—90 minutes
Number of Questions—63 MC and 6 GI

This practice test will give you some indication of how you might score on the multiple-choice portion as well as the free-response portion of the AP Biology exam. Of course, the exam changes every year, so it is never possible to predict a student's score with certainty. This test will also pinpoint strengths and weaknesses on the key content areas covered by the exam.

DIRECTIONS Each of the questions or incomplete statements of this portion of the exam is followed by four possible answers or suggestions. Choose the single response that best answers the question or completes the statement. There is no penalty for guessing. Simple four-function calculators may be used on this portion of the exam. Use the Equations and Formulas guide as needed for selecting the proper equation or formula to solve the Grid-In Questions.

MULTIPLE-CHOICE QUESTIONS

1. Which functional group gives amino acids and fatty acids their acidic behavior?
   (A) amine
   (B) carbonyl
   (C) carboxyl
   (D) hydroxyl

2. The result of fertilization is a diploid zygote. What is the result of meiosis in plants?
   (A) somatic cells
   (B) two diploid cells
   (C) four haploid cells
   (D) brain cells

3. In Ligers (the hybrid of a lion and tiger) the hybrid has reduced fitness. Which of the following explains this process?
   (A) hybrid breakdown
   (B) mechanical
   (C) behavioral
   (D) reduced hybrid viability

4. A female bird does not recognize the song of a male bird species. This is the result of what type of reproductive isolation?
   (A) temporal
   (B) mechanical
   (C) behavioral
   (D) ecological

5. Which of the following is the most important property of the water in a pond during prolonged freezing conditions?
   (A) The surface tension is increased, allowing larger invertebrates to skim on the surface.
   (B) Its density decreases as it freezes.
   (C) It becomes more neutral.
   (D) Its capacity to hold dissolved oxygen increases.

6. The most recent common ancestor for all animals, if alive today, would belong to which of the following groups?
   (A) bacteria
   (B) plants
   (C) protists
   (D) fungi

7. Water moves through a plant due to all of the following EXCEPT
   (A) cohesion.
   (B) evaporation at the leaf surface.
   (C) adhesion.
   (D) exocytosis.

GO ON TO NEXT PAGE
205

8. A kidney is made up of many nephrons across the membrane of which many substances move. Which of the following substances is incorrectly matched with the type of transport with which it would move into or out of a nephron?
(A) salt – active transport
(B) glucose – facilitated diffusion
(C) water – osmosis
(D) antibody – diffusion

9. Enzymes are affected by all of the following environmental conditions EXCEPT
(A) increased temperature.
(B) decreased pH.
(C) salt concentration.
(D) oxygen concentration.

10. Which of the following mechanisms controls the cell cycle?
(A) interphase and mitosis
(B) cycling and cyclin-dependent kinases
(C) homologous chromosomes
(D) independent assortment

11. When chimpanzees use sticks to extract termites from a nest, their behavior is best described as
(A) gene flow.
(B) learned by imitation.
(C) courtship.
(D) regulated by the release of hormones.

12. In photosynthesis, the products of _____ are directly used in _____.
(A) glycolysis; the Calvin cycle
(B) the light reactions; the Calvin cycle
(C) the Calvin cycle; light reactions
(D) the Calvin cycle; glycolysis

13. A population is defined as a
(A) group of individuals of the same species living in the same geographic area.
(B) group of many species living in the same geographic area.
(C) group of individuals of the same species living in different geographic areas.
(D) group of individuals of the same species which are extinct.

14. All of the following are properties of amino acid side groups (R-group) EXCEPT
(A) polar.
(B) nonpolar.
(C) peptide bond.
(D) acidic.

15. Which of the following is not associated with meiosis?
(A) gametes
(B) crossing over
(C) replication
(D) tetrad

16. An allele is considered dominant if
(A) its effects mask the expression of the allele with which it is paired.
(B) it amplifies the expression of the allele with which it is paired.
(C) it has no effect on the allele with which it is paired.
(D) its effects are masked by the allele with which it is paired.

17. Because the Geologic Record shows that rust did not form on rocks until much later in Earth's history, it can be assumed that
(A) oxygen was present in earth's early atmosphere.
(B) iron particles were present in earth's early atmosphere.
(C) oxygen was not present in earth's early atmosphere.
(D) iron particles were not present in earth's early atmosphere.

18. In humans, all of the following are true EXCEPT
(A) A body cell has 23 homologous pairs of chromosomes.
(B) Gender is determined by X and Y chromosomes.
(C) An egg cell has 23 chromosomes.
(D) Human females are XY and males are XX.

Use the following answer options for Questions 19–21. Match the structures of the cell with the correct description/function.
(A) cristae of mitochondria
(B) Golgi body
(C) smooth endoplasmic reticulum
(D) lysosome

19. contains hydrolytic enzymes

20. contains enzymes important to the production of ATP

21. synthesizes lipids

22. The rejection of a transplanted heart can be caused by which part of the cell membrane?
(A) recognition proteins
(B) cholesterol
(C) channel proteins
(D) receptor proteins

23. All of the following are members of a community EXCEPT
(A) pH of the soil.
(B) population.
(C) bacteria.
(D) primary consumers.

Use the following terms to answer Questions 24–26. Terms may be used once, more than once, or not at all.
(A) $C_{12}H_{22}O_{11}$
(B) NH_2CH_2COOH
(C) $CH_3(CH_2)_{16}COOH$
(D) glycerol

24. This molecule is the backbone of common animal fats holding the other components together.

25. This molecule is considered saturated because of its single carbon-carbon bonds.

26. This molecule could form a peptide bond with a similar molecule.

27. In meiosis, if each daughter cell has six chromosomes, how many sister chromatids would be present at the start of meiosis?
(A) 3
(B) 6
(C) 12
(D) 24

Questions 28–30 refer to the diagram below. An ether-based solvent was used to separate the pigments from a spinach leaf. After 30 minutes, four colored bands appeared.

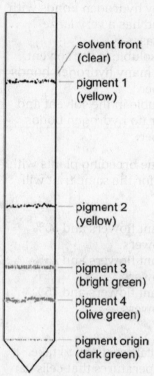

solvent front (clear)

pigment 1 (yellow)

pigment 2 (yellow)

pigment 3 (bright green)

pigment 4 (olive green)

pigment origin (dark green)

28. Chlorophylls a and b would be represented by
(A) pigments 1 and 2.
(B) pigments 3 and 4.
(C) pigments 1 and 4.
(D) pigment 3 only.

29. Using the following formula:

Rf = Distance pigment migrated/ Distance of solvent

The pigment with the largest Rf value would be
(A) pigment 1.
(B) pigment 2.
(C) pigment 3.
(D) pigment 4.

GO ON TO NEXT PAGE

30. What factors had the greatest influence on the migration of pigment 1?
    (A) It is very soluble in the solvent and has a very large molecular mass.
    (B) It forms many hydrogen bonds with the paper and has a very large molecular mass.
    (C) It is slightly soluble in the solvent, and it forms many hydrogen bonds with the paper.
    (D) It is very soluble in the solvent and forms few or no hydrogen bonds with the paper.

31. Crossing two true breeding plants with different alleles for the same trait will produce
    (A) all hybrids.
    (B) 50% dominant flowers and 50% recessive flowers.
    (C) 75% dominant flowers and 25% recessive flowers.
    (D) 25% dominant flowers and 75% recessive flowers.

32. Enzymes
    (A) allow chemical reactions to take place at temperatures that cells can tolerate.
    (B) will only lower the activation energy of an exergonic reaction.
    (C) are usually composed of RNA.
    (D) will only be used as an energy source in an endergonic reaction.

33. The most accurate description of an organism with AABB genotype is
    (A) heterozygous.
    (B) homozygous recessive.
    (C) homozygous dominant.
    (D) a hybrid.

34. Which is NOT a correct match between stimulus and ion movement?
    (A) Arrival of an action potential at a synapse—calcium ions move into the neuron.
    (B) Arrival of an action potential along the axon—sodium ions move out of the neuron.
    (C) ATP triggers the sodium-potassium pump—sodium ions are pumped out of the cell.
    (D) An action potential reaches a muscle fiber and causes a cellular response.

35. Which of the following will occur if potato slices are placed in a hypertonic solution?
    (A) Water leaves the cell in order to reach equilibrium.
    (B) Water enters the cell in order to reach equilibrium.
    (C) Salt enters the cell in order to reach equilibrium.
    (D) Salt leaves the cell in order to reach equilibrium.

36. Which of the following is a process that can involve the products of the endomembrane system?
    (A) plasmolysis
    (B) exocytosis
    (C) turgor pressure
    (D) phagocytosis

37. An organism's cell is heterozygous (Aa) for one trait. If that cell undergoes meiosis to form gametes, which of the following are possible?
    (A) only A gametes
    (B) both A and a gametes in equal proportion
    (C) only a gametes
    (D) three A gametes for every one a gamete

38. Which of the following processes does not potentially lead to an increase in genetic variation?
    (A) conjugation
    (B) transduction
    (C) transposition
    (D) translation

39. Regarding early Earth, an increase in atmospheric oxygen was the result of
    (A) anaerobic metabolism.
    (B) photosynthesis.
    (C) glycolysis.
    (D) fermentation.

40. Plants and insects have an intricate relationship where each species is a selective agent for traits of the other. The honeybee would have the greatest impact on which of the following traits in plants?
(A) fertilization
(B) pollination
(C) sporophyte formation
(D) endosperm formation

41. Which trophic level of a food web would best be represented by a carnivorous insect such as a praying mantis?
(A) primary producer
(B) decomposer
(C) secondary consumer
(D) primary consumer

Use the following terms to answer Questions 42–44. Terms may be used once, more than once, or not at all.
(A) Krebs cycle
(B) Calvin cycle
(C) electron transfer phosphorylation
(D) glycolysis

42. Carbon dioxide is released as a result of this stage.

43. This is the first stage of fermentation.

44. This process forms four ATP per glucose molecule, through substrate-level phosphorylation.

45. In a family of four children, all with the same father but two different mothers, the two children from Mother 1 are normal and the children from Mother 2 have a genetic disorder. If the father is normal, which of the following is a possible explanation of the inheritance of the disorder?
(A) The defective gene must be on the Y chromosome.
(B) The defective gene is recessive and must be on the X chromosome.
(C) The defective gene is in the mitochondrial DNA of the father.
(D) The defective gene is in the mitochondrial DNA of Mother 2.

46. Estrogen is released from the anterior pituitary gland in the brain, but acts on target cells in the ovaries. This is best explained as
(A) an endocrine signal that travels a long distance through the blood.
(B) a signal pathway that travels a long distance through the nervous system.
(C) an immune pathway that travels a long distance through the blood.
(D) a method of cell communication used by cells with direct contact.

47. Which of the following is an example of a density independent factor?
(A) wildfire
(B) disease
(C) predators
(D) parasites

48. In photosynthesis, light reactions
(A) occur in the stroma.
(B) occur in the thylakoid membrane.
(C) provide oxygen to build sugars in the Calvin-Benson cycle.
(D) receive electrons from the electron transport chain.

49. Which sequence of mRNA would result from the transcription of the following sequence ATCGAT?
(A) UACGUA
(B) TAGCTA
(C) ATCGAT
(D) UAGCUA

50. Mike takes good care of his favorite plant. He keeps it in the sun, fertilizes it every few months, and waters it three times a week. Why is Mike's plant dying?
(A) It is a plant that lives in the dark only.
(B) It needs bacteria to be added to the soil in order for roots to absorb the water.
(C) It is not getting enough sodium and should be given sodium in the water every day.
(D) It is being overwatered and the roots are rotting.

GO ON TO NEXT PAGE

51. Sea stars are a predator found off the coast in California. They eat barnacles and mussels. When they are removed from an ecosystem, the diversity of invertebrates drastically decreases. When sea stars are present, the diversity greatly increases. What term is used to describe sea stars in this example?
    (A) keystone species
    (B) indicator species
    (C) exotic species
    (D) invasive species

52. The function of tRNA is
    (A) to copy sections of DNA.
    (B) to unwind DNA for replication.
    (C) to assemble fatty acids in the correct order.
    (D) to deliver the correct amino acid to the ribosome.

53. Which of the following is NOT a possible result of a mutation in an animal cell's DNA?
    (A) neutral mutation
    (B) positive or beneficial mutation
    (C) negative or detrimental mutation
    (D) resistance mutations

54. Enzymes
    (A) are unaffected by pH.
    (B) are used up in the reaction that they catalyze.
    (C) can have an active site that isn't functional.
    (D) can be composed of lipids.

55.

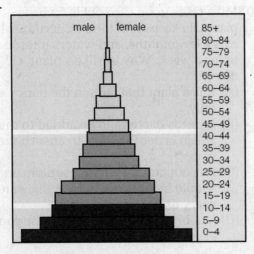

The age structure shown in the graphic is representative of a
    (A) population showing zero growth.
    (B) population showing rapid decline.
    (C) population showing a slow decline.
    (D) population showing an increase.

56. How are bacteria and viruses different?
    (A) Bacteria have a nucleus and viruses do not.
    (B) All bacteria use DNA as the genetic material and all viruses use RNA.
    (C) Bacteria have protein but viruses do not.
    (D) Bacteria are cells and viruses are not.

57. The following all contain DNA EXCEPT
    (A) plasmids.
    (B) nuclei.
    (C) pili.
    (D) mitochondria.

58. After transcription of eukaryotic DNA,
    (A) mRNA leaves the nucleus and moves to the cell membrane.
    (B) introns are snipped out.
    (C) introns are translated.
    (D) exons and introns are translated separately.

59. If all of the hydrogen bonds in a DNA molecule were to break,
    (A) the phosphate groups would break away from the nitrogenous bases.
    (B) the phosphate groups would break away from deoxyribose.
    (C) the strands of DNA would break away from each other.
    (D) the nucleotides would destabilize.

60. A single cell in a person's brain has become cancerous. It doubles its DNA and divides much faster than a normal brain cell. The most likely change that would have caused this condition took place in the
    (A) nucleus.
    (B) lysosome.
    (C) microtubule.
    (D) mitochondria.

61. The interaction between populations where one species is harmed and the other is benefited is termed
    (A) commensalism.
    (B) parasitism.
    (C) competition.
    (D) mutualism.

62. Humoral immunity is triggered by
    (A) antibodies.
    (B) cytokines.
    (C) histamines.
    (D) antigens.

63. Genetic diversity within a species is important for which of the following reasons?
    (A) It allows species to adapt to changing environments.
    (B) It allows populations to migrate to new geographic locations.
    (C) It allows weaker organisms to go extinct.
    (D) It allows environmental factors to have no impact on a population.

GRID-IN QUESTIONS

Note: All answers should use correct significant digits.

1. In a population of 1,000 moths, 160 show the homozygous recessive trait of white wings. The rest display the dominant trait of gray wings. How many moths will be heterozygous gray?

2. Scientists are trying to determine under what conditions a plant can survive. They collect the following data and would like to know the water potential of the plant cell. The solute potential is –0.6 MPa and the pressure potential is –1.0 MPa. What is the water potential?

3. There are 2,000 mice living in a field. If 1,000 mice are born each month and 200 mice die each month, what is the per capita growth rate of mice over a month?

4. If the half life of an isotope is 8 hours, how much of a 100g sample would remain after 1 day?

5. The following data were collected from a population of Drosophila (fruit flies).

Phenotype	# of Flies Observed
Red eyes	134
White eyes	66

In this monohybrid genetic cross where red eyes are dominant to white, determine the chi square value (to two significant digits).

6. Grasshoppers in Madagascar show variation in their back-leg length. Given the following data, determine the standard deviation.

Length in cm
2.0
2.2
2.2
2.1
2.0
2.4
2.5

STOP
END OF SECTION I

IF YOU FINISH BEFORE TIME IS CALLED, YOU MAY CHECK YOUR WORK ON THIS SECTION. DO NOT GO ON TO SECTION II UNTIL YOU ARE TOLD TO DO SO.

GO ON TO NEXT PAGE

AP BIOLOGY EXAMINATION
SECTION II: Free-Response Essays
Suggested Writing Time—80 minutes
Number of Questions—2 MP and 6 SP

DIRECTIONS This section begins with a 10-minute reading period to allow you to read the questions. You may take notes, but you cannot begin your final response until this period is over. You will then have 80 minutes to answer the following questions. You can continue planning and organizing your response, but this time will come out of your 80 minutes. Answers must be in essay form. Outline form is unacceptable. Diagrams with labels may be used to supplement your answer. Diagrams alone, however, are inadequate. Unless the directions indicate otherwise, respond to all parts of each question. It is recommended that you take a few minutes to plan and outline each answer. Spend approximately 20–25 minutes per multi-part question and 3–10 minutes per single-part question. Support your essay with specific examples where appropriate. Be sure to number each of your answers. If a question has multiple parts, make sure the answer to each part is clearly labeled.

MULTI-PART QUESTIONS

1. Water potential is the tendency of water to move from one place to another. Pumpkin cores were placed in sucrose solutions at 22°C and normal atmospheric pressure. The following data were gathered.

Individual Data for Pumpkin Cores				
Contents in Beakers	Initial Mass	Final Mass	Mass Difference	% Change in Mass
Water	29.15	32.12		
0.2 M Sucrose	28.45	29.41		
0.4 M Sucrose	30.92	29.84		
0.6 M Sucrose	29.25	27.14		
0.8 M Sucrose	32.09	28.54		
1.0 M Sucrose	31.67	27.58		

(a) Complete the above table.
(b) Graph the percent change in mass. Label both the X and Y axes.

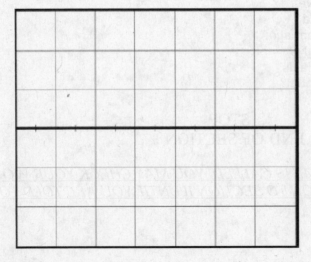

(c) Explain how you determined the value for the molar concentration of the pumpkin cells. Explain how the molar concentration value is related to pressure potential.

2. Chromosomes pass genetic information from one cell to another in cell generation.
   (a) Discuss the relationship between DNA, genes, and chromosomes.
   (b) What is a nondisjunction event?

SINGLE-PART QUESTIONS

1. The Hardy-Weinberg equation can be used to determine if a population is evolving and what is driving that evolution. State and explain three of the five conditions of Hardy-Weinberg equilibrium.

2 What is different between commensalism and mutualism?

3. Describe the structure and function of the cell membrane.

4. Explain, using one example of your choice, how negative feedback works to maintain homeostasis.

5. In a population of sociable weavers (small birds that live in the African savanna) body weight was recorded for 977 birds and graphed below. What conclusion can be drawn about the type of selection weavers undergo?

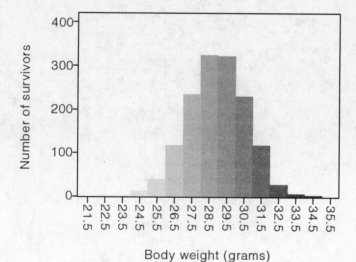

Body weight (grams)

GO ON TO NEXT PAGE

6.

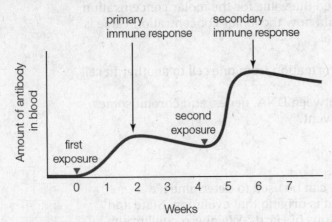

Explain the graph. What does the graph represent?

END OF EXAMINATION

ANSWERS FOR SECTION I

MULTIPLE-CHOICE ANSWER KEY

SCORING Using the table below, score the multiple-choice portion of the test. Correct answers earn points, while incorrect answers are not penalized. A greater number of correct answers would be associated with higher exam scores. You will find explanations of the answers below and on the following pages.

1. C	14. C	27. C	40. B	53. D
2. C	15. C	28. B	41. C	54. C
3. D	16. A	29. A	42. A	55. D
4. C	17. C	30. D	43. D	56. D
5. B	18. D	31. A	44. D	57. C
6. C	19. D	32. A	45. D	58. B
7. D	20. A	33. C	46. A	59. C
8. D	21. C	34. B	47. A	60. A
9. D	22. A	35. A	48. B	61. B
10. B	23. A	36. B	49. D	62. D
11. B	24. D	37. B	50. D	63. A
12. B	25. C	38. D	51. A	
13. A	26. B	39. B	52. D	

EXPLANATIONS FOR THE MULTIPLE-CHOICE ANSWERS

1. **C.** The carboxyl (COOH) functional group is easily ionized in water and releases an H^+ (*Biology*, 12th ed., page 38/13th ed., page 41).

2. **C.** Mitosis is the process of making two genetically identical diploid somatic cells. Meiosis is the process of making four genetically different haploid gametes (*Biology*, 12th ed., pages 164–165/13th ed., pages 198–199).

3. **D.** In reduced hybrid viability, the offspring often have reduced fitness and more health problems, leading to a shorter life expectancy (*Biology*, 12th ed., pages 290–291/13th ed., pages 285–285).

4. **C.** Behavioral isolation occurs when courtship rituals are no longer recognized (*Biology*, 12th ed., pages 290–291/13th ed., pages 284–285).

5. **B.** Although dissolved oxygen is an important commodity to aerobic organisms, it is useless if the pond freezes. By floating to the top, ice insulates the pond, preventing it from freezing solid (*Biology*, 12th ed., page 28/13th ed., pages 30–31).

6. **C.** While bacteria were the first organisms on Earth and cyanobacteria one of the first photosynthetic organisms, both are prokaryotic. Plants are eukaryotic but autotrophs (photosynthetic). Protists are eukaryotic and can be heterotropic, both of which are characteristics of animals (*Biology*, 12th ed., pages 351–353/13th ed., page 355).

7. **D.** Evaporation at the leaf surface causes tension that pulls the water through the plant. Cohesion allows the water molecules to stick together, and adhesion allows water to stick to the sides of the xylem. Therefore, they all work together in moving water through a plant (*Biology*, 12th ed., pages 498–499/13th ed., pages 476–477).

8. **D.** An antibody is a protein consisting of four polypeptide chains. Its large size makes it unable to cross a membrane through diffusion (*Biology*, 12th ed., pages 84–89/13th ed., pages 92–93).

9. **D.** Enzymes are influenced by temperature, pH, and salt concentrations (*Biology*, 12th ed., pages 98–99/13th ed., pages 82–83).

10. **B.** Cyclins and cyclin-dependent kinases are used to regulate the cell cycle. The concentration of these proteins determines if the cell cycle continues or is terminated (*Biology*, 12th ed., pages 150–151/13th ed., pages 184–185).

11. **B.** This behavior is learned by imitation (*Biology*, 12th ed., page 791/13th ed., page 777).

12. **B.** The products ATP and NADPH made in the light reactions directly enter the Calvin cycle in order to make sugar (*Biology*, 12th ed., page 111/13th ed., page 105).

13. **A.** A population is a group of individuals of the same species living in the same geographic area. This is the smallest unit that can undergo evolution (*Biology*, 12th ed., page 278/13th ed., page 272).

14. **C.** Peptide bonds occur between a nitrogen and carbon of the adjoined amino acids in a polypeptide chain. They are not part of side groups (*Biology*, 12th ed., page 45 and Appendix V/13th ed., page 46).

15. **C.** During prophase I in meiosis, crossing over occurs, which is the exchange of genetic material between homologous chromosomes. The paired set of homologous chromosomes is a tetrad. The end result of meiosis is four haploid gametes (*Biology*, 12th ed., pages 160–161/13th ed., pages 198–199).

16. **A.** When paired with a recessive gene, a dominant gene will be expressed while the recessive gene is masked (*Biology*, 12th ed. page 171/13th ed., page 207).

17. **C.** The study of rust formation on rocks throughout the Geologic Record shows that free oxygen developed later in the earth's atmosphere and, therefore, was not available for chemical reactions on early Earth (*Biology*, 12th ed. page 318/13th ed., pages 314–315).

18. **D.** Human gender is determined by X and Y chromosomes, where males have XY and females XX (*Biology*, 12th ed., page 157/13th ed., pages 197 and 224).

19. **D.** Lysosomes in eukaryotic cells are membrane-enclosed sacs that contain hydrolytic enzymes (*Biology*, 12th ed., page 67/13th ed., pages 64–65).

20. **A.** Cristae are the inner membrane folds of the mitochondria which hold ATP synthase, the enzyme used to produce ATP (*Biology*, 12th ed., page 68/13th ed., page 66).

21. **C.** The smooth endoplasmic reticulum makes lipids while the rough endoplasmic reticulum produces proteins (*Biology*, 12th ed., page 66/13th ed., pages 64–65).

22. **A.** Recognition proteins identify cells as belonging to an organism. The host immune system will attempt to eliminate (reject) a transplanted heart if the donor's proteins aren't a good match (*Biology*, 12th ed., page 81/13th ed., pages 88 and 660).

23. **A.** A community, by definition, consists of biotic factors (*Biology*, 12th ed., page 818/13th ed., page 810).

24. **D.** Glycerol joins with three fatty acids as it serves as the backbone of triglycerides, a common animal fat (*Biology*, 12th ed., page 42/13th ed., page 44).

25. **C.** All of the carbons in the hydrocarbon portion of this fatty acid have the maximum number of hydrogens bound to them (*Biology*, 12th ed., page 42/13th ed., page 44).

26. **B.** This is the amino acid glycine. It is typically bound to another amino acid in polypeptide chains by peptide bonds (C-N) (*Biology*, 12th ed., page 44/13th ed., page 46).

27. **C.** Before meiosis starts, the DNA is replicated. Then each chromosome is composed of two sister chromatids (*Biology*, 12th ed., pages 160–164/13th ed., pages 198 and 199).

28. **B.** Chlorophyll a is bright green and chlorophyll b is olive green. Both are large molecules that form hydrogen bonds with the cellulose in the chromatography paper and therefore do not travel very far (*Biology*, 12th ed., page 108/13th ed., pages 102–103).

29. **A.** The R_f value is the quotient distance (the distance the pigment migrated/distance of solvent) (*Biology*, 12th ed., page 108/13th ed., pages 102–103).

30. **D.** The two main factors that influence the movement of pigments during paper chromatography are the solubility in the solvent and its attraction to the paper. Based on its migration, pigment 1 was very soluble and has little attraction to paper (*Biology*, 12th ed., page 108/13th ed., pages 102–103).

31. **A.** Crossing an AA plant with an aa plant will result in 100% of the F1 flowers to have a genotype of Aa (*Biology*, 12th ed., page 173/13th ed., pages 206–207).

32. **A.** Enzymes lower the activation energy required to initiate a chemical reaction. This allows chemical reactions to occur at temperatures that do not harm cells (*Biology*, 12th ed., page 96/13th ed., pages 80–81).

33. **C.** Homozygous dominant describes an organism with a pair of dominant alleles (*Biology*, 12th ed., page 171/13th ed., pages 204–205).

34. **B.** An action potential along a neuron stimulates gated channels to open, allowing sodium ions to rush into a neuron, not out (*Biology*, 12th ed., page 558/13th ed., page 547).

35. **A.** A hypertonic solution contains a higher concentration of solute (therefore a lower concentration of water) than the cells immersed in

it. Water will diffuse out of the cell and the cytoplasm will shrink (*Biology*, 12th ed., page 89/13th ed., page 90).

36. **B.** The vesicles that bud from the Golgi bodies carry materials for export. They merge with the cell membrane and expel their contents through the process of exocytosis (*Biology*, 12th ed., page 67/13th ed., page 65).

37. **B.** When heterozygous organisms produce gametes, the alleles separate and are packaged into separate gametes (*Biology*, 12th ed., page 172/13th ed., page 206).

38. **D.** Translation is the process of making a polypeptide chain from mRNA and does not directly deal with DNA. Conjugation is the cell-to-cell transfer of DNA. Transduction is the viral transmission of DNA/RNA. Transposition is the movement of DNA segments (*Biology*, 12th ed., page 341/13th ed., page 333).

39. **B.** Photosynthesis releases oxygen as a byproduct. In anaerobic respiration, fermentation, and glycolysis, oxygen is not needed (*Biology*, 12th ed., page 322/13th ed., pages 314–315).

40. **B.** Though some plants are pollinated by wind, insects, birds, and other animals are attracted to specific flowers in order to carry the pollen from one plant to another. In addition, some plants will only function when stimulated or triggered by the pollinator. But in return, the animals get the nectar for food (*Biology*, 12th ed., pages 510–511/13th ed., pages 372–373).

41. **C.** Secondary consumers feed upon primary consumers which in turn feed on primary producers (*Biology*, 12th ed., page 840/13th ed., page 830–831).

42. **A.** Carbon dioxide is released during the Krebs cycle of aerobic respiration (*Biology*, 12th ed., page 129/13th ed., page 122).

43. **D.** Glycolysis precedes both alcoholic and lactate fermentation (*Biology*, 12th ed., page 132/13th ed., page 118).

44. **D.** Glycolysis produces four ATP per glucose. However, it must invest two ATP, so the net gain is only two ATP (*Biology*, 12th ed., page 127/13th ed., pages 120–121).

45. **D.** Mitochondrial DNA is maternally inherited and because both children from Mother 2 have the disorder, she must have a defected gene in the mitochondrial DNA (*Biology*, 12th ed., page 308/13th ed., pages 300–301).

46. **A.** Endocrine signals are often produced in different regions than where they act. The signals (hormones) travel through the blood to reach target cells (*Biology*, 12th ed., page 598/13th ed., page 586).

47. **A.** Density independent factors can affect population numbers independently of population density (*Biology*, 12th ed., page 803/13th ed., page 797).

48. **B.** The light reactions take place in the thylakoid membrance and the Calvin cycle occurs in the stroma of the chloroplast. (*Biology*, 12th ed., page 112 & 115/13th ed., page 106).

49. **D.** The process of transcription follows the base pair rules. However, Uracil (U) is substituted for Adenine (A) (*Biology*, 12th ed., page 219/13th ed., page 152).

50. **D.** Plants that have too much water in the soil are not able to dry out and therefore the roots rot. Too much water also prevents the cells from getting adequate oxygen. When the roots do not work properly, the plant dies (*Biology*, 12th ed., pages 484–485/13th ed., page 462).

51. **A.** A keystone species has a disproportionately large impact on a community. When a keystone species is present, the biodiversity increases. When it is not present, the diversity decreases (*Biology*, 12th ed., page 830/13th ed., page 822).

52. **D.** A tRNA molecule matches its anticodon with the codon of the mRNA strand to deliver the correct amino acid to the ribosome for protein assembly (*Biology*, 12th ed., page 216/13th ed., page 155).

53. **D.** Animals can have mutations that have no effect on the protein, a positive effect, or a negative effect (*Biology*, 12th ed. page 278–279/13th ed., page 272–273).

54. **C.** Allosteric enzymes will have their active site inoperative if their allosteric site isn't properly stimulated (*Biology*, 12th ed., page 100/13th ed., pages 84–85).

55. **D.** A pyramid shaped structure is indicative of a population with a majority of its people in either pre-reproductive years or reproductive years (*Biology*, 12th ed., pages 334 and 330/13th ed., pages 324 and 330).

56. **D.** Viruses are protein coats with genetic material such as DNA or RNA inside. They are not cells as they do not have a membrane structure (*Biology*, 12th ed., page 787/13th ed., page 781).

57. **C.** Pili are protein filaments that project from the surface of some bacteria (*Biology*, 12th ed., page 60/13th ed., page 58).

58. **B.** Introns are removed; exons are joined and travel to the ribosome for translation (*Biology*, 12th ed., page 220/13th ed., page 153).

59. **C.** The strands of DNA are held together by hydrogen bonds; without these bonds the strands would separate (*Biology*, 12th ed. page 207/13th ed., pages 150–151).

60. **A.** DNA is located in the nucleus and mutations would occur during DNA replication which also takes place in the nucleus of a cell (*Biology*, 12th ed., pages 64–65/13th ed., pages 62–63).

61. **B.** Parasitism is where one species benefits and the other is harmed. With mutualism, both species benefit. In commensalism, one species benefits and the other has neutral interaction (*Biology*, 12th ed., page 818/13th ed., pages 810–815).

62. **D.** An antigen is a molecule or particle that is recognized as nonself (*Biology*, 12th ed., page 680/13th ed., page 650).

63. **A.** Genetic diversity in a species allows natural selection to occur and allows individuals with the genes best suited to the changing environmental conditions to survive and reproduce (*Biology*, 12th ed., pages 162–163/13th ed., pages 219–227).

GRID-IN ANSWERS

SCORING Answers and explanations for questions in this section are given below. When comparing your answer to the provided answer, pay close attention to the number of significant digits, and for answers with values between zero and one, to the inclusion of the place-holding zero before the decimal point. A correct answer in this section is weighted equally to a correct answer in the multiple choice section of the exam. There is no penalty for an incorrect answer.

1. 480

   $p + q = 1$

   $p^2 + 2pq + q^2 = 1$

   $q^2 = 160/1,000$

   $q^2 = 0.16$

   $q = 0.4$

   $p = 1 - 0.4$, or 0.6

   $2pq = 2 \times 0.6 \times 0.4$, or 0.48

   $0.48 \times 1,000 = 480$

   (*Biology*, 12th ed., pages 280–281/ 13th ed., pages 274–275).

2. −1.6 MPa

   Water Potential (Ψ)

   $\Psi_W = \Psi_s + \Psi_p$

   $= -0.6\text{MPa} + (-1\text{MPa})$

   $= -1.6\text{MPa}$

   (*Biology*, 12th ed., pages 88–89/ 13th ed., pages 90–91).

3. 0.4 growth rate

   Population Growth = $dN/dt = B - D$

   1,000 births/2,000 mice = 0.5

   200 deaths/2,000 mice = 0.1

   Per capita growth rate = Per capita birth rate − Per capita death rate

   $0.5 - 0.1 = 0.4$

   (*Biology*, 12th ed., page 800/13th ed., page 794).

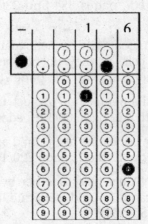

4. **12.5 grams**

   # of ½ lived = 1 half live/8 hours × 24 = 3

   Amount remaining = Original amount × $1/2^{\text{(number of half lives)}}$

   $100g × 2^{(-3)}$

   $100g × 1/8 = 12.5$ grams

   (*Biology*, 12th ed., page 268/13th ed., page 262).

5. **6.8**

   $$X_2 = \frac{\Sigma (o - e)^2}{e}$$

   Because it is a 3:1 monohybrid cross, the expected # of red flies is 200 × 0.75 = 150.

   The # of white flies is 200 × 0.25 = 50

   $[(66 - 50)^2 / 50] = 6.8$

   $X_2 = 6.8$

   (*Biology*, 12th ed., pages 188–189/13th ed., pages 206–208).

6. **0.19**

   $$s = \sqrt{\frac{\Sigma(x - \bar{x})^2}{N - 1}}$$

   Mean = (2 + 2.2 + 2.2 + 2.1 + 2.0 + 2.4 + 2.5)/7 = 2.2

   Sample Size = 7 – 1 = 6

   $(2.0/2.2)^2/6 + (2.2/2.2)^2/6 + (2.2/2.2)^2/6 + (2.1/2.2)^2/6 + (2.0/2.2)^2/6 + (2.4/2.2)^2/6 + (2.5/2.2)^2/6 =$

   .006666 + 0 + 0 + .001666 + .006666 + 0.015

   $\sqrt{0.36}$

   s = 0.19

   (*Biology*, 12th ed., pages 264–265/13th ed., pages 258–259).

ANSWERS FOR SECTION II

SCORING It is difficult to come up with an exact score for this section of the test. Correct statements are awarded points. You are not penalized for incorrect statements unless you have contradicted one of your correct statements. Diagrams that are not explained by your statements and bullet points or lists are not awarded points. If you compare your answers to the answers provided below, you can get a general idea of the percentage of the questions for which you would get credit. More thorough answers will earn more points and are associated with higher exam scores of 4 or 5.

FREE-RESPONSE ANSWERS

MULTI-PART

1. a.

		Individual Data for Pumpkin Cores		
Contents in Beakers	Initial Mass	Final Mass	Mass Difference	% Change in Mass
Water	29.15	32.12	2.97	10.19
0.2 M Sucrose	28.45	29.41	0.96	3.37
0.4 M Sucrose	30.92	29.84	−1.08	−3.49
0.6 M Sucrose	29.25	27.14	−2.11	−7.77
0.8 M Sucrose	32.09	28.54	−3.55	−12.44
1.0 M Sucrose	31.67	27.58	−4.09	−14.83

b.

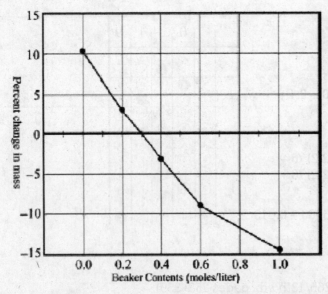

c. No single core reading could provide the equivalent molar concentration of the pumpkin tissue. We also had no way of measuring the pressure potential of the pumpkin cores. Consequently, we had to establish the molarity at zero pressure. The cores that had an increase in mass had a positive pressure potential. Conversely, those that had a decrease in mass had a negative pressure potential. By graphing the percent of change in mass of the pumpkin cores, we could estimate the molar concentration at zero change in mass by interpreting our graph. By using this value, we could then use zero as a pressure potential (*Biology*, 12th ed., pages 88–89/13th ed., pages 90–91).

2. a. The genetic information of a eukaryotic cell is packaged in chromosomes. Each eukaryotic species has a set number of chromosomes in the nucleus of every cell. Chromosomes are made of DNA and proteins. Genes are regions of DNA that code for a specific protein. Therefore genes are segments of DNA. Tightly-coiled DNA is termed "chromosomes."

   b. A nondisjunction event occurs when one or more pairs of chromosomes do not separate properly during mitosis or meiosis. The effect is an abnormal chromosome number after fertilization. An example of a nondisjunction event is Down Syndrome where there is a trisomy of chromosome 21. This can be seen on a karyotype which is a display of chromosome pairs in a cell that is arranged by the size and shape of the chromosomes (*Biology*, 12th ed., pages 194–195 /13th ed., page 228).

SINGLE-PART

1. The five conditions of Hardy-Weinberg equilibrium include no net mutations, large population size, no gene flow, random mating, and no natural selection. No net mutations means that there will not be a change in allele frequency based on mutations. The population size must be large enough so that, if there are random mutations, it does not have an overall effect on the composition of the gene pool. Populations must be isolated so that there is no potential for gene flow resulting from immigration and emigration of individuals among populations. Random mating is mating that occurs by chance and not selection. Sexual selection and artificial selection would be examples of nonrandom mating. No natural selection means that there is no differential reproductive success. In other words, all individuals have the same chance to survive and produce the same number of offspring (*Biology*, 12th ed., pages 280–281/13th ed., pages 274–275).

2. Both commensalism and mutualism are types of symbiotic relationships. Commensalism is where one organism benefits while the other is not harmed or helped (neutral). Mutualism is where both organisms benefit. An example of a mutalistic relationship is clown fish and sea anemones. The clown fish benefit by having a place to live, and sea anemones benefit as the clown fish scare away other fish that want to eat the anemones (*Biology*, 12th ed., page 818/13th ed., page 810).

3. The cell membrane is a selectively permeable barrier and therefore regulates what can enter or leave the cell. All types of cells have a cell membrane. The structure is a phosholidid bilayer with a hydrophobic region in the middle of the bilayer and a hydrophilic region on the outside and inside of the cell. Proteins are embedded in the membrane and allow for transport, recognition, adhesion, and communication.

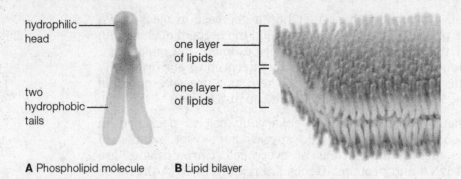

A Phospholipid molecule   **B** Lipid bilayer

(*Biology*, 12th ed., pages 78–79/13th ed., pages 88–89).

4. Negative feedback is used by organisms to regulate a specific physiological process or to return to a set point. Operons can be examples of negative feedback and can be used to regulate gene expression in bacteria. For the tryptophan operon, which makes the amino acid tryptophan, when too much tryptophan is present in a cell, it acts as a co-repressor and turns off the genes that make it. This maintains the correct amount of the amino acid in the cell. Other possible examples include temperature regulation in animals and plant response to water limitiations (*Biology*, 12th ed., page 236/13th ed., pages 170–171).

5. This graph represents stabilizing selection because the intermediate form of the trait (in this case body weight) is favored by natural selection and the extremes are not (*Biology*, 12th ed., page 284/13th ed., page 278).

6. This graph represents the primary and secondary immune response. The first time a host immune system sees a pathogen it produces antibodies. In the process of making antibodies (which occurs in B-cells) additional cells are made that remember the antigen. The second exposure to the same pathogen causes a larger population of B-cells to be formed much more quickly than in the primary response, and therefore the host is less likely to become ill (*Biology*, 12th ed., page 671/13th ed., page 661).

Practice Test 2

AP BIOLOGY EXAMINATION
Section I: Multiple-Choice and Grid-In Questions
Time—90 minutes
Number of Questions—63 MC and 6 GI

This practice test will give you some indication of how you might score on the multiple-choice portion as well as the free-response portion of the AP Biology exam. Of course, the exam changes every year, so it is never possible to predict a student's score with certainty. This test will also pinpoint strengths and weaknesses on the key content areas covered by the exam.

DIRECTIONS   Each of the questions or incomplete statements of this portion of the exam is followed by four possible answers or suggestions. Choose the single response that best answers the question or completes the statement. There is no penalty for guessing. Simple four-function calculators may be used on this portion of the exam. Use the Equations and Formulas guide as needed for selecting the proper equation or formula to solve the Grid-In Questions.

MULTIPLE-CHOICE QUESTIONS

1. What is the result of meiosis?
   (A) doubling of the genetic material
   (B) halving of the genetic material
   (C) copying the genetic material
   (D) maintaining the genetic material

2. Mendel's theory of independent assortment states that
   (A) only one of two alleles for a gene gets passed from a parent to one of its offspring.
   (B) gametes separate independently after meiosis.
   (C) alleles of one gene are inherited separately from other alleles for another gene.
   (D) tetrads perform crossing over to increase variation among offspring.

3. Which of the following does not characterize most Archaea?
   (A) cell wall
   (B) no nucleus present
   (C) metabolic diversity
   (D) mitochondria to produce energy

4. All of the following are true about a neuron EXCEPT
   (A) Myelin can insulate its axon.
   (B) Its sodium-potassium pumps require energy from ATP.
   (C) Its sodium-potassium pumps start to work when a stimulus is received.
   (D) It receives stimuli via its dendrites.

5. What can cancer be described as?
   (A) unregulated cell division that interferes with normal function
   (B) the normal fate of some cells in the body
   (C) the result of apoptosis triggered by ultraviolet radiation
   (D) premature cell death caused by mutations

6. A characteristic of parasitism is
   (A) that parasites spread slowly when host population density is high.
   (B) that it reduces fitness in both the parasite and the host.
   (C) that the parasite and host change together over time.
   (D) that the relationship will eventually evolve to be mutualistic.

GO ON TO NEXT PAGE

225

7. In hydrolysis
   (A) water forms as a product.
   (B) enzymes remove an –OH group.
   (C) polymers get larger.
   (D) monomers are products.

8. Which of the following statements is correct?
   (A) Sexual reproduction creates clones.
   (B) Maternal and paternal chromosomes are identical.
   (C) There are multiple forms of a gene.
   (D) Genes only influence differences in single traits.

9. Introns are removed from RNA. The exons remaining to code for a protein composed of 300 amino acids would require how many nitrogen bases?
   (A) 100
   (B) 300
   (C) 600
   (D) 900

10. Female horses mated with male donkeys produce mules whose chromosomes don't match up. This is an example of
    (A) Mendel's law of segregation.
    (B) post-zygotic reproductive isolation.
    (C) nondisjunction during gamete formation in one parent.
    (D) a chromosomal mutation.

11. Cell differentiation is caused by
    (A) whether mitosis or meiosis is occuring in the cells.
    (B) selective gene expression in different cell types.
    (C) loss of genetic material by some cell types.
    (D) apoptosis of some cells.

12. All of the following are abiotic components of an ecosystem EXCEPT
    (A) decomposers.
    (B) elevation.
    (C) rainfall.
    (D) soil pH.

13. As long as per capita growth rate remains constant and greater than zero, then
    (A) zero population growth will occur.
    (B) the death rate must be greater than the birth rate.
    (C) the population would never reach its biotic potential.
    (D) exponential growth will occur.

14. Nonspecific defenses of the human immune system include
    (A) antibodies.
    (B) cytotoxic T lymphocytes.
    (C) macrophages.
    (D) plasma B lymphocytes.

Use the following terms to answer Questions 15–18. Terms may be used once, more than once, or not at all.
(A) plasma membrane
(B) cell wall
(C) ribosomes
(D) nucleus

15. This structure is not found in animal cells.

16. This structure is found inside both prokaryotic and eukaryotic cells.

17. This structure is part of the extracellular matrix of mushroom and spinach cells.

18. This structure is where translation takes place in eukaryotic cells.

19. The forearms of a cat, a whale, and a human are considered to be structural homologies primarily because
    (A) they evolved a similar function from different ancestors.
    (B) they evolved an identical structure due to a common ancestor.
    (C) they evolved a similar structure with different functions from a common ancestor.
    (D) they evolved an identical function from different ancestors.

20. Which of the following terms is paired with the incorrect description?
    (A) interphase—cytoplasmic division
    (B) allele—version of a gene
    (C) fertilization—the process of sperm and egg coming together
    (D) zygote—the product of an egg and sperm coming together

21. Most of the water that enters the digestive system is absorbed across the lining of the small intestine into capillaries. This happens because
    (A) the small intestine is lined with villi and microvilli that increase surface area.
    (B) many hydrolysis reactions take place in the lumen of the small intestine.
    (C) the water potential is higher in the blood than in the lumen of the small intestine.
    (D) water molecules are actively transported into the blood by aquaporins.

22. If a pure-breeding black cat is crossed with a pure-breeding cat with white hair, and they produce three kittens with grey hair, the simplest explanation is
    (A) a mutation.
    (B) an X-linked gene.
    (C) a lethal gene.
    (D) an incompletely dominant gene.

23. All of the following are involved with DNA replication EXCEPT
    (A) topoisomerase.
    (B) helicase.
    (C) DNA polymerase.
    (D) codons.

24. The chromosome number of a body cell in *Arabidopsis* is 12. What is the chromosome number of a gamete?
    (A) 2
    (B) 6
    (C) 12
    (D) 24

25. A termite is observed following a trail of ink. If a biologist were to further study the ink, which of the following would she most likely expect to find?
    (A) A pigment molecule in the ink resembles a signal molecule produced by termites of that species.

(B) The solvent in the ink resembles a chemical used by geneticists to anesthetize fruit flies.
(C) The interior of a nearby termite mound is the same color as the ink.
(D) The ink changes the termite's behavior by causing a mutation in its brain cells.

26. Two species living in the same area and sharing many similarities, such as nest sites and food sources, are in a relationship known as
    (A) mutualism.
    (B) parasitism.
    (C) commensalism.
    (D) competition.

27. In the second generation of a cross between individual (EEGG) and individual (eegg), the most common genotype will be
    (A) EEGG.
    (B) EeGG.
    (C) EeGg.
    (D) eeGg.

28. Living in groups provides all of the following benefits EXCEPT
    (A) Group members can alert others about predators.
    (B) There are increases in hunting success.
    (C) There is a decrease in disease transmission.
    (D) Individuals are hidden from view by the group.

29. Why do human males tend to have a greater frequency of expressing an X-linked recessive genetic disorder than females?
    (A) Females have two dominant genes for the disorder.
    (B) Males have one X and one Y chromosome.
    (C) Males transcribe genes faster than females.
    (D) Male chromosomes contain a larger percent of exons than female chromosomes.

GO ON TO NEXT PAGE

30. In a predator-prey relationship
    (A) the predator population size does not vary, but the prey population size does.
    (B) the predator and prey population sizes rise and fall, forming a sawtooth graph over time.
    (C) only prey can act as a keystone species.
    (D) the predator is at a lower trophic level because they tend to be fewer in number.

31. Which of the following sequences is complementary to the DNA strand 5'-AGATCA-3'?
    (A) 5'-TCTAGT-3'
    (B) 5'-AGAUCA-3'
    (C) 3'-TCTAGT-5'
    (D) 3'-AGAUCA-5'

32. Master genes that control the formation of specific body parts are
    (A) promoter genes.
    (B) homeotic genes.
    (C) polymerases.
    (D) topoisomerases.

33. Which of the following occurs during the initiation phase of translation?
    (A) A polypeptide forms.
    (B) The stop codon is reached by the ribosome.
    (C) Peptide bonds form between amino acids.
    (D) mRNA binds with the small ribosomal subunit.

34.

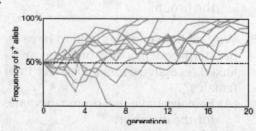

A The size of these populations of beetles was maintained

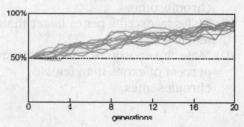

B The size of these populations of beetles was maintained

Which of the following is the most likely reason for differences in the populations depicted in graph A from those in graph B?
    (A) The populations in A were smaller than those in B, so genetic drift occurred.
    (B) The populations in A were exposed to a predator species, and the populations in B were not.
    (C) The populations in B had a greater exposure to ultraviolet radiation than the populations in A.
    (D) The populations in B were undergoing stabilizing selection, and those in A were undergoing disruptive selection.

35. A phylogenetic tree is most useful for illustrating which of the following?
    (A) genetic drift
    (B) gene flow
    (C) ages of fossils
    (D) common ancestry

36. The Mesozoic era, sometimes called the Age of Dinosaurs, is marked by rock layers in which dinosaur fossils are present. Some mammalian fossils also date from the Mesozoic era, but are few in number and type as compared to more recent fossils from the Cenozoic era. Which of the following is the accepted explanation for this increase in mammal species?
    (A) The mammal species were effective predators that outcompeted the dinosaurs.
    (B) The extinction of the dinosaurs eliminated competition, so mammals underwent adaptive radiation.
    (C) Different dinosaur species gradually evolved into the mammal and bird species of today.
    (D) The large dinosaurs had a low surface area to volume ratio as compared to small mammals.

37. Which of the following makes it difficult to create a phylogenetic tree for Bacteria?
(A) Horizontal gene transfer is common among Bacteria.
(B) Mitosis does not occur in Bacteria.
(C) Bacteria have circular or looped chromosomes.
(D) Bacteria do not have mitochondria.

38. The RNA World hypothesis
(A) cannot be valid because no organisms today have RNA as their hereditary molecule.
(B) is supported by the existence of catalytic RNA molecules.
(C) states that RNA viruses are the earliest forms of life on Earth.
(D) explains how protein synthesis works in all organisms.

39. Evidence of common ancestry for all organisms on Earth includes
(A) the ability to form amino acids in laboratory simulations of early Earth's conditions.
(B) identical ribosome structure in all living organisms.
(C) mRNA codons that are translated to the same amino acid in all living organisms.
(D) the ability of all organisms to perform aerobic respiration.

The following diagram illustrates how you can get ATP energy from fats, complex carbohydrates, and proteins. Use this diagram to answer the questions 40–41.

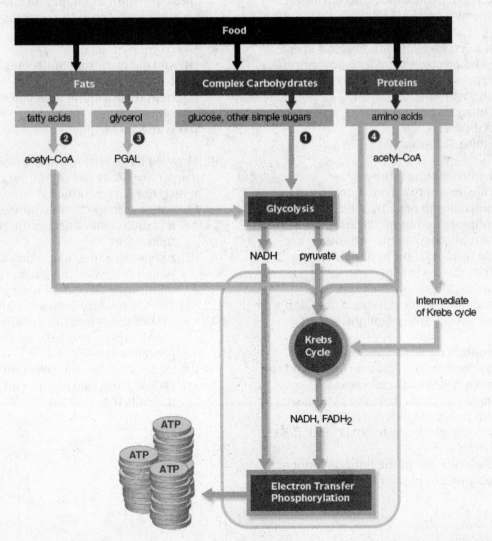

40. You can get fat by eating too many carbohydrates. Given that many chemical reactions in cells are reversible, which of the following molecules is most likely converted to fat by your cells?
(A) NADH
(B) ATP
(C) amino acids
(D) acetyl-coA

41. What is the role of NADH and FADH$_2$?
(A) They are phosphorylated when they transfer their electrons directly to ATP.
(B) When they transfer electrons directly to ADP, ATP is formed.
(C) They transfer their phosphate groups directly to ADP and their electrons directly to oxygen.
(D) When they transfer electrons to oxygen, proton movement transfers energy to make ATP.

42. The shaded box surrounding the Krebs cycle and electron transfer phosphorylation represents
(A) a lysosome.
(B) a muscle cell.
(C) a ribosome.
(D) a mitochondrion.

43. Chemosynthetic organisms
(A) transfer energy from inorganic molecules to organic food molecules.
(B) are more common at Earth's surface than photosynthetic organisms are.
(C) use fermentation to obtain energy from their environment.
(D) violate the second law of thermodynamics because they don't get energy from sunlight.

44. Chlorophyll molecules absorb free energy from light. This energy is used to
(A) make ATP inside chloroplasts.
(B) move electrons from the cytoplasm into the thylakoids.
(C) transfer electrons to NAD$^+$ and make NADH.
(D) make glucose in the light dependent reactions of photosynthesis.

45. Nitrogen is a major component of
(A) lipids.
(B) proteins.
(C) nucleic acids.
(D) both proteins and nucleic acids.

46. Occasionally a person is born with webs of skin between his fingers. What is the best explanation for this?
(A) The cells in these webs are an abnormal growth called tumors.
(B) The cells in these webs have a mutation that prevented apoptosis from occuring.
(C) The person's mother ate some genetically modified duck meat while pregnant.
(D) Speciation has occurred.

47. Which of the following is most likely to move through a cell membrane's channel proteins in the process called facilitated diffusion?
(A) oxygen molecules
(B) steroid hormone molecules, such as testosterone
(C) peptide hormone molecules, such as glucagon
(D) water molecules

48. How do large enzyme molecules such as salivary amylase get out of the cells in which they are produced?
(A) active transport: they move through a protein embedded in the plasma membrane
(B) exocytosis: they are inside vesicles which fuse with the plasma membrane to release their contents
(C) facilitated diffusion: they are at a higher concentration inside the cell than outside, and they move through protein channels
(D) phagocytosis: the cells that need the salivary amylase engulf and digest the cells that make it

49. The contents of a lysosome are typically more acidic than the surrounding cytoplasm, and it contains digestive enzymes. If the membrane of a lysosome were compromised and its contents were released, which of the following would be expected to happen?
(A) Nothing, because the cell has multiple lysosomes.
(B) The cell's genes might mutate due to being exposed to the harmful chemicals.
(C) The cell might die, because the lysosome enzymes are no longer separated from important proteins in the cytoplasm.
(D) The cell would actively transport hydroxide ions into its cytoplasm to neutralize the acids.

50. In the *lac* operon of *Escherichia coli* bacteria, the presence of lactose stimulates the production of enzymes that result in lactose digestion. When the lactose has been digested, enzyme production stops. This is an example of
(A) negative feedback.
(B) quorum sensing.
(C) chemosynthesis.
(D) signal transduction.

51. The large tsunami that affected an agricultural area of Japan in 2011 has had many effects. Which of the following effects would be of least concern?
(A) The fields were flooded with salt water, and the salt could make it difficult for future crops to absorb water from the soil.
(B) The flood waters washed marine animals to inland areas; these organisms might outcompete the native species and become invasive.
(C) Cars, trucks, and planes damaged by the surge of water might have leaked fossil fuels which were not able to be contained quickly and might have seeped into the soil.
(D) Radiation leaks from a nuclear power plant might have caused mutations in the surviving animals and plants in its vicinity.

52. The humoral immune response in mammals includes
(A) antibodies produced by B lymphocytes after vaccination.
(B) formation of a blood clot.
(C) destruction of infected cells by cytotoxic T lymphocytes.
(D) destruction of bacteria by phagocytic white blood cells.

53. Which is the most accurate explanation of why houseplants will bend toward sunny windows?
(A) A plant hormone, auxin, is unevenly transported by cells at the plant's growing tips and causes cells in the shaded side of the stem to elongate.
(B) The plant is responding to night length; it will bend towards the window during the summer months, but not when the nights are longer than a critical value.
(C) The plant is changing position because of turgor pressure inside its cells; cells on the side facing the light lose pressure due to increased photosynthesis.
(D) Cells that face the sun are damaged by increased exposure to ultraviolet radiation; they are unable to grow as quickly as cells on the shaded side of the plant stem.

54. Which of the following is an example of innate behavior in response to environmental cues?
(A) A dog runs to the kitchen whenever it hears an electric can opener.
(B) A chimpanzee uses a stick to get termites out of a mound.
(C) A caged European robin hops repeatedly towards the north side of its cage in the spring.
(D) A blue jay avoids eating viceroy butterflies after having tasted a monarch butterfly.

GO ON TO NEXT PAGE

55. Hershey and Chase helped show that DNA stores and transmits genetic information by
(A) discovering the base-pairing rules.
(B) applying x-ray diffraction methods to DNA samples.
(C) building a model based on the experimental work of other scientists.
(D) using isotopes of sulfur and phosphorus for bacteriophage cultures.

56. In prokaryotes, control of gene expression usually involves
(A) proteins that affect transcription of the gene.
(B) molecules that affect translation of the gene.
(C) removing segments from the transcribed RNA.
(D) homeotic genes.

57. Transcription factors in eukaryotes include
(A) operons.
(B) operators.
(C) inducers.
(D) activators.

58. A change in DNA that substitutes a nucleotide and has a positive effect on the organism's ability to survive and reproduce is best described as
(A) neutral.
(B) lethal.
(C) beneficial.
(D) impossible.

59. Trisomy-21, also known as Down syndrome, results from what type of mutation?
(A) an extra set of chromosomes, known as polyploidy
(B) an extra single chromosome, resulting from nondisjunction
(C) an autosomal dominant gene, which is always expressed if present
(D) a missing portion of a chromosome, resulting from errors during crossing over

60. One reason why a vaccine for HIV has not been developed is
(A) DNA viruses mutate very quickly.
(B) reverse transcriptase makes errors that the host cell's repair mechanisms miss.
(C) HIV is a lytic virus that reproduces very quickly inside the host cell.
(D) viral reassortment causes HIV to gain genes from other viruses infecting the host cell.

61. One major difference between the nervous system and the endocrine system is
(A) endocrine cells use sodium-potassium pumps when they are not releasing a chemical signal.
(B) all neurotransmitters affect cells by binding to receptors on their cell surfaces while all hormones affect cells by binding to receptors in their cytoplasm.
(C) hormones can affect cells located far from the cells where they are produced, while neurotransmitters affect adjacent cells.
(D) neurotransmitters are used for stimulation, and hormones are used for inhibition.

62. A neuron releases neurotransmitters when
(A) potassium ions enter the cell's cytoplasm by active transport.
(B) vesicles bind with the plasma membrane.
(C) Schwann cells transmit an impulse to the synapse.
(D) myelin is removed from the axon.

63. A student examined two populations of domestic cats, one on an inhabited island close to the coast of Maine and the other in town in western Massachusetts. She noticed that all of the cats on the island were all black, all white, or had a combination of black and white patches of fur. However, in western Massachusetts, cats had orange fur coloration in addition to or instead of black and white. Which of the following is the least likely explanation of these observations?

(A) The cats on the island are reproductively isolated from other cat populations.

(B) The cats on the island have less genetic variation due to genetic drift.

(C) Predators on the island were able to find and catch cats with orange fur more easily than they could find cats without orange fur.

(D) The cats on the island have undergone allopatric speciation.

GRID-IN QUESTIONS

1. To the nearest tenth of a percent, what percentage of forested area was lost in South America from 1990 to 2010?

	Forested Area (in millions of hectares)		
Region	1990	2000	2010
Africa	750	709	674
Asia	576	570	592
Europe	989	998	1,005
Oceania	199	198	191
North America	676	677	678
Central America	26	22	19
South America	946	882	864
World total	4,168	4,061	4,033

2. A student cuts two blocks of agar containing phenolphthalein. The blocks are initially pink, but when exposed to acetic acid, the phenolphthalein indicator loses its color. The original dimensions of the two blocks and the dimensions of the still pink portion of one block are included in the table below. To the nearest tenth of a percent, what percentage of the second block's volume should also be pink?

	Block 1	Block 2
Initial length (cm)	3.0	2.0
Initial width (cm)	4.0	3.0
Initial height (cm)	5.0	10.0
Final length (cm)	1.6	
Final width (cm)	2.6	
Final height (cm)	3.6	

3. According to the Acid Rain Monitoring Project at the University of Massachusetts, the pH measured at King Phillip Brook on April 10, 2011, was near 5, while the pH measured at Robbins Pond on that same date was near 8. Using the following formula, determine to the nearest whole number how many times greater the hydrogen ion concentration was at King Phillip Brook.

4. A student crosses two pea plants, one with the genotype Aa Gg Rr tt and the other with the genotype aa Gg Rr Tt. The genes are not linked. If the student collects 384 seeds from the resulting pea pods and plants them, how many of the offspring plants would be expected to show the recessive form of all four traits?

GO ON TO NEXT PAGE

5. Refer to the diagrams below. To the nearest micrometer, how much longer is the chloroplast than the mitochondrion?

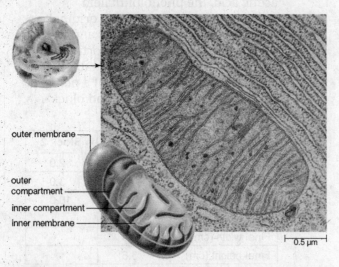

outer membrane

outer compartment

inner compartment

inner membrane

0.5 μm

Mitochondrion

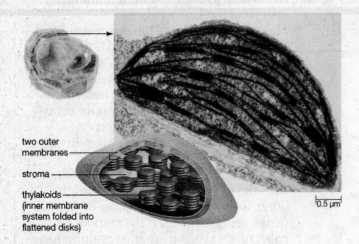

two outer membranes

stroma

thylakoids (inner membrane system folded into flattened disks)

0.5 μm

Chloroplast

6. The following table lists the reported cases of West Nile virus in humans in Colorado from 2003 through 2010. How many times more cases were reported in 2003 than were reported, on average, in the years 2008–2010?

Year	Reported Cases of West Nile Virus
2003	2,947
2004	291
2005	106
2006	345
2007	578
2008	71
2009	103
2010	81

STOP
END OF SECTION I

**IF YOU FINISH BEFORE TIME IS CALLED, YOU MAY CHECK YOUR WORK ON THIS SECTION. DO NOT GO ON TO SECTION II UNTIL YOU ARE TOLD TO DO SO.**

AP BIOLOGY EXAMINATION
SECTION II: Free-Response Essays
Suggested Writing Time—80 minutes
Number of Questions—2 MP and 6 SP

DIRECTIONS This section begins with a 10-minute reading period to allow you to read the questions. You may take notes, but you cannot begin your final response until this period is over. You will then have 80 minutes to answer the following questions. You can continue planning and organizing your response, but this time will come out of your 80 minutes. Answers must be in essay form. Outline form is unacceptable. Diagrams with labels may be used to supplement your answer. Diagrams alone, however, are inadequate. Unless the directions indicate otherwise, respond to all parts of each question. It is recommended that you take a few minutes to plan and outline each answer. Spend approximately 20–25 minutes per multi-part question and 3–10 minutes per single-part question. Support your essay with specific examples where appropriate. Be sure to number each of your answers. If a question has multiple parts, make sure the answer to each part is clearly labeled.

MULTI-PART QUESTIONS

1. Eukaryotic organisms usually have genes they inherited from one or two parents, through mitotic asexual reproduction or through meiosis followed by fertilization.
   (a) Explain how prokaryotic cells reproduce asexually.
   (b) List and describe three methods by which prokaryotic cells can obtain genes from cells other than their parents.
   (c) Explain how one of these methods can be a contributing factor in the increase of types of disease-causing bacteria that are resistant to multiple antibiotics.

2. The food web below represents the organisms of a large community. The arrows show the direction of energy flow in the system.

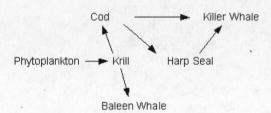

   (a) Identify the organism(s) at the third trophic level.
   (b) The cod populations of some communities have become drastically reduced in number due to overfishing. Discuss what effect this might have had on the killer whale population in this community.
   (c) Global climate change is predicted to cause increased water temperatures. Explain how an increase in temperature might affect this community.

SINGLE-PART QUESTIONS

1. If heat-sensitive film is used to photograph organisms in an air-conditioned pet store, some animals are much more readily visible than others. Give one example of an organism you would have difficulty finding and one organism you would easily find in the pet

GO ON TO NEXT PAGE

store using this method; then explain how each would respond if the electricity went off during a summer heat wave.

2   Explain, using one example of your choice, how positive feedback works to amplify a response in an organism.

3. Choose one of the following types of wastes produced by organisms:

    ▪ nitrogen metabolism wastes
    ▪ carbon dioxide
    ▪ undigested food wastes

    Discuss the distinctly different means by which three animals living in different environments get rid of those wastes.

4. Four important types of RNA are involved in the synthesis of proteins in cells. List three of these types and describe their functions.

5. The ability of an enzyme to function is dependent upon the shape of its active site. List three factors which can affect the shape of an enzyme's active site and describe the effect of each.

6. How is the structure of a mitochondrion related to its function?

END OF EXAMINATION

ANSWERS FOR SECTION I

MULTIPLE-CHOICE ANSWER KEY

SCORING Using the table below, score the multiple-choice portion of the test. Correct answers earn points, while incorrect answers are not penalized. A greater number of correct answers would be associated with higher exam scores. You will find explanations of the answers below and on the following pages.

1. B	14. C	27. C	40. D	53. A
2. C	15. B	28. C	41. D	54. C
3. D	16. C	29. B	42. D	55. D
4. C	17. B	30. B	43. A	56. A
5. A	18. C	31. C	44. A	57. D
6. C	19. C	32. B	45. D	58. C
7. D	20. A	33. D	46. B	59. B
8. C	21. A	34. A	47. D	60. B
9. D	22. D	35. D	48. B	61. C
10. B	23. D	36. B	49. C	62. B
11. B	24. B	37. A	50. A	63. D
12. A	25. A	38. B	51. B	
13. D	26. D	39. C	52. A	

EXPLANATIONS FOR THE MULTIPLE-CHOICE ANSWERS

1. **B.** The results of meiosis are egg and sperm cells which are haploid gametes and therefore contain half the genetic information of a diploid somatic cell (*Biology*, 12th ed. pages 156–159/13th ed. pages 190–193).

2. **C.** The law of independent assortment states that a gene is distributed into gametes independently of how other genes are distributed (*Biology*, 12th ed. page 174/13th ed. pages 208–209).

3. **D.** Arhaea are prokaryotic cells and therefore have no membrane-bound organelles (including no nucleus or mitochondria). They can have many modes of nutrition including photoheterotrophic, photo-autotrophic (photosynthetic), chemoautotrophic (chemosynthetic), chemoheterotrophic, or photochemoautotrophic (*Biology*, 12th ed. pages 344–345/13th ed. pages 336–337).

4. **C.** When a neuron is at rest, sodium-potassium pumps use active transport to maintain a gradient. When adequate stimulus is received, channels open and the gradient is reversed (*Biology*, 12th ed. page 557/13th ed. page 545).

5. **A.** Cancer is described as a disease caused by cells that divide abnormally, disrupting cell division (*Biology*, 12th ed. pages 150–151/13th ed. pages 184–185).

6. **C.** Novel host species can be more likely to die than traditional host species because the novel host species have not evolved defenses to the infecting parasite as compared with a host that has co-evolved

with the infecting parasite (*Biology*, 12th ed. page 826/13th ed. page 818).

7. **D.** Hydrolysis is a cleavage reaction that splits water and adds its components to the smaller molecules that form as polymers are broken apart. Monomers often result from a hydrolysis reaction (*Biology*, 12th ed. page 39/13th ed. page 40).

8. **C.** The multiple forms of a gene are called alleles. These are small differences in a single trait that make individuals unique. Asexual reproduction creates clones, and maternal and paternal chromosomes have the same genes but different forms (alleles) (*Biology*, 12th ed. page 156/13th ed. page 190).

9. **D.** Three nitrogen bases are used to code for each amino acid in a protein, therefore 3 × 300 = 900 (*Biology*, 12th ed. page 220/13th ed. page 154).

10. **B.** This is a type of postzygotic isolating mechanism is called reduced hybrid fertility (*Biology*, 12th ed. pages 290–291/13th ed. pages 284–285).

11. **B.** The signaling molecules encoded by master genes diffuse from the source, causing a concentration gradient. Depending on their concentration, these molecules have varying effects on development (*Biology*, 12th ed. page 765/13th ed. page 756).

12. **A.** Abiotic factors are non-living factors; decomposers are living organisms such as bacteria or fungus (*Biology*, 12th ed. pages 802–803/13th ed. pages 796–797).

13. **D.** The size of a population will increase by the same proportion in every successive generation (*Biology*, 12th ed. page 800/13th ed. page 794).

14. **C.** Macrophages are white blood cells that engulf and digest foreign materials and damaged cells. T cells and B cells that make antibodies respond to specific antigens (*Biology*, 12th ed. pages 664–667/13th ed. pages 654–655, 660–661).

15. **B.** Animal cells lack a cell wall. Bacteria, plants, and fungi have cell walls (*Biology*, 12th ed. page 70/13th ed. page 70).

16. **C.** Ribosomes are the site of protein synthesis in all cells (*Biology*, 12th ed. page 56/13th ed. page 60).

17. **B.** The cell wall is part of the extracellular matrix of plants, fungi, and some other organisms (*Biology*, 12th ed. pages 70–71/13th ed. pages 70–71).

18. **C.** Ribosomes are the site of translation in all cells (*Biology*, 12th ed. page 222/13th ed. page 156).

19. **C.** Homologous structures have a similar structure and function because they have a common ancestor. Analogous structures, which have a similar function without a common ancestor are said to have evolved through morphological convergence (*Biology*, 12th ed. pages 304–305/13th ed. pages 298–299).

20. **A.** Interphase is when DNA is replicated before nuclear division (mitosis or meiosis). Cytokinesis is the division of cytoplasm which

results in new cells (*Biology*, 12th ed. pages 142–145, 148, 156–157/13th ed. pages 178, 182, 190–191).

21. **A.** Surface area plays an important role in absorption, and the villi and microvilli provide a large amount of surface area for that absorption to take place (*Biology*, 12th ed. pages 57, 708 /13th ed. pages 55, 701).

22. **D.** With incomplete dominance, a heterozygous individual with a blended phenotype is produced (*Biology*, 12th ed. page 176/13th ed. page 210).

23. **D.** Codons are segments of three nucleotides found on an mRNA strand (*Biology*, 12th ed. pages 220/13th ed. page 154).

24. **B.** Gametes are haploid cells that contain half the genetic information of a diploid somatic cell (*Biology*, 12th ed. pages 156–157/13th ed. pages 190–191).

25. **A.** The pigment molecule can be similar in structure to a pheromone used by termites to communicate with each other, such as when marking trails followed between their mound and a source of food (*Biology*, 12th ed. page 786/13th ed. page 780).

26. **D.** A struggle for existence ensues, as two species cannot use identical resources indefinitely and coexist. Extinction might eventually occur, but it is not an immediate result (*Biology*, 12th ed. page 820/13th ed. page 812).

27. **C.** A second generation cross between EeGg and EeGg would yield 25% EeGg (*Biology*, 12th ed. page 175/13th ed. page 209).

28. **C.** Infectious diseases or parasites are readily transmitted in groups (*Biology*, 12th ed. page 791/13th ed. page 785).

29. **B.** Males have only one X chromosome, which offers them less protection against X-linked genetic disorders than females, who have two X chromosomes (*Biology*, 12th ed. page 190/13th ed. page 224).

30. **B.** Predator and prey populations can show a cycle where the predator population becomes more dense after the prey population does; then the prey decrease in density as more are eaten; then the predator density drops due to lack of food (*Biology*, 12th ed. pages 822–823/13th ed. pages 814–815).

31. **C.** According to Watson and Crick's double helix model, the strands go in opposite 5'-3' directions. Chargaff's base-pairing rules match adenine (A) to its complement thymine (T) and guanine (G) to cytosine (C) (*Biology*, 12th ed. pages 206–207/13th ed. pages 138–139).

32. **B.** Homeotic genes encode transcription factors that can bind to promoters (*Biology*, 12th ed. page 234/13th ed. pages 166–167).

33. **D.** mRNA and the small ribosomal subunit bind; later the large subunit binds with the mRNA/small unit to form the initiation complex (*Biology*, 12th ed. page 222/13th ed. page 156).

34. **A.** Genetic drift can result in an allele becoming fixed in small populations. Graph A shows seven of twelve populations having an allele become fixed (*Biology*, 12th ed. page 288/13th ed. page 282).

35. **D.** Phylogenetic trees are used to show common ancestry (*Biology*, 12th ed. pages 302–303/13th ed. pages 296–297).

36. **B.** Adaptive radiation of mammals took place after dinosaurs disappeared (*Biology*, 12th ed. pages 296–297/13th ed. page 290).

37. **A.** Phylogenetic trees depict common ancestry and vertical gene transfer. Horizontal gene transfer of several types even allows for exchange of genetic material between Archaea and Bacteria (*Biology*, 12th ed. pages 340–341/13th ed. page 333).

38. **B.** The RNA world hypothesis suggests that RNA could have been the earliest genetic material because RNA can also act as an enzyme. Viruses are acellular and are not considered to be organisms (*Biology*, 12th ed. pages 321, 334/13th ed. pages 312–313, 324).

39. **C.** Most organisms share the same genetic code, even though some unicellular organisms have a few codons that indicate different amino acids than are indicated for other organisms (*Biology*, 12th ed. page 220/13th ed. page 155).

40. **D.** Acetyl-coA can be diverted from the Krebs cycle and used to make fatty acids (*Biology*, 12th ed. pages 134–135/13th ed. pages 128–129).

41. **D.** NADH and $FADH_2$ transfer electrons to the mitochondrial electron transport chain. The movement of electrons along the chain pumps protons to the outer compartment. When these protons diffuse through ATP synthase, energy is transferred to attach a phosphate group to ADP (*Biology*, 12th ed. pages 130–131/13th ed. pages 124–125).

42. **D.** The Krebs cycle and electron transport take place in the mitochondrion (*Biology*, 12th ed. page 125/13th ed. page 122).

43. **A.** Chemoautotrophs can get energy from inorganic molecules such as hydrogen sulfide. They are the main producers of the deep ocean sea floor (*Biology*, 12th ed. page 339/13th ed. page 331).

44. **A.** During the light-dependent reactions of photosynthesis, light energy is used to form a proton gradient; when the protons diffuse through ATP synthase, ATP is made. The electrons that move during the light-dependent reactions originate from water in the inner thylakoid compartment and they are transferred to $NADP^+$ to make NADPH. The electrons from NADPH and energy from ATP are used in the Calvin cycle to make glucose (*Biology*, 12th ed. pages 111–113/13th ed. pages 105–107).

45. **D.** Amine groups of amino acids and the nucleotide bases of nucleic acids contain nitrogen atoms (*Biology*, 12th ed. pages 44–47/13th ed. pages 46–49).

46. **B.** Programmed cell death, or apoptosis, is common during development. If the cells are unable to respond to chemical signals from other cells due to a mutation that affects receptors for those signals, the cells will persist (*Biology*, 12th ed. page 765/13th ed. page 757).

47. **D.** While water molecules can pass through a phospholipid bilayer, the speed by which they pass increases due to the presence of protein channels called aquaporins. Oxygen is small and nonpolar, so it

diffuses very easily without assistance. Glucagon, a peptide hormone, binds to receptors on the cell surface. Steroid hormones, being lipid soluble, move through the phospholipid bilayer, though more slowly than oxygen due to their larger size (*Biology*, 12th ed. pages 82–82, 600–601, 730/13th ed. pages 90, 588–589, 722).

48. **B.** Enzymes are proteins and are secreted via the endomembrane system as vesicles from the Golgi bodies fuse with the plasma membrane (*Biology*, 12th ed. pages 66–67, 86–87/13th ed. pages 64–65, 94–95).

49. **C.** The membranes inside eukaryotic cells can isolate toxic substances. Lysosomes in white blood cells, for example, can digest bacteria and cell parts (*Biology*, 12th ed. pages 67–68/13th ed. pages 60, 65).

50. **A.** Negative feedback is a change that causes a response that reverses that change. While it is also associated with homeostasis and hormone levels, this type of prokaryotic genetic control mechanism involves negative feedback (*Biology*, 12th ed. pages 236, 466–467/13th ed. pages 170, 536).

51. **B.** Marine animals are adapted to living in salt water. When the surge receded, many of those left behind would have died from exposure to air. Those that entered bodies of freshwater would have gained water by osmosis and not been able to maintain homeostasis (*Biology*, 12th ed. pages 722–724/13th ed. pages 716–717).

52. **A.** The humoral immune response is another name for the antibody-mediated immune response, in which B cells produce antibodies that have shapes complementary to pathogen surface shapes called antigens (*Biology*, 12th ed. pages 670–671/13th ed. page 662).

53. **A.** In phototropism, pigments called phototropins affect the flow of auxin, directing it towards cells on the shaded side of the shoot tip. Those cells elongate more than the cells on the sunlit side (*Biology*, 12th ed. pages 530–531/13th ed. pages 514–515).

54. **C.** Innate behavior is not learned or altered by experience. The robin's movement to the north is influenced by environmental cues such as magnetic field. The chimpanzee's tool use is an example of observational learning. The blue jay's avoidance of the monarch and the dog's response to the can opener are operant conditioning, a type of learning (*Biology*, 12th ed. pages 784–785, /13th ed. pages 776–777, 779).

55. **D.** Alfred Hershey and Martha Chase grew bacteriophage on bacterial cultures provided with specific sulfur and phosphorus isotopes. When those viruses later infected other cells, the phosphorus isotopes entered the cells, while the sulfur isotopes remained outside. This demonstrated that the phosphorus-containing nucleic acids rather than sulfur-containing proteins must contain hereditary information (*Biology*, 12th ed. page 205/13th ed. page 137).

56. **A.** A repressor protein can bind to the operator and block transcription of bacterial genes arranged in an operon (*Biology*, 12th ed. page 236/13th ed. page 170).

57. **D.** Transcription factors in eukaryotes can be repressors or activators, depending on whether they stop or speed up transcription (*Biology*, 12th ed. page 230/13th ed. page 164).

58. **C.** A beneficial mutation will increase in a population over time (*Biology*, 12th ed. page 279/13th ed. page 273).

59. **B.** Nondisjunction during meiosis results in a gamete that is missing one chromosome or has one extra chromosome. People with Down syndrome have an extra copy of chromosome 21 when nondisjunction a parent's gamete occurred (*Biology*, 12th ed. page 194/13th ed. page 228).

60. **B.** HIV is an RNA retrovirus that uses its own reverse transcriptase enzyme to create DNA inside the host cell. This enzyme is error prone (*Biology*, 12th ed. pages 336–337/13th ed. pages 328–329).

61. **C.** Hormones are released into, and travel through, the blood to reach all areas of the body. Neurotransmitters are released into the synapse between the end of the axon and a cell on which they can have an effect (*Biology*, 12th ed. pages 560–561, 598/13th ed. pages 548–586).

62. **B.** Exocytosis of neurotransmitters from synaptic vesicles occurs when an action potential causes an influx of Ca^{++} ions at the axon terminal (*Biology*, 12th ed. pages 560–561/13th ed. page 548).

63. **D.** The cats on the island could be geographically and thus reproductively isolated from cats on the mainland. The island cats can be descended from a small founder population or can simply be few in number, so it is possible that the allele for orange fur was never present or was eliminated by change. It is also possible that the orange color would be more visible to predators. However, allopatric speciation is unlikely because the island is close to the mainland and some gene flow is possible; new residents might bring cats from other areas, for example (*Biology*, 12th ed. pages 288–292/13th ed. pages 282–286).

GRID-IN ANSWERS

SCORING Answers and explanations for questions in this section are given below. When comparing your answer to the provided answer, pay close attention to the number of significant digits, and for answers with values between zero and one, to the inclusion of the place-holding zero before the decimal point. A correct answer in this section is weighted equally to a correct answer in the multiple choice section of the exam. There is no penalty for an incorrect answer.

1. **8.7**

   (946 million hectares in 1990 – 864 million hectares in 2010)/946 million hectares in 1990

   = 82 million/946 million

   = 0.0866

   (*Biology*, 12th ed. page 387/13th ed. page 377).

2. **13.8**

   $V = l\,w\,h$

   The acetic acid diffused to a depth of 0.7 cm, causing a reduction of 1.4 cm in color for each dimension of the first block.

   The rate of diffusion is expected to be the same in the second block, so the expected final dimensions for the second block would be (2.0 – 1.4) = 0.6 cm length; (3.0 – 1.4) = 1.6 cm width; and (10.0 – 1.4) = 8.6 cm height.

   The unaffected volume of the second block is therefore 0.6 cm (length) × 1.6 cm (width) × 8.6 cm (height) = 8.256 cm³.

   The total volume of the second block is 2.0 cm (length) × 3.0 cm (width) ×10.0 cm (height) = 60.0 cm³.

   The portion of this block expected to remain pink is therefore 8.256/60.0 = 0.1376

   (*Biology*, 12th ed. pages 82–83/13th ed. page 90).

3. **1,000**

pH = –log [H⁺]

The hydrogen ion concentration at King Phillip Brook was 10^{-5} and the hydrogen ion concentration at Robbins Pond was 10^{-8}

$10^{-5}/10^{-8} = 10^3 = 1,000$

(*Biology*, 12th ed. page 30/13th ed. page 32).

4. **6**

The probability of having aa offspring is 1/2; the probability of having gg offspring is 1/4; the probability of having rr offspring is 1/4; and the probability of having tt offspring is 1/2.

Thus, the probability of having an offspring with all four recessive traits is $1/2 \times 1/4 \times 1/2 \times 1/4 = 1/64$.

1/64 of the 384 offspring, or 6 offspring, should be recessive for all four traits.

(*Biology*, 12th ed. pages 172–174/13th ed. pages 207–209).

5. **2**

The length of the mitochondrion is approximately 2.75 micrometers, while the length of the chloroplast is approximately 4.75 micrometers. 4.75 – 2.75 = 2, when rounded to the nearest whole number.

(*Biology*, 12th ed. page 69/13th ed. page 67).

6. **34.67**

Mean = Sum of all data points/Number of data points

A total of 255 cases were reported from 2008 through 2010, for an average of 85 cases per year.

2,947 cases (reported in 2003)/
85 cases (average for 2008–2010)
= 34.67

(*Biology,* 12th ed. pages 346–347/13th ed. pages 328–329).

ANSWERS FOR SECTION II

SCORING It is difficult to come up with an exact score for this section of the test. Correct statements are awarded points. You are not penalized for incorrect statements unless you have contradicted one of your correct statements. Diagrams that are not explained by your statements and bullet points or lists are not awarded points. If you compare your answers to the answers provided below, you can get a general idea of the percentage of the questions for which you would get credit. More thorough answers will earn more points and are associated with higher exam scores of 4 or 5.

FREE-RESPONSE ANSWERS

MULTI-PART

1. (a) Prokaryotes do not have a nucleus or multiple chromosomes, as eukaryotic cells do; therefore their asexual reproduction is less complicated. Prokaryotic cells replicate their single looped chromosome. This chromosome and its duplicate are both attached to the cell membrane. As the cell grows, new membrane is added between the two chromosomes. When the cell is large enough, the cytoplasm is divided. This process is called binary fission.

    (b) Prokaryotes can get genes they have not inherited by processes collectively called horizontal gene transfer. Three types of horizontal gene transfer are transformation, transduction, and conjugation. In transformation, a bacterial cell absorbs DNA from its environment. This happens more often if the cell has been heat-shocked, or stressed in some way; such a cell is described as being "competent." In transduction, DNA is transferred from one bacterium to another by means of a virus. When a virus is made, it can include not only viral DNA, but also bacterial DNA which it can carry to a new host. In conjugation, a prokaryote with a certain type of plasmid is able to join its cytoplasm with another prokaryote via a sex pilus. It transfers this plasmid to the other cell.

    (c) If an antibiotic resistance gene is located on a plasmid, that plasmid might be transferred by means of conjugation. Conjugation can occur between different types of prokaryotes, even between Archaea and Bacteria. If a bacterium that is resistant to one type of antibiotic receives a plasmid containing a gene that confers resistance to another type of antibiotic, that bacterium has now become resistant to multiple drugs (*Biology*, 12th ed. pages 340–341/13th ed. pages 332–333).

2. (a) Trophic level refers to an organism's feeding level in the community. When one organism eats another, energy is transferred from the prey to the predator. Phytoplankton are the primary producers and are at the first trophic level. Krill are primary consumers and are at the second trophic level. Baleen whales and cod eat the krill, so they are at the third trophic level.

(b) The killer whales in this community are eating the cod and are competing with the harp seals to do so. The killer whales are also eating the harp seals. If the cod population is reduced in size, the carrying capacity of the ecosystem for both the killer whales and the harp seals will also be reduced. Because they are at higher trophic levels, the population size for both killer whales and harp seals is likely to already be small. Even smaller populations will be more subject to genetic drift and also to competitive exclusion or extinction.

(c) If the water temperature rises, the levels of dissolved oxygen in the water will be reduced. This will affect the ability of the krill and cod to get adequate supplies of oxygen from the water. If their populations become reduced, the baleen whale, killer whale, and harp seal populations will all be negatively affected; their populations could reduce in size or could face extinction (*Biology*, 12th ed. pages 844–845/13th ed. pages 834–835).

SINGLE-PART

1. Heat-sensitive film used in a pet store would easily show a mammal, such as a dog, and would not as clearly show a reptile, such as a chameleon. This is because the mammal is an endotherm while the reptile is an ectotherm. If the temperature rose in the pet store, the reptile's temperature would rise, remaining at about the same temperature as the room. However, the mammal's temperature would remain constant. The dog might also respond by panting and by sweating at glands in its feet; both result in evaporative cooling, where the dog's body transfers heat energy to the water, causing its change in state (*Biology*, 12th ed. pages 733–734/13th ed. pages 725–726).

2. In positive feedback, the product of a reaction stimulates the reaction to continue. One example of this involves fruit ripening. A ripening fruit produces the gaseous plant hormone ethylene. As the fruit ripens, more ethylene is produced and further ripening is stimulated. This effect is behind both the axiom "One bad apple spoils the barrel" and the use of paper bags to ripen fruits such as peaches; the barrel or paper bag traps the ethylene gas and ripening occurs quickly (*Biology*, 12th ed. page 527/13th ed. page 513).

Note: Other examples may be used, including the functioning of oxytocin during labor.

3. Jellyfish, insects, and humans not only produce different nitrogen waste products, but also use very different means by which they get rid of those wastes. Jellyfish produce ammonia, which is very soluble in water, and lose it to their aqueous environment by means of diffusion. Insects produce uric acid, which is very insoluble in water. Organs called Malpighian tubules remove uric acid from the blood and transport it into the gut; the uric acid is expelled from the body along with digestive wastes. Ammonia is converted to urea in the kidneys of humans and other mammals; the urea travels through the blood and is removed by the nephrons of the kidneys. The urine travels to the urinary bladder via ureters, and is later expelled via the urethra. Urea is less soluble than ammonia, but more soluble than uric acid (*Biology*, 12th ed. pages 722–724/13th ed. pages 716–717).

Note: The above is one possible example. Due to the diversity of animals that oculd be used as examples, there are many more options that may be used.

4. The four types of RNA mentioned are messenger or mRNA, transfer or tRNA, ribosomal or rRNA, and microRNA. Messenger RNA consists of a copy of DNA instructions for the assembly of a protein; in eukaryotes it is often edited, with introns being removed before translation. Transfer RNA transports amino acids to ribosomes for assembly; at one looped end it has a set of nucleotides called the anticodon which indicate the amino acid it carries at the opposite end of the molecule. Ribosomal RNA, along with proteins, is the structural component of the ribosome's subunits. MicroRNA consists of very short double strands involved in the form of eukaryotic gene control known as RNA interference or RNAi (*Biology*, 12th ed. pages 216–223, 231/13th ed. pages 150–157, 165).

5. Three factors that can affect the shape of an enzyme's active site are environmental pH, the presence of an allosteric inhibitor, and a mutation in the gene that codes for the enzyme. Enzymes have a particular shape at their optimum pH. If the pH changes, certain amino acid R groups will interact in a different manner; this can affect the tertiary or quarternary structure of the enzyme, possibly changing the shape of the area where it binds to the substrate (its active site). An allosteric inhibitor binds to another part of the enzyme; its presence also affects the way in which R groups interact and causes a con-formational change in the active site so that it no longer has a shape which can bind to the substrate. A mutation that causes an amino acid to be changed can also affect the shape of an enzyme. In particular, if an amino acid with a nonpolar R group is replaced by an amino acid with a polar R group (or vice versa), the way in which the enzyme folds in its tertiary and quarternary structure will change, and its active site might not be able to bind to the substrate (*Biology*, 12th ed. pages 98–100, 224–225/13th ed. pages 82–85, 158–159).

Note: Other examples may be used, including environmental salinity, environmental temperature, and cofactors. Competitive inhibitors do not change the shape of the active site and would not be a correct answer.

6. A mitochondrion has a double membrane which not only separates its reactions from the cell's cytoplasm, but also enables it to set up an electrochemical gradient to drive the formation of ATP. The folding of the inner membrane provides an increased surface area for the exchange of protons between the inner and outer compartments. The Krebs cycle takes place in the inner compartment. The mitochondrion has its own chromosome and ribosomes which allow it to produce some of the enzymes needed for aerobic respiration (*Biology*, 12th ed. pages 68, 128–131/13th ed. pages 66, 122–125).